FLORAL DESIGN & INTERIOR LANDSCAPE MANAGEMENT

(Courtesy, California Cut Flower Commission)

FLORAL DESIGN LANDSCAPE

DIANNE A. NOLAND

Horticulture Instructor
University of Illinois at Urbana-Champaign

AgriScience & Technology Series

Jasper S. Lee — Series Editor

& INTERIOR MANAGEMENT

PEARSON

Prentice
Hall
Interstate

Upper Saddle River, New Jersey

Cover photo: California Cut Flower Commission

ISBN 0-13-036429-0

2 3 4 5 6 7 8 9 10   07 06 05 04

Preface

Floral Design & Interior Landscape Management is a comprehensive book about the floral industry. The book explores the many segments of the floral industry and the beautiful products and services it provides. The reader will learn that flowers and foliage plants enrich our lives with beauty and function.

This book begins with the scope and variety of the floral industry and the many exciting career possibilities. The international nature of the distribution of flowers and foliage is highlighted. Both the art and science of floral design and the interior landscape are covered. Chapters focus on caring for and handling fresh flowers, as well as on designing with everlastings. Floral design basics, specific design techniques, and advanced floral work, such as wedding flowers and sympathy work, are covered. Business aspects highlight pricing design work, creating a business plan, and operating a retail floral shop. Suitable plants for specific areas and the growing needs of plants are explored in the art and science of interior landscaping.

All aspects of floral design and interior landscape design are covered in one book to provide exactly what is needed in today's horticulture programs. A student- and teacher-friendly approach is used with many colorful photographs and line drawings to enrich the educational experience. Activities are outlined that spark interest outside the classroom.

Acknowledgments

Numerous people contributed to make *Floral Design & Interior Landscape Management* a reality. Special recognition goes to the late Dr. John Culbert, Professor Emeritus, University of Illinois, who was my floral design instructor and mentor, and to the Ramanis from Switzerland for my first supervised horticulture experience.

Floral design students at the University of Illinois deserving special recognition include Erin Robinson Dodds, Molly Karnes, Kathryn Dieter Newman, Jennifer Hall Dennis, and Amy Fredericksen. To my 100-plus students each semester since 1980, a hearty thank-you for helping me hone my teaching and presentation skills.

Many others deserve thanks for their contributions, including:

- Ronald J. Biondo
- Dr. Jasper S. Lee
- Dr. Daniel Warnock
- Abbott's Florist
- Art Floral
- Kuhn Flowers
- Society of American Florists
- *Florists' Review*
- The National FFA Organization

Special appreciation is due to my husband, Dave, and son, Drew, for their support. I also thank my parents and my friend Peggy for their encouragement. Much credit goes to Ronald L. McDaniel, Rita Lange, and Kim Romine of the Center for Agricultural and Environmental Research and Training (CAERT), Inc., for their editorial and design expertise. Appreciation is also expressed to Dan Pentony, Prentice Hall Interstate consultant, for his assistance.

Dianne A. Noland

Contents

Floral Design & Interior Landscape Management

CHAPTER 1

The Floral Industry

OBJECTIVES

This chapter is about the floral industry. It has the following objectives:

1 Describe the scope and value of the floral design industry.

2 Identify careers found in the floral design industry.

3 Identify needed occupational safety practices in the floral industry.

TERMS

buyer
career success
cut flowers or fresh flowers
cut foliage
floral designer
floral industry
floriculture
flower exporter
importer

interiorscaping firm
leadership
National FFA Organization
National Junior Horticultural
    Association (NJHA)
personal growth
plant care technician or
    interior landscape
    technician

retail floral manager
retail florist
salesperson
supervised experience (SE)
wholesale floral manager
wholesale florist

1–1. The floral industry involves the design and care of fresh flowers and foliage.

ON'T Forget! Valentine's Day is next week and you must get just the right gift for that special someone. What about candy? A card? No. The perfect gift to express your feelings would be fresh, fragrant flowers. Should the gift be roses, tulips, or lilies? What color should they be? How many? Should the gift be just one type or would a mixture be better? The great news is that you have a large choice in flowers, foliage, and design styles.

Have you ever wondered about the names of the flowers that you see at the florist? Have you ever marveled at the skill that some people have in arranging flowers? If you have, then you may have taken the first step in learning about the floral industry. You may even want to learn more about floral design and how to express yourself with flowers.

THE FLORAL INDUSTRY

The *floral industry* is comprised of businesses that sell, distribute, handle, design, and deliver fresh flowers, cut foliage, and foliage plants. Partners in the floral industry include flower exporters, wholesale florists, retail florists, floral supply companies, and interiorscaping firms. All of these businesses are a major part of *floriculture*. Floriculture is defined literally as the "culture of flowers" but includes florist shops, flower retailers, wholesale florists, production greenhouses, and floral supply companies. The floral industry is an international, multibillion-dollar industry.

1–2. Fresh flowers and foliage are harvested for use in beautiful floral designs.

The floral industry and florists work with a very beautiful but also perishable product—cut flowers and foliage. *Cut flowers* or *fresh flowers* are the flowering portions harvested or cut from plants. *Cut foliage* are leafy segments removed from potted or field-grown plants to add texture and unique shape in floral designs.

The floral industry has many opportunities for rewarding and creative careers that involve flowers and plants. Some of these career opportunities include employment with a flower export firm, a wholesale florist, a retail florist, or an interiorscaping company. Other possibilities are positions in sales or research and development with floral supply companies. Let's explore some of the career fields and find out more about floriculture.

*F*LOWER EXPORTERS

The flowers in a bouquet may originate from many countries throughout the world. The businesses that are responsible for purchasing and then supplying flowers and foliage to many parts of the world are called *flower exporters*.

Scope of the Business

A flower-exporting company buys floral crops from all over the world and ships them to anyplace in the world where the flowers are needed. Sometimes the greenhouse growers themselves are flower exporters directly to the wholesale or retail florist. A flower exporter must know the most timely and effective travel routes to ship floral crops because of their perishable nature. Many exporters are not directly handling the plant materials but are routing them from growers or flower auctions.

There are several distribution routes for floral crops. The shortest route is directly from the local grower to the consumer. In the international market, the floral crops usually move along a much more involved path—from the greenhouse grower, to the exporter to a wholesale florist, then to a retail florist, and finally to you, the customer.

The international distribution of floral crops is possible today because of the speedy and efficient shipping of the growers' products to markets or international airports.

1–3. A typical international flower distribution route.

Regular air traffic linking and heightened communications technologies also help in making the process more efficient and fast. Although the distances that an individual flower may travel are great, the time of delivery to a buyer may actually be quite short. For example,

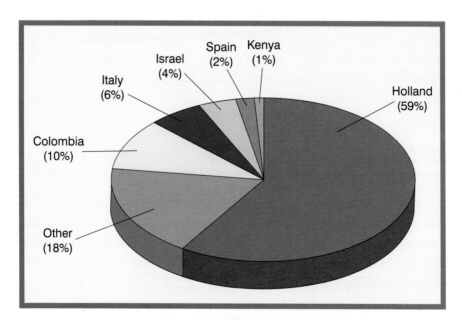

1–4. Percentage of world flower exports by country.

1–5. The international flower auction in Aalsmeer, The Netherlands.

a rose could be (1) harvested in Israel in the morning, (2) sold to an exporter in Holland later that morning, (3) shipped from the Amsterdam airport that afternoon, (4) delivered to a Portland, Oregon, wholesaler the next morning, and (5) placed on display in a retail flower shop in Portland by the afternoon of that second day. Quite remarkable!

Earlier in our history, nearly all cut flowers sold in the United States were also grown in local greenhouses. Transportation and refrigeration were not yet developed to the degree to allow for longer shipping distances. When transportation, mainly air travel, became reliable and reasonable in cost, other countries with climates better suited to growing certain types of cut flowers became important suppliers of floral crops to the United States. Today, imported cut flowers account for a larger percentage of the major cut flowers and foliage sold in the United States, including 90 percent of carnations, 71 percent of roses, and 89 percent of cut chrysanthemums. The United States is a major *importer* in the world market. Remember when a country imports, it brings goods "into their ports." Acting as an importer, the businesses in the United States buy goods and bring them into the country.

Today, the center of the international wholesale cut flower market is located in Holland (The Netherlands). Flowers from all over the world are flown to flower auctions in Holland, while buyers from around the world also converge there to buy the flowers at the auctions. Other countries that are major exporters include Italy, Kenya, Columbia, South America, and Ecuador in Central America.

CAREERS IN FLOWER EXPORTING

A typical floral exporting firm may have positions of owner or manager (depending on the size of the company), buyer, and salesperson. The effective owner or manager should oversee the operation, provide goal-setting and organizational skills to direct the company, and hire, train, and oversee the employees. An effective buyer should have a broad knowledge of cut flowers and foliage as well as plants and should know where to locate plant materials. A talented buyer is also a trend-watcher who knows about new flower varieties and colors and new growing and shipping markets. The sales force contacts prospective customers to determine their floral needs and arranges for appropriate delivery times. Computer and communications skills are also very important. Experience in other areas of the floral industry may be helpful.

Positions at international flower auctions would include plant manager, care and handling supervisors and workers, packaging and shipping specialists, transportation manager and workers, and auction room specialists as well as bookkeeping and business specialists. For entry-level positions, knowledge of flower types and their conditioning needs is helpful. Effective training in packaging and shipping would also be necessary. A willingness to work early hours is a must. Most auctions are literally empty by 10 A.M. each day.

An internship may be an effective way to learn about these types of careers and "get your foot in the door." A summer internship may be that first step in a floral exporting career.

WHOLESALE FLORISTS

The **wholesale florist** purchases cut flowers, cut foliage, plants, and hard goods from a number of suppliers and then resells and delivers these goods to retail businesses. Wholesalers have the important function of finding products that the retailers want to buy at the proper time.

Scope of the Business

The wholesale florist receives goods from around the world and resells the materials to retailers. Wholesale florists sell only to businesses that have a resale license. Local retailers may be near enough to shop in person, but many retail customers (whether distant or not) simply call the wholesaler to have the goods delivered by truck, van, or air.

Wholesalers work with both perishable materials and non-perishable hard goods. The effective wholesaler is concerned about the freshest perishable product and should have trained employees who know the proper care and handling techniques of fresh flowers and foliage. Many wholesale florists handle large quantities of potted plants and need to know proper storage prac-

1–6. Wholesale florists buy and sell flowers as well as plants and supplies. (Courtesy, Society of American Florists)

tices. Some wholesalers have a small greenhouse specifically used to keep potted plants in good condition until they are sold.

Occasionally, wholesale florists provide educational opportunities for local retail florists by hosting design shows and seminars on important issues for the retail florist. Floral designers or industry speakers are brought in to provide a service to the wholesale florists' customers—the retail florists.

CAREERS

The wholesale florist has many key positions, such as owner, wholesale floral manager, buyers for fresh or cut flowers and hard goods, sales staff, delivery personnel, and plant care specialists. These positions are all important to the company.

A *wholesale floral manager* oversees the operations and employees of the business. He or she estimates retail demand for products, hires and supervises the staff, and prepares, along with the owner, long-range goals and plans. The position requires experience in the floral or business industry, good people skills, business knowledge, and good organizational skills.

Another important job in the wholesale florist business is the buyer. A *buyer* locates sources of perishables and supplies and arranges the purchase of these goods. The buyer may work with floral exporters, growers, and other wholesale florists to purchase products. In a large business, there may be buyers both for perishables and for hard goods or supplies. A good cut flower buyer must be very knowledgeable about the wide variety of cut flowers and foliage available on the market and be open to purchase new materials just coming on the market. He or she will also know the best times or seasons to purchase materials from different parts of the world. A hard goods buyer will find the best quality and price for the retailers' needs such as ribbon, vases, tape, knives, and numerous other products.

A *salesperson* is an important position in the wholesale florist. The salesperson may be the only contact a retailer has with the wholesale florist. The salesperson phones individual customers, usually weekly, to take orders and determine the delivery times, places the order, and keeps in contact with the retailer about any necessary substitutions.

Other positions at the wholesale florist would be delivery personnel. The delivery people should have the appropriate license required for the delivery vehicle, have a good driving record, have organizational skills for packing and unloading the vehicle, and often will be trained to provide the care and handling of the fresh product received from either growers or flower exporters. In a large company, care of the fresh floral product would be handled by the care and handling specialist. This individual would process the flowers properly and remove any cut plant material that is non-saleable.

Retail florists

A variety of floriculture crops and products are sold to customers through retail outlets. Traditionally, the **retail florist** provides a variety of floral design products and services, such as wedding or funeral flowers, cut flowers, plants, and other related gift items. Retail florists can range in size from small independent businesses to floral companies with several satellite operations or franchises.

1–7. To attract customers, retail florists create beautiful displays of their products.

Scope of the Business

The retail florist shop is a business that provides a versatile range of floral designs that cover all the holidays and all of a person's life events, such as a baby's birth, birthdays, weddings, anniversaries, promotions, everyday flowers, and death. The services of delivery and set-up at a site are a trademark of many full-service florists. The retail florist sells fresh flowers by the stem along with greenery or foliage, and both flowering and foliage plants.

Other related products are often sold to enhance the floral design such as balloons, cards, mugs, food items, statuary, and a variety of gift items. Items for the do-it-yourself person are also available for purchase such as vases, ribbon, tape, floral foam, and floral preservatives.

Some florists expand their services and offer event planning, providing flowers as well as invitations, linens, and anything needed for a successful event. Depending on the owner's interests, the operation may also expand to include a display greenhouse or production greenhouse, a garden center, interiorscaping or landscaping services, holiday decorating services, and even a coffee shop.

Careers

The positions that are necessary to successfully run a retail floral shop may include some or all of the following: owner, retail floral manager, floral designers, salesperson or order-taker, delivery personnel, care and handling specialist, and plant care supervisor. The owner is the person who acquires the building, designs the shop name and business plan, determines products and services offered, and provides the focus and goals for the business. An

1–8. The retail florist sells "emotion" to celebrate special occasions, such as the birth of a child, or two.

owner has ideally worked in several shops to learn the business or has learned by being a part of a family business. A retail florist owner should have a good character with integrity and consistency, people and organizational skills, business knowledge, communication skills, and be a good judge of skill, character, and potential in hiring employees initially (the manager may assume these duties later).

The *retail floral manager* coordinates the day-to-day operations of the business. The typical duties may include hiring and managing shop personnel, buying and maintaining the shop's inventory, determining future shop's specials, coordinating window displays, and working with budgets. With the growth of a shop, an effective floral manager delegates duties to skilled floral designers or other workers.

The *floral designer* designs all types of floral work from wire service orders to custom floral designs. Floral designers with more training and experience are usually assigned the more difficult projects such as wedding and custom floral work. The floral designer may also be assigned other duties, such as window display, order taking, and care of plants.

In larger shops, salespeople take the orders of the customers who walk in or phone. Other duties may include cooler or display upkeep and plant care and cleaning. The salesperson should be knowledgeable about the shop's products, prices, and services. Familiarity with

1–9. Floral designers create designs to harmonize with an event.

shop specials, wire service offerings, and flowers and foliage is very important. A friendly, helpful, professional demeanor, good communication skills, and computer skills (or legible handwriting) are valuable to the effective salesperson.

The delivery person is responsible for the floral design arriving to the correct address in good condition. Familiarity with the area, good driving skills, proper licenses, professional appearance and manner, and some knowledge of basic design (in case of an upset vase) are necessary for an effective delivery person.

Other floral employees include the care and handling specialist who receives, unpacks and properly conditions the fresh flowers and foliages that arrive at the shop. The plant care specialist orders, receives, and maintains the various potted plants needed to supply the retail customer needs. In smaller stores, floral designers, delivery or sales personnel may also perform theses duties. Knowledge of fresh flower and foliage care (see chapter 3) is important for the care and handling specialist; knowledge of potted plant needs, such as lighting, watering and fertilization, is required for the plant care specialist (see chapter 14).

FLORAL SUPPLY COMPANIES

Retail florists create floral designs with many specialized tools, products, and supplies. Companies that sell floral hard goods, such as ribbon, vases, floral tape, floral preservatives, and other specialized florist needs are the *floral supply companies*. Floral supply companies focus their inventories on hard goods and tools and not fresh flowers or foliages.

Scope of the Business

If a retail florist needs or uses a tool or a specific supply item, there is probably a floral supply company that can supply it. Floral supply companies may be specialists in one particular type of product, such as vases, floral foam products or tools; other floral supply companies carry a wide variety of items. Floral supply companies supply products manufactured in every corner of the world from baskets made in China to floral preservative powder manufactured near Chicago.

1–10. Floral supply companies provide retail florists with a wide array of products and tools.

Floral supply companies that specialize in a particular product may also have a product development or research and development segment in the company. These types of companies are seeking to meet the great demand for new and better products.

OTHER CAREERS

The interesting careers available in the floral supply area range from sales personnel to research and development specialists. The salesperson may travel to the customer to show the products in person, take orders, and answer questions. Follow-up calls may also be necessary. An effective salesperson knows the product extremely well, communicates the positive aspects of it, and is friendly and helpful to the customer.

Employees who work in the research and development part of the company need knowledge of the floral industry and its needs, problem-solving skills, a creative mind to develop something new, and possibly a university degree.

1–11. Plants provide beauty and a feeling of nature in an interior space.

INTERIORSCAPING FIRMS

When a beautiful lush green sea of plants adorns a shopping area, hotel or a restaurant, probably an interiorscaping company has provided that lovely "jungle". A typical *interiorscaping firm* uses plants to enhance interior spaces by providing a welcoming beauty and a functional purpose of screening unsightly views or directing pedestrian traffic flow. An interiorscaping company design interior landscapes.

Scope of the Business

An interiorscaping firm works with a client to analyze the site, choose suitable plants, and order and install the plants. A maintenance contract is a major service that interiorscaping companies provide for the client. The plant care technician may visit the site weekly or as needed to water, fertilize, or remove unsightly foliage or flowers. A flower or plant rotation program is another aspect of interiorscaping. Contracts for rotation or replacement can vary from once a month to every three to six months.

To diversify, some interiorscaping firms may provide decorations for grand openings, banquets, parties, or conventions as well as seasonal displays for Christmas and other holidays. Interiorscapers may also start their own retail foliage business or even a flower shop. Since decorative containers are used in many interiorscapes, some firms also sell a variety of containers.

Careers

Possible careers in the interiorscaping or the interior landscape field are owner or manager, plant buyer, and plant care technician. Let's explore the new position of plant care technician.

An *plant care technician or interior landscape technician* is a valuable position in an interiorscaping firm. The technician is trained in proper watering, fertilizing, cleaning the leaves (or removing leaves), and insect and disease control for a variety of interior plants. Early detection and treatment of insect or disease problems in an interiorscape is very important. Knowledge of plant types and their growing needs and typical insect pests and diseases is crucial to success as a plant care technician. A pesticide applicator's license is required for interior pesticide use. A professional manner and cost-efficient way of performing duties is also valuable to the successful interior landscape technician.

EMPLOYERS' EXPECTATIONS

Working in the floral industry can be a rewarding and creative challenge. Floral employers will expect a new employee to have some basic knowledge of the florist industry and be willing to learn through training. Previous experience will be necessary for some positions, such as a main floral designer or a research and development specialist, but many positions

Table 1-1. Desirable Employee Qualities

Loyalty	Friendliness
Honesty	Good motivation
Integrity	Willingness to learn
Dependability	Initiative
Adaptability	Enthusiasm
Cooperativeness	Ability to accept criticism
Positive attitude	Ability to work with people

1–12. Professional attitude, attire, and actions are the keys to success. (Courtesy, Kuhn Flowers, Jacksonville, FL)

can be learned with training by the employer or by completing an internship or supervised work experience.

What are desirable work qualities for the employee? Loyalty to the company, willingness to learn, a friendly helpful attitude, truthfulness, dependability, and integrity are all desirable attributes for the successful employee. A positive attitude and enthusiastic manner are highly desirable employee traits. Workers who are self-starters and move on to new tasks without being specifically instructed are highly prized. The ability to accept criticism and to learn from mistakes is another important trait of a flexible adaptable employee.

Proper attire and grooming along with a professional demeanor will serve a potential employee well during the interview and while on the job. To convey a professional image, many floral industry employers provide a uniform with a nametag, especially to the service employees such as plant care technicians or floral designers servicing a wedding.

SUPERVISED EXPERIENCE

Valuable work experiences can be gained through **supervised experience (SE)** programs. SEs provide students with opportunities to apply classroom instruction through real-world experiences in the floral industry. Students practice specific job skills in one of four ways, including exploratory, placement, ownership, or research and experimentation projects. Typical supervised experiences in the floral industry are placement or employment with a local retail or wholesale florist, a flower exporter, or an interiorscaping firm.

The agriculture/horticulture instructor, the parents, and the employers work with students to determine career interests and plan the experience. These key people also provide guidance and supervision as the experience progresses. Most students start with a fairly simple SE and then progress to more advanced projects as they learn more about the industry. Student recognition for SEs can be gained through FFA.

STUDENT YOUTH ORGANIZATIONS

The National FFA Organization

The premier student organization for young people interested in the floral industry is the *National FFA Organization*. In fact, FFA is designed for students enrolled in agriculture/horticulture and is an integral part of the classroom instruction. The National FFA Organization is the largest student organization in the United States.

1–13. Students can gain helpful real-world experiences through supervised experience programs. (Courtesy, The National FFA Organization)

The focus of FFA is threefold. It is to promote premier leadership, personal growth, and career success. *Leadership* is the ability to direct and influence other people to meet individual or group goals. *Personal growth* deals with social skills, citizenship, and topics associated with self-esteem. *Career success* involves skills and traits that will help a person succeed in the world of work.

FFA offers many exciting experiences, including travel, meeting new people, and participation in floriculture and horticulture career development events. A student's knowledge about the floral industry can be recognized with awards at chapter, regional, state, and national levels.

1–14. Students can test their floral skills through FFA career development events. (Courtesy, The National FFA Organization)

National Junior Horticultural Association (NJHA)

Another organization for young people interested in the floral industry is the *National Junior Horticultural Association (NJHA)*. NJHA programs focus on Horticulture, Youth, Careers, Education, and Leadership (HYCEL). NJHA activities are designed to work with existing programs, such as 4-H, FFA, scouts, youth gardening groups, and horticulture/agriculture education.

SAFETY FIRST IN THE FLORAL INDUSTRY

Knowing the potential hazards of an occupation can help everyone be safer. The floral industry has some potential occupational hazards, such as the common use of knives and other cutting tools, handling of conditioning and hydrating solutions, possible allergic reactions to particular plant material, and pesticide use in the greenhouse and interior landscape industry.

♦ Sharp knives and shears—Florists frequently use shears and knives in re-cutting flowers and foliage. A novice floral designer can use shears at first and then use a knife when it becomes more familiar.

Recommended safety practices:

- Concentrate your full attention when cutting.
- Learn to control the knife.
- Make a small, quick pull with the knife to cut a stem.
- Keep the shears and knife sharpened and clean for the most effective use.

1–15. Properly holding and controlling a knife is an important floral design skill.

♦ Floral solutions—Florists use several types of conditioning solutions for making flowers last longer. Although most solutions are not toxic to humans, mixing the solutions too strong can cause browning and harm to flowers. One particular type of hydrating solution called STS or silver thiosulfate is toxic and should be handled and disposed of properly. This chemical should not be poured down the drain but disposed as a hazardous chemical. Fortunately, there are other hydrating solutions that do not contain silver and can be handled and disposed of easily.

Recommended safety practices:

- Read the directions and mix floral solutions properly.
- Know the solutions and chemicals being used and their proper disposal.
- If a solution has a silver compound, dispose as a hazardous chemical.

◆ Allergic reactions—Occasionally, a floral designer or other employee may experience an allergic reaction to some type of flower or foliage. This is entirely an individual response, but once the person is aware of the allergic reaction, gloves should be worn so that contact can be kept to a minimum.

Recommended safety practices:

- Be aware of possible allergic reactions to plant materials.
- Wear gloves and long sleeves when handling.

◆ Pesticide use—When pesticide use is necessary for interior potted plants, the employee must be a licensed pesticide applicator. Since chemical use is potentially dangerous, the licensing process generally involves instruction by professionals, home study, and a rigorous testing. Always follow recommended safety procedures.

Recommended safety practices:

- Enroll in a pesticide-training course and pass the licensing exam.
- Learn proper handling and disposal techniques.
- Wear safety clothing.
- Spray during off-hours with properly working spray equipment.

REVIEWING

MAIN IDEAS

The floral industry is made up of businesses that distribute, handle, design, and deliver fresh flowers, cut foliage, and foliage plants. Partners in this industry include flower exporters, wholesale florists, retail florists, floral supply companies, and interiorscaping firms. These businesses form a major part of floriculture. Many interesting careers are available in the floral industry.

Flower exporters locate, buy, sell, and deliver all types of floral crops anywhere in the world. For a typical international flower distribution route, the path is from the grower to a flower exporter to a wholesale florist to a retail florist to you, the customer. The flower market in Holland is the center of the international wholesale floral trade.

Wholesale florists purchase cut flowers, cut foliage, plants, and floral supplies from suppliers and then resell these products to retail floral businesses. Careers in this part of the floral industry include wholesale floral manager, buyer, salesperson, and delivery person.

Retail florists provide a variety of floral designs and services to cover major events in a person's life. There are several interesting careers, such as owner, retail floral manager, floral designer, salesperson or order-taker, delivery person, care and handling specialist, and plant care supervisor. An owner should draw from several retail work experiences and from business training before opening or purchasing a new operation. The retail floral manager handles the day-to-day operations of the business, including hiring and supervising personnel, buying and budgeting, and maintaining inventory. The floral designer creates the daily floral design orders as well as custom wedding and floral work delivered on site.

Floral supply companies offer a variety of tools, supplies, and floral products for purchase by retail and wholesale florists. Careers range from sales personnel to research and development specialists.

Interiorscaping firms create beautiful indoor gardens for businesses, hotels, restaurants, and stores. The interiorscaper or interior landscape technician designs, buys, installs, and maintains indoor plants within the interiorscape.

Most employers expect their workers to have some knowledge of the field but are willing to provide training. Important traits for an employee are loyalty, dependability, honesty, integrity, and a positive self-starter attitude. To convey a professional demeanor, the employee should dress appropriately.

The floral industry has some potential occupational hazards, such as the common use of knives and other cutting tools, the handling of conditioning and hydrating solutions, possible allergic reactions to a particular plant material, and pesticide use in the greenhouse and interior landscape industry. Learning the recommended safety procedures will create a safer work environment.

QUESTIONS

Answer the following questions using complete sentences and correct spelling.

1. What is the scope of the floral industry?

2. What does a flower exporter do?

3. How do flowers get from a greenhouse in Germany to you? Describe a typical route.

4. What is the difference between a wholesale florist and a retail florist?

5. What is the job of a buyer? What are some important job skills or knowledge?

6. What products and services might a typical retail florist provide?

7. What are the responsibilities of a retail floral manager?

8. Why are floral supply companies important to the retail florist?

9. What are valuable employee qualities or attitudes?

10. How does an SE program help prepare someone for a career in the floral industry?

EVALUATING

Match the term with the correct definition. Write the letter of the term on the line provided.

a. flower exporter
b. supervised experience (SE)
c. self starter
d. wholesale florist
e. National FFA Organization

f. retail florist
g. floral industry
h. importer
i. buyer
j. floral designer

_____1. A person who moves on to another task without being instructed to do so.

_____2. Business that supplies flowers and foliage to all parts of the world.

_____3. A person who designs all types of floral work.

_____4. Opportunity to apply classroom instruction through real-world experiences.

_____5. Business that purchases flowers, foliage, and supplies to resell to retail businesses.

_____6. Premier student organization for young people interested in the floral industry.

_____7. Business that provides a variety of floral design products and services.

_____8. Business or group that purchases goods to bring into the country.

_____9. Businesses that distribute, handle, design, and deliver fresh flowers, foliage, and foliage plants.

_____10. A person who locates and purchases a variety of perishable products and floral supplies.

EXPLORING

1. Visit a local retail florist. Make a list of all the different types of floral designs and the occasions for which each would be appropriate. Record other types of products for sale, including foliage plants, silk designs, and gifts and cards.

2. Make an appointment with a wholesale florist manager or salesperson for a 10-minute interview. Before the interview, make a list of questions about the types of positions that interest you. Ask about any training or knowledge needed. Dress appropriately and conduct the interview in a professional manner.

CHAPTER 2

The History of Floral Design

OBJECTIVES

This chapter is about the history of floral design. It has the following objectives:

1 Identify major influential periods of floral design history.

2 Identify the major design style(s) for each influential period.

3 Relate the influence of earlier periods to today's designs.

TERMS

American Colonial period
chaplet
Dutch Flemish period
English tradition
Egyptian period
free form
French period or the Grand
     era

garland
Georgian era
Greek and Roman period
ikebana
Italian Renaissance period
Japanese influence
language of flowers
line arrangement

line mass
mass arrangement
nosegay
strewing
topiary
tussie mussie
Victorian era
wreath

LORAL design has a rich and varied history dating back to very early cultures. Flowers were used to beautify surroundings, for personal enjoyment, to express feelings, and to enhance religious ceremonies or important festivals and events. The study of the history and traditions of floral design throughout the ages provides great insight into the use of flowers today.

2–1. Flowers have played an important role in all civilizations since the beginning of recorded history. (Courtesy, California Cut Flower Commission)

EARLY FLORAL DESIGN PERIODS

EGYPTIAN PERIOD (2800–28 B.C.)

Egyptians were historically the first people to use flowers for decorative purposes. Cut flowers were placed in bowls, vases, or jars to use in religious ceremonies and for festivals during the **Egyptian period**. Flowers also served a decorative purpose in the home.

2–2. Garlands and wreaths were first fashioned by the Egyptians.

2–3. Chaplets, originally given by the Greeks to honor their heroes and athletes, may today adorn members of a bridal party.

The Egyptians valued simplicity and highly stylized repetition. A typical arrangement would be a wide-mouthed bowl with an orderly sequence of a fully opened water lily, a leaf, and then a bud, repeating around the rim of the bowl.

Flowers, foliage, and fruits were often woven together into wreaths, garlands, flower collars, and chaplets. A **wreath** forms a circular shape; a **garland** is a strand or roping of plants, that can be shaped depending on the place and the designer. **Chaplets** were either garlands or wreaths worn on a person's head.

THE GREEK AND ROMAN PERIOD (600–146 B.C. AND A.D. 28–325)

The Greeks and Romans were greatly influenced by the Egyptian period. Garlands, wreaths, and chaplets were the main floral designs during the **Greek and Roman period**. Flowers were given to honor their heroes and gods during festivals, athletic events, and religious ceremonies. The **strewing** (scattering) of flowers and loose petals at banquets and festivals was typical of this period. Flowers arranged in vases or bowls were uncommon during this era.

Influence on Today's Designs

Wreaths and garlands are still very popular today. The wreath is a popular door decoration during the holidays or year-round. Wreaths may also be placed either on a wall or on a table as a centerpiece. Garlands are popular for adorning cake tables or head tables at weddings. Evergreen garlands (or roping) add a festive touch to stairways and banisters during the Christmas season. The strewing of petals by a flower girl at a wedding is a common practice.

JAPANESE INFLUENCE

Ikebana, or Japanese flower arranging, has been practiced as an art form since 621 A.D. This form of floral design was influenced by early Chinese art. The floral designs of the **Japanese influence** emphasize careful and significant placement of every flower, branch, or leaf. Space and flowing rhythm also characterize this design style. The placement of three main flowers or branches signifies heaven (shin), man (soe), and Earth (tai).

The three main classifications of Japanese floral arrangement are

1. Formal or classical style (Rikka and Shoka).

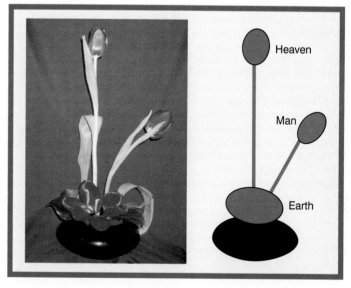

2–4. The three main placements in a Japanese design are heaven (shin), man (soe), and Earth (tai).

2. Informal or naturalistic style (Nageire and Moribana).

3. Abstract or freestyle.

Ikebana designs are used for religious and tea ceremonies as well as for home decoration.

Influence on Today's Designs

Japanese flower arranging has influenced contemporary line and line mass designs of today. The use of space in contemporary floral design was given greater importance due to the influence of this design style.

INFLUENTIAL PERIODS OF FLORAL DESIGN

2–5. The design style of the Renaissance period is symmetrical with no flower stems showing.

MIDDLE AGES (FIFTH TO FIFTEENTH CENTURIES)

The flower arranging of the Middle Ages in Europe continued with the Greek and Roman traditions. Flowers were strewn on the floor and were made into wreaths and garlands. Although flowers were important during this period, very little information is known about additional uses, except for their use in food, beverages, and medicine.

ITALIAN RENAISSANCE (FIFTEENTH AND SIXTEENTH CENTURIES)

The *Italian Renaissance period* signifies a greater interest in the arts. This period is considered the beginning of flower arranging as it is known today. Flowers were placed in vases, urns, and bowls for their beauty and for their symbolic meanings. The rose portrayed love; the white lily meant chastity. The white lily became known as the Madonna lily because it appeared in so many paintings of the Annunciation, showing the angel Gabriel and the young Mary.

For church and state occasions, floral design styles were colorful, large, full, and symmetrical with no stems showing. Casual arrangements for the home included short-stemmed, tight clusters of colorful flowers. Colorful arrangements of fruits, vegetables, and flowers placed casually on trays or in baskets were introduced during this period. Wreaths and garlands were still popular.

Influence on Today's Designs

Today's designs are greatly influenced by this period and the use of many flowers in a vase. Incorporating fruits and vegetables within flower arrangements is still a common sight for banquets, buffets, and other festive events. To some extent, people today still attach meanings to certain flowers. Roses are the flowers most commonly given at Valentine's Day. Roses continue to signify love.

DUTCH FLEMISH PERIOD (SEVENTEENTH CENTURY)

2–6. Dutch Flemish designs were large and extravagant mixtures of flowers with accessories placed near the vase.

The **Dutch Flemish period** was a time of great horticultural interest. Flowers were introduced from all parts of the world and were used to create elaborate mixed designs during this period. The designs were carefully styled, large, and flamboyant arrangements with either symmetrical or asymmetrical balance. Careful attention was paid to the selection and placement of the flowers. Fruit, shells, bird nests or birdcages, and other objects of nature were also added as accessories. During the latter part of this period, flowers were shown in all views—front, sides, and back. Space and depth were emphasized more as compared to the Renaissance style. Many containers were used, including urns, glass vases, goblets, low baskets and bowls, and Delft vases.

Floral designs during this period were favored both for the wealthy and the middle class and for both formal and informal occasions. Many paintings of this period show floral designs as an important part of the composition.

Influence on Today's Designs

The lavish, colorful mixtures of the Dutch Flemish floral designs have influenced many contemporary floral designs, including banquet centerpieces and hotel lobby designs. The use of accessories is still a prominent part of many arrangements. Today's designs also use depth and display flowers from many angles, which originated in the Dutch Flemish period.

FRENCH PERIOD OR GRAND ERA (SEVENTEENTH AND EIGHTEENTH CENTURY)

The *French period or the Grand era* was influenced by the French monarchy beginning with Louis XIV. The emphasis during this period was on classic form. Floral designs were refined and elegant compared to the often overdone flamboyance of the earlier Dutch Flemish arrangements. Fan-shaped, round, and crescent-shaped designs were favored. Other designs featured in the Grand era were tall designs (two to three times the container height) as well as small casual bouquets (equal to, or shorter than, the container height). Roses were very popular along with all the spring bulb flowers—lilacs, lilies, and the newly introduced gladioli.

Containers, including vases, urns, and flasks, were very ornate and made of porcelain, metal, or glass. Shell- and leaf-shaped dishes and baskets or bowls were also characteristic of this period.

2–7. Highly ornamented vases and classic refined style characterized the Grand era of France.

Influence on Today's Designs

The fan and crescent arrangements of the Grand era are still designed today. The emphasis on classic form and not the extravagance of the earlier period is also commonly chosen for today's designs.

ENGLISH TRADITION

The English have a long history and love of flowers and plants. The conquering Romans introduced decorating with wreaths and garlands. Tending of kitchen or cottage gardens dates back to the Middle Ages. In the fifteenth and sixteenth centuries, the English picked flowers for casual bouquets to bring into their homes. An early requirement for flowers in the **English tradition** was their fragrance. The English favored fragrant flowers because they believed that the perfume would rid the air of pestilence. Fashionable English ladies carried **nosegays** (handheld bouquets) for their fragrance as well as for decoration. Another name for the nosegay was **tussie-mussie** (tuzzy-muzzy). *Tuzzy* is an old English word for a knot of flowers.

The English enjoyed both casual and formal designs. The William and Mary reign from 1689 to 1702 marked the height in popularity of the very formal and symmetrical style of gardening. With the popularity of formality, the **topiary** form was developed, first in the garden by pruning shrubs into symmetrical shapes, and then later in floral design.

2–8. Nosegays or tussie-mussies were created and carried by fashionable English ladies as a defense against unsavory odors.

2–9. Topiary forms became popular in England during the reign of William and Mary.

2–10. The English created the first centerpiece during the Georgian era.

*E*ARLY ENGLISH PERIOD— GEORGIAN ERA (EIGHTEENTH CENTURY)

The **Georgian era** was named for the English kings, George I, II, and III. During the Georgian period, floral designs varied from small, casual, mixed bouquets in glass, or metal, bud vases or vases and small tussie-mussies, to large, mixed flower arrangements in urns, baskets, and vases. The arrangement height of the tall designs was usually one and one-half times the container height. These smaller bouquets are also believed to be the first centerpieces. Dried flower arrangements also became popular during this time. The English are also credited with inventing the miniature arrangement.

The containers were numerous, such as urns, bud vases, stem cups with handles, baskets, jars, jugs, bowls, bottles, vases, and five-fingered posy-holders. Ceramic wall pockets and Delft enclosed bricks with holes for flowers were introduced for flower arranging during the Georgian period.

2–11. A variety of containers were used by the English to arrange flowers. (Tussie mussie holders, stem cups with handles, and enclosed bricks with flower holes)

Influence on Today's Designs

The English developed many popular items for today's flower enthusiasts, such as the centerpiece, the nosegay (the forerunner of the wedding bouquet), the topiary, and also the miniature. Flowers arranged in a bud vase are still a simple but pleasant way to display a few select blossoms. Dried flower arrangements are also still enjoyed today.

LATER ENGLISH PERIOD—VICTORIAN ERA (NINETEENTH CENTURY)

The **Victorian era** was named for Queen Victoria who ruled England from 1837 to 1901. The Victorian era contributed the most to establishing floral design as an art. The art of floral design was taught and thoroughly covered in books and magazines of that era. This era established many rules and techniques of floral design. Two design styles were popular—large, abundant, masses of flowers and small, mixed, informal bouquets. The larger designs were generally round or oval with draping or trailing plant materials, such as fuchsias or bleeding hearts, to give a touch of the romantic. No obvious center of interest was created. Flowers of all types, especially new or unusual flowers, were favored. Foliage was prominently incorporated into designs, often at the edges to soften the framework.

The **language of flowers** was studied and used to convey meaning—to communicate with others, especially during courtship. The tradition of sending flowers to ladies before social events was begun during this period. The Victorians were much more elaborate and thorough in attaching meanings to plants. Rosemary in a design meant remembrance. Roses varied in their meaning depending on the color. For example, red meant love, white was silence, and yellow meant infidelity. Heliotrope meant eternal love; larkspur symbolized fickleness.

Popular containers were urns, vases, bottles, epergnes (see Figure 1–12), tussie-mussie holders, wall pockets, cornucopias,

2–12. Victorian designs were large oval or round masses of abundant flowers and foliage with trailing plant materials to lend a romantic look.

2–13. Epergnes were popular Victorian containers with multiple levels to hold flowers, foliage, and fruit or vegetables.

and baskets. Glass was very popular although many containers were made out of metal, ceramic material, and porcelain. The Victorians loved accessories, such as fans, figurines, shells, knickknacks, and glass paperweights.

Influence on Today's Designs

The Victorian era marked the beginning of floral design as an art form. Floral design became a creative field to study. The emphasis on the art and necessity of training during the Victorian era set the stage for the modern day florist.

The romantic look of the Victorian era is still a popular one today. Draping or trailing material added to soften an arrangement's silhouette makes a beautiful contemporary romantic design. The addition of foliage is also an important component of today's designs.

AMERICAN STYLES

Colonial Period (Eighteenth Century)

The European design styles greatly influenced the early American floral styles. **American Colonial period** styles were much simpler and contained flowers and foliage that were native to the United States. The addition of grains, grasses, and dried flowers made American design styles very unique compared to their European counterparts. Colonial ladies often arranged flowers of the same kind in bowls or baskets and then added filler flowers, such as baby's breath. Other casual designs for the home were generally very colorful mixtures of simple naturalistic styles in vases, pots, or jars. Fan-shaped and triangular arrangements were very popular for more formal events for the home or church. Five-fingered vases, epergnes, urns, and stem cups were other commonly used containers.

INFLUENCE ON TODAY'S DESIGNS

The incorporation of dried materials with fresh flowers was introduced during this period and is still a popular technique today. Simple natural arrangements of one kind or simple colorful mixtures continue to be popular designs for the home.

TWENTIETH CENTURY AMERICA

The floral designers of the twentieth century enjoyed the simplicity of the Japanese ikebana designs and adapted them to a form called the *line arrangement*. The large, colorful mixture of flowers of the European arrangements were simplified and called *mass arrangements*. The mass designs were based on geometric shapes.

The *line mass* style (also called Western line arrangements) was created by twentieth- century American designers. Line mass blended the colorful mass style of the Europeans with the spacious and dramatic line style of the East.

Free form styles were invented in the 1950s. The use of line and expressiveness brought a new dimension to floral design. Unique, individual expression allowed for creative uses of flowers, foliage, and accessories. Often, the rules of design were reinvented or ignored to allow for creativity.

2–14. Line mass designs combine the line and space of the Japanese influence with the colorful masses of the European style.

Influence on Today's Designs

The line mass style and the free form style added a new dimension to the florist industry beginning in the 1950s and 1960s. Variations of these design styles are still popular today. The space and linear component of the line mass continue to add vitality and drama to designs. Expressiveness is still important and allows for unique interpretations and uses of plant materials.

REVIEWING

MAIN IDEAS

Throughout history, flowers and floral design have been an important part of religious, community, and home decoration and enjoyment. Learning about the past can help us to relate our current floral practices and techniques to other cultures and periods of history.

The first people to design with flowers were the Egyptians who made wreaths, garlands, and chaplets. The Romans and Greeks strewed numerous flowers and petals at banquets. The Japanese influence gave us beautiful line and spaciousness in floral art.

The Europeans were very influential floral designers. The Italian Renaissance is considered the beginning of appreciation of flowers placed in containers and used in the home. The Dutch Flemish period added a flamboyance and extravagant style to floral design. The Grand era of France emphasized elegance and classic form. The English, including the Georgian period, contributed many design styles, such as the nosegay, centerpiece, topiary, and the miniature. During the Victorian era, floral design rules and techniques were established, and floral design was considered an art after that period.

The American Colonial period was responsible for the addition of dried grains or flowers to the fresh flower arrangements. The line mass was developed as a blend of the Japanese line and the European mass arrangements during the middle 1900s by the Americans. Free form designs were invented to allow for creative expression and unique use of plant materials.

QUESTIONS

Answer the following questions using complete sentences and correct spelling.

1. Why should a floral designer of today know about the history of floral design?

2. What were the floral decorations of the earliest cultures?

3. What style has three major placements of flowers or branches?

4. What period is considered the beginning of the appreciation of flowers placed in containers and brought into the home?

5. What are the characteristics of the Dutch Flemish style of floral design?

6. Who developed the first centerpiece?

7. Why were the forerunners of today's wedding bouquets developed? Who developed these bouquets?

8. Who first developed the "rules" of floral design?

9. What is the language of flowers and when was it used?

10. Who added dried flowers or grains to fresh flower arrangements?

11. What is a line mass design and what influenced its creation?

12. What design style has very few rules, if any?

EVALUATING

Match the term with the correct definition. Write the letter of the term on the line provided.

a. chaplet
b. Egyptians
c. Victorian period
d. garland

e. ikebana
f. Dutch Flemish
g. strewing
h. mass arrangement

i. Grand era
j. tussie mussie

_____1. The scattering of petals and flowers.

_____2. Fragrance was an important aspect of these tightly clustered flowers.

_____3. Created designs with very stylized and repetitive flower and leaf placements.

_____4. Worn on the head as a decoration or to honor a person.

_____5. Emphasizes line and significant placement of every flower or piece of plant material.

_____6. Extravagant, colorful arrangements with accessories, such as shells, bird nests, or fruit.

_____7. Roping or strands of woven flowers and foliage.

_____8. Designs with geometric shapes and numerous flowers.

_____9. Floral design became an art.

_____10. Design emphasis was on classic form and elegance, not flamboyance.

EXPLORING

1. Visit a local florist. List the general types of floral designs that are available for sale. Determine the period(s) of history that influenced each type of floral design.

2. Choose a favorite period of floral design history. Gather the plant materials, container, and accessories (if applicable) and make an authentic floral design for that period.

3. Visit a museum and note the use of flowers in the paintings. Choose five paintings from different periods and sketch the floral designs. For each painting, list the floral design style and shape, types of flowers, container, and accessories and determine the period in history.

CHAPTER 3

Care and Handling of Fresh Flowers and Foliage

OBJECTIVES

This chapter is about the care and handling of fresh flowers and foliage. It has the following objectives:

1 Know the basic requirements of cut flowers.

2 Understand the causes of deterioration and death of flowers.

3 Describe the steps of effective conditioning of flowers and foliage.

4 Explain the importance of using floral preservatives.

5 Learn about commercial packing and shipping.

TERMS

acidic	hard water	senescence
alkaline	harden	softened water
bent neck	highly buffered	stem blockage
conditioning	phloem	total dissolved salts (TDS)
deionizer	photosynthesis	transpiration
ethylene inhibitor	precooled	turgid
grades	respiration	
green rose	salinity	

ALL floral designers want their flowers to last as long as possible. Although every type of flower has an inherent genetic life span, each flower type can be enjoyed for the maximum time by learning more about its after-harvest care. Floral designs can be enjoyed days longer by understanding some key aspects of the care and handling of fresh flowers and foliage. Using floral preservatives and other pre-treatments and practicing good storage techniques extends the life of fresh-cut flowers.

Floriculture has an international scope. Flowers and foliage are grown in many parts of the world. Packaging and shipping are a very important part of the care and handling process. The flowers in just one arrangement may have originated in such diverse places as Ecuador, Holland, Israel, Italy, California, and Australia.

3–1. Extend the enjoyment of fresh flowers by learning proper care and handling techniques.

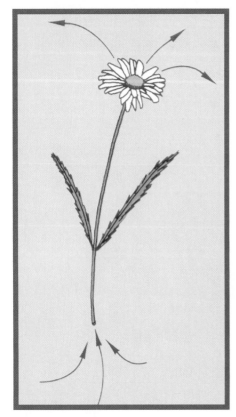

3–2. As the fresh flower transpires (loses water), sufficient water must be taken in through the cut end of the stem.

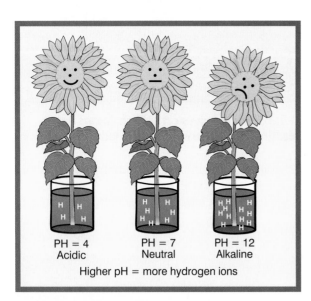

PH = 4   PH = 7   PH = 12
Acidic   Neutral   Alkaline

Higher pH = more hydrogen ions

3–3. Water with an acidic pH is ideal for fresh-cut flowers. Adding floral preservatives will correct alkaline and neutral pH.

BASIC CUT FLOWER REQUIREMENTS

Even though a fresh flower has been removed from the plant, it continues living (and sometimes, growing), like tulips and anemones. With special care, fresh flowers can be enjoyed for a long time. The basic needs of fresh-cut flowers and foliage are high-quality water, sugars for food, a healthy environment, and sanitation.

HIGH-QUALITY WATER

Flowers are 90 percent water. It is important that all parts of the plant—stems, leaves, flowers—be *turgid* (filled with water). As the flowers transpire or give off water, additional high-quality water is needed to supplement that loss.

To check for water quality, a water analysis can be determined by a trusted water treatment company. Adding the correct kind and amount of floral preservative is usually sufficient to make minor adjustments in water quality. In severe cases, a water purification system may be needed.

The pH of the water is also important. The pH refers to the relative concentration of hydrogen ions in a solution and ranges from 1 to 14 with 1 through 6 being *acidic*, 7 neutral, and 8 through 14 being *alkaline*. Water pH varies by region and may be alkaline or acidic. Since acidic solutions are better for water uptake, an alkaline pH would need to be lowered by the use of floral preservatives.

Water is also classified as hard or soft. **Hard water** is water that contains high amounts of minerals, which also make the water alkaline. If the pH is on the lower end of alkaline (8 or 9), the water can be efficiently corrected with floral preservatives. Hard water with very high pH values of 11 through 14 is also ***highly buffered*** or very resistant to change in pH. Additional acid may be needed to reduce the pH or the use of a ***deionizer*** may be needed to remove the minerals in the water. ***Softened water*** is water that has been treated with salts in the form of sodium to remove the minerals. Softened water is not the answer to water quality because of the added salts; it actually does more damage to flowers than hard water.

A water analysis also measures the water ***salinity*** or the ***total dissolved salts (TDS)*** in the water. A high salt content (TDS) in the water is very detrimental to flowers; the salt clogs the xylem (the water-conducting tissue within the stem) and may cause weakened stems and wilting. High-quality water should have readings of less than 200 parts per million (ppm).

FOOD–SUGARS

Sugars, namely sucrose and dextrose, are the food source for cut flowers. Flowers have two ways of getting the sugars (or carbohydrates) that they need.

1. From stored sugars in the plant at the time of harvest.
2. From supplemental sugars provided by using the proper amount of floral preservative.

HEALTHY ENVIRONMENT

The fresh flowers that you harvest need the proper environment to last for the longest possible time. Provide a clean air environment within the workroom or cooler to avoid ethylene gas exposure. Ethylene is a colorless, odorless gas that is emitted by aging fruit (especially apples), foliage, or flowers and from exhaust and faulty or incomplete burning of fossil fuels.

Provide the proper temperatures for both conditioning and storage. ***Conditioning*** is the preparation of cut plant materials for arranging by allowing for adequate solution uptake. The temperature of the water in which to condition the flowers upon arrival or after harvesting should be a comfortable bath water temperature, approximately 100 to 110°F. Use a thermometer the first

3–4. Condition flowers in warm (110°F) preservative solution.

time to be sure of the proper temperature. The warm water is more easily transported up through the xylem and also contains less air than cold water. Never use hot water since it may damage or scald the stem. The use of cold water may result in stem blockage because of the trapped air within the water.

Allow flowers to condition and take up water at room temperature for several hours. Placing buckets of freshly conditioned flowers into the cooler will slow the uptake of water. Room temperature is preferable for efficient uptake of the conditioning solution.

Once the flowers have been conditioned or **hardened** (filled with water and ready to be arranged), the flower buckets should be kept in a cool place, such as a cooler. The ideal temperature to store flowers is 34 to 38°F. Flowers will freeze at temperatures below 32°F; check the cooler and watch for any fluctuations. Foliage, especially boxed ones, will store well at 32°F. Store flowers and arrangements in cool areas away from sunlight and cold and hot air drafts.

Table 3–1. Basic Needs for Fresh-Cut Flowers

Needs	Notes
High-Quality Water	
Proper pH of 3 to 4.5 (acidic)	Acidic solutions (1) inhibit bacterial or microbial growth, and (2) allow for more efficient movement into and through stems than acidic or alkaline solutions.
	Usually corrected by proper amount and kind of floral preservatives.
Low total dissolved salts (TDS) of 200 ppm or less	Pure water is the best for flowers. Water with high salts causes wilting and weakening of stems. Avoid softened water.
Food	
Sugars	Harvest when flower has the most stored foods, usually late afternoon. Supplement with floral preservatives.
Healthy Environment	
Clean air—avoid ethylene exposure	To avoid ethylene exposure, keep fruit (especially apples) out of the cooler or any confined place with flowers. Other sources include faulty heating units, aging flowers. Practice sanitation.

Proper temperatures
    Conditioning—warm water and room temperature
    Storage—cool temperatures
	Warm water is quickly transported up the xylem. Room temperature is ideal to allow flowers to take up water and to open.

Sanitation	
Provide clean water Use clean tools (knives, shears) and containers	Avoid the buildup of bacteria and other microbes that cause the stems to be clogged.

SANITATION

Cleanliness or sanitation is important to a long life for a fresh flower. A designer should always clean their hands, their tools (such as knives or floral shears), and the containers for storing or arranging flowers. Avoid introducing bacteria or other organisms into the vase solution.

Disinfected work areas and clean coolers or storage areas are also important to eliminate the production of ethylene.

CAUSES OF FLOWER DETERIORATION AND DEATH

Once the flower or foliage has been harvested from the mother plant, its source of nourishment is cut off. It is up to the conscientious floral designer to supply all the needs of the cut flower to make it last for the longest possible time. Take note of the causes of deterioration and death of plant materials.

GENETIC LIFE

Each flower or foliage has an inherent or "built in" length of life depending on its genetic makeup. Proper care of plant materials will allow them to last their maximum genetic life span. Different varieties or types will last varying amounts of time because of breeding; choosing the longest-lasting kinds is beneficial. For example, many new rose varieties are bred to last longer.

Let's look at the wide range of lasting qualities that different flowers have.

Flower	Inherent Genetic Life (Approximate)
Daylily	1 day
Dutch iris	3–5 days
Spring bulbs	
Tulips, Daffodils	3–5 days
Roses	5–7 days
Snapdragons	5–7 days
Carnations	10–14 days
Chrysanthemums	14–21 days

| Daffodils (3–5 days) | Carnations (10–14 days) |

3–5. Be aware of the varying genetic life spans of different cut flowers.

3–6. The flowers in a floral design may last for differing times. After 4–5 days, remove the faded tulips and anemones and redesign the long lasting proteas (black tips), leucadrendron (yellow leaf-like flowers), and roses for a longer desired effect. (Courtesy, California Cut Flower Commission)

Since a floral design may have several kinds of flowers, the lasting qualities of the flowers may vary. In an arrangement with both snapdragons and chrysanthemums, the snapdragons will fade first and need to be replaced. A vase arrangement of spring flowers may all last the same amount of days. In some cases, the filler flowers (statice, sea lavender, or baby's breath) or the foliage may last longer than the flowers.

WILTING

Wilting is the most noticeable symptom of the deterioration of a flower. The causes of wilting may be unavoidable, as in the cause of an aged or spent flower, or may be totally avoidable by practicing proper care and handling techniques. Some causes of wilting are excessive water loss and lack of absorption.

Excessive Water Loss

A fresh flower loses water through **transpiration** (plant water loss) due to warm temperatures and low relative humidity (air moisture). Store flowers in a cooler or other cool place at or near 34 to 38°F with high humidity of 80 to 90 percent. Avoid drafty areas of either hot or cold. Also avoid over-handling flowers when arranging. Hot hands can damage flowers and increase transpiration. Do not position a flower by holding the flower head; always handle the flower stem.

Lack of Absorption

A common cause of premature flower wilting is **stem blockage**. Blockage results when the xylem becomes clogged at the stem end by air, bacteria, or other microorganisms, salts, undissolved floral preservative powder, or other debris, like sand or soil. The stem end may also begin to heal at the original cut and block the flow of water up the xylem.

*T*IMING OF HARVEST

Knowing the proper time of day and the proper stage of development at which to harvest flowers will also extend the life of fresh flowers.

Time of Day

3–7. Avoid over-handling or mishandling fresh flowers while arranging them.

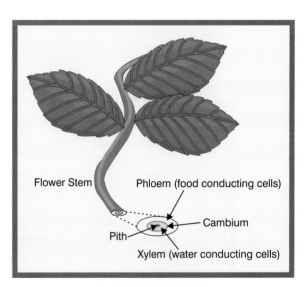

Flower Stem

Phloem (food conducting cells)

Cambium

Pith

Xylem (water conducting cells)

3–8. Xylem moves water up through the stem: phloem supplies food (carbohydrates, sugars) manufactured in the leaves to the rest of the plant.

Never harvest flowers when they are wilted! Avoid cutting flowers during the middle of the day on a hot day. It is important that the flowers and foliage have the highest amounts of stored foods and water.

Harvesting the flower or foliage at the proper time of day ensures that the most stored foods are present in the plant. Late afternoon or evening is an optimum time to harvest because the plant has been engaged in **photosynthesis**, the process of making sugars

Late Afternoon Best **Early Morning Next Best**

3–9. Harvest flowers when the most stored foods are present—late afternoon or evening. Early morning is the next preferred time because the flowers are full of water (turgid).

(food for the plant) from water and carbon dioxide, all day long. The **phloem**, the food-conducting tissue of the flower stem, is responsible for supplying the rest of the plant with its food, that is, the sugars that keep the cut flower healthy, colorful, and alive.

Morning is the next best time to cut flowers from the garden or greenhouse. At that time of the day, the plant is turgid or full of water. In the morning, the cut flowers are not experiencing water stress and can take up water (preservative solution) well.

Stage of Flowering

The ideal stage to cut the majority of flowers is just before the flower is fully open. Exceptions to this rule are daisies, which should be cut fully open, and the spring bulb flowers, such as tulips, daffodils, or iris, which may be harvested in the bud stage. Harvesting the spring bulb flowers in bud will allow a few extra days of vase life. Callas should be harvested at exactly the desired stage of opening because the flowers (from "tubes" to fully open) do not continue to develop after harvesting.

3–10. Most flowers are harvested just before peak—just before the flowers are fully open. _Left_—magenta spray roses; _right_—sunflowers and delphiniums. (Courtesy, California Cut Flower Commission)

3–11. Exceptions to harvesting just before peak.

Daisies cut when fully open.

Spring flowers cut in bud stage.

Left—pink gerbera daisies. *Right*—white Marguerite daisies.

Left—tulips and iris. *Right*—yellow tulips (with pink callas in tube stage and yellow fully open gerbera daisies).

Improper Environmental Conditions

The flower's food supply is used up more quickly in higher than optimum storage temperatures. The rate of **respiration**, the process of the plant using its stored food, increases with warm temperatures. An increased respiration rate leads to an early death or **senescence** of the flower. To prolong the life of a fresh flower, respiration must continue but at a slower pace. Cool temperatures reduce the respiration rate. Other benefits of cool temperatures are less ethylene is produced and the development of bacteria or other clogging microbes is slowed down.

ETHYLENE GAS EXPOSURE

Ethylene gas is a natural plant hormone that is produced by aging flowers, foliage, fruits, and vegetables. Keep flower storage areas clean and free of aging, decaying plant materials. Use clean containers, buckets, and tools. Avoid exposing fresh flowers to ethylene gas by never placing fruit, especially apples, in the flower cooler. Have the heating system in the building checked for efficient operation since incomplete or faulty burning of fuels or improper venting may also produce ethylene.

3–12. Ethylene damage on chrysanthemums.

Table 3-2. Ethylene Sensitive Flowers

Alstroemeria
Anemone
Baby's Breath
Bouvardia
Carnations, standard and mini
Cornflower
Delphinium
Lily
Snapdragon

Another way to combat the influence of ethylene gas is to purchase ethylene sensitive flowers from reputable growers and wholesalers who pretreat their flowers with **ethylene inhibitors**. These products block or tie up the ethylene within the flower and reduce its impact. Storing the flowers at proper cool temperatures also decreases the influence of ethylene on flowers.

Not all flowers are affected by ethylene gas. However, it is important to know the symptoms and to take precautionary measures, as previously mentioned, to reduce the effect of ethylene-induced disorders. Symptoms of ethylene gas exposure include:

◆ "sleepy" carnations (flower appears wilted or the petals feel soft or mushy—uniformly, not just the outer petals)

◆ large amount of falling or already fallen petals or florets

◆ standard or football—drop petals

◆ snapdragons—drop florets

◆ uniformly yellowing leaves

DISEASED OR DAMAGED

When purchasing flowers or selecting them to cut from the garden, the best quality ones should be selected. Plant materials with evidence of disease, insect damage, or broken and damaged plant parts should be avoided. Choose flowers and foliage that have good color; inspect the leaves and stems for any disease or damage.

PROPER STEPS TO CONDITION PLANT MATERIALS

HARVESTING TIPS

The two best times to harvest are late afternoon and morning. Wilted flowers should not be cut. Harvest flowers just before they fully open and at their peak of color. Spring bulbs may be cut when in bud stage. Use clean, sharp scissors or knife and cut the flower slightly longer than needed for the chosen floral design.

BUYING TIPS

When purchasing flowers, choose the freshest ones by looking for good typical color, green undamaged leaves, and a turgid appearance and feel (for carnations). Flowers, like roses, should be purchased at the proper stage of development, which is when at least half of the sepals have unfurled. A *green rose*, which is a rose with the green sepals still prominently enclosing the bud, may not open at all because it is not fully developed.

| Green rose (too soon) | Proper stage of development |

3–13. Look for roses to buy or harvest that are at the proper stage of development.

3–14. Avoid buying old roses with many opened petals.

Roses that are past their prime will have many loosened petals or may have changed or "blue" coloring. "Old" bunched roses will appear to be buds but are soft, not firm. A gentle touch will confirm it.

Buy from florists or wholesalers who provide a quality product and practice proper care and handling, including pretreating the appropriate ethylene-sensitive flowers. Interview your flower sources to find out if they use floral preservatives.

STEPS FOR CONDITIONING FLOWERS AND FOLIAGE

The following steps for conditioning flowers will increase both the longevity of your flowers and the efficiency of your operation.

1. Unpack and inspect (for proper amount and quality) the flowers immediately upon receiving them. Report any missing or poor-quality flowers.

2. Prioritize the order of processing the flowers—condition wilt-prone (gerberas, bouvardia, baby's breath) and expensive (lilies, orchids, roses) ones first.

3. Remove sleeves, ties, and any foliage that will be below the water level to prevent rotting and bacterial formation.

4. Recut all stems; remove 1/2 to 1 inch (under warm water is the ideal situation, especially for roses).

5. Use specific treatment solutions as needed, such as a hydration solution or an ethylene inhibitor solution.

6. Place in a floral preservative solution mixed at the proper concentration.

   • Too little—Increased bacterial growth, which causes stem blockage and shortened vase life.

   • Too much—May result in toxicity (yellowed leaves, petal dropping) and reduced vase life.

   • For bud opening—Some products will give specific directions for the proper amount to use to effectively open bud-harvested flowers, such as standard carnations and gladiolas

7. Let the flowers remain at room temperature in a well-lit area for two to three hours to allow for the uptake of the floral preservative solution.

8. Place the flowers in a cooler set at 34 to 38°F, with high humidity (80 to 90 percent), and constant lighting.

9. The flowers are ready to be used in a design!

SPECIAL TREATMENTS

As you become more interested and familiar with different types of flowers and foliage, you will need to know some special treatments that will benefit certain types of plants.

Underwater Cutting

Cutting stems under water will ensure that water, not air, enters the stem (xylem). Individual flowers can be held underwater in a sink or bucket and recut. Also, commercial underwater cutters are available that will allow you to recut an entire bunch of flowers. Underwater cutting is especially suggested for roses. Replace water regularly to avoid the spread of bacteria.

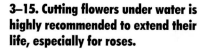
3–15. Cutting flowers under water is highly recommended to extend their life, especially for roses.

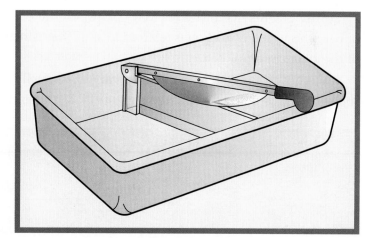

Woody Stems or Branches

Plant materials that have woody stems should be conditioned in preservative solution mixed with very warm water. The use of warm water will maximize water uptake.

Flowering branches may be forced into flower earlier by pruning them from flowering trees (crab apples, forsythia, apple, cherry, or plum trees) before the tree flowers outdoors. Recut and place the branches into very warm preservative solution. The solution may need to be changed periodically (very warm water each time) until the desired opening of the flower buds is reached.

Stems with Milky Sap

Some flowers exude a milky sap when cut from the mother plant. Examples are poinsettias, the related spurges or euphorbias, and poppies. If not conditioned quickly or properly, the sap will solidify at the cut end and block the uptake of preservative solution. The following techniques will allow optimum water uptake of stems with milky sap:

1. A quick dip (five seconds) in boiling water with the flower heads protected. The stems are then immediately placed into a regular preservative solution.

2. Placement into very warm preservative solution.

3. Careful use of heat near the cut flower end (a match flame)—do not burn the cut end!

Reviving Roses

A rose bud may be just a few days old when the entire bud obviously wilts and bends down. This wilted condition is referred to as a ***"bent neck"*** rose. It is caused by blockage of the xylem by air or debris.

If you notice the condition quickly (within 24 hours), you can revive the flower. Remove the bent neck rose from the arrangement. Place the entire stem into a warm preservative

3–16. A "bent neck" rose is a common site.

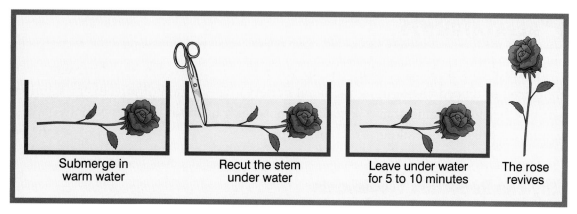

Submerge in
warm water

Recut the stem
under water

Leave under water
for 5 to 10 minutes

The rose
revives

3–17. A bent neck rose can be revived.

solution, either in a sink or pan, and immediately recut the stem under water. Allow the rose to remain submerged for 5 to 10 minutes. When the rose has revived, place it in the design.

FLORAL PRESERVATIVES

WHY USE THEM?

Using floral preservatives can almost double the vase life of most fresh flowers. Numerous university and corporate tests have shown these results consistently over the years with a variety of flower types.

INGREDIENTS AND THEIR FUNCTION

Effective floral preservatives have three main ingredients. Each of these ingredients has an important function in keeping flowers and foliage fresh and long lasting. Either powder or liquid formulations should be used in high-quality water.

Ingredient	Function
A sugar source	Supplemental food source
An acidifier	Inhibits stem plugging by preventing future microbial growth
A bactericide	Kills any bacteria present in the vase or on the stems

PRETREATMENTS

Pretreatments are specific solutions into which newly harvested or newly arrived flowers are placed or dipped before using the floral preservative solution. Pretreatment solutions may be ethylene reducing or may be valuable for quickly hydrating the stems. Both of these treatments will help to prolong flower life.

Ethylene Reduction Treatments

Ethylene reduction treatments should be used for ethylene-sensitive flowers. An ethylene reduction treatment is only needed once. So check to see if the grower or wholesaler treated the floral product before shipping the flowers.

Hydrating Solutions

A hydrating solution can be beneficial for nearly every flower but is specifically great for flowers that are slow in their water uptake or wilt-prone, such as gerberas, roses (helps with bent neck), bouvardia, or anthuriums. The use of hydrating solutions is valuable for extending flower life for flowers in general everyday enjoyment but also for important floral displays or functions lasting for several days to a week.

Solutions are available premixed (quick and ready to use) or in concentrate (mixed as needed). Various solutions can be used as a quick 5- to 10-second dip while others suggest 30- to 60-minute treatments. Careful reading and following of the instructions will be very important to their proper mixing and use.

HOME REMEDIES

Over the years, various home remedies have been used to make flowers last longer. Some have been moderately successful; some do not work at all. A few home remedies that will work when added to water include (1) non-diet, non-cola soft drinks; (2) lemon juice; and (3) mouthwash. In our unscientific but fun classroom experiments, soft drink "floral preservatives" are tested compared to commercial floral preservatives and plain tap water. The soft drinks are mixed equally by volume with tap water. Winners for different years have tied or come in second place to commercial preservatives. Examples of some of the home remedy winners are lemon-lime drinks, root beer, iced tea with lemon, grape and orange sodas, and fruit juice-based soft drinks. Each of these winners has two common ingredients—sugar and citric acid. Tap water usually finishes in last place, except for the year that a salty sport drink was included in the experiment. The highly concentrated salty drink was so harmful to flowers that the stems broke at the nodes within three to four days.

Other home remedies that do not work include aspirin, pennies, and plant fertilizer. Always evaluate a home remedy to see if it has sugar and citric acid (and a bactericide) before using it. Many of these home treatments will actually clog the stem and do more harm than good.

COMMERCIAL PACKING AND SHIPPING

INTERNATIONAL SCOPE OF FLORICULTURE

The flowers sold in florist shops in the United States may have been grown both domestically (within our country) or internationally. The countries where flowers are commonly grown for shipment to the United States and all over the world include:

Region	Countries
North America	United States—California, Florida, Hawaii
Europe	Holland (The Netherlands), France, Italy, Spain
South America	Columbia
Middle East	Israel
Asian	Australia, Singapore
Africa	South Africa, Kenya, Ivory Coast
Central America	Mexico, Jamaica, Guatemala, Costa Rica, Honduras, Ecuador

Packing

Individual growers harvest flowers in the field or greenhouse. The flowers are separated into groups or **grades** before they are bunched. Grades may be based on quality, such as unblemished flowers and foliage, uniformity, or size. Roses and other crops are also graded according to stem length, stem strength, and uniformity. Roses are commonly purchased as shorts, mediums, long, fancy, and extra fancy. The stem lengths start at 9 inches and are graded by 2-, 3-, or 4-inch increments, depending on the grower. Utility grade roses have blemished foliage, off-color flowers, or possibly weak stems.

Flowers are then bunched before shipping. Bunches are made up of flowers of all the same color. The stem ends are usually bound with a string, rubber band, or a twist-tie.

Sleeves are placed over the bunch for protection. Some flowers, such as Fuji mums and gerberas, are individually sleeved to protect the delicate flower.

Knowing the commercial size of bunches for major types of flowers is very important when ordering or buying flowers from a wholesale florist. Roses and carnations are packaged as a bunch of 25; other major crops, such as irises, gladioli, standard chrysanthemums, snapdragons, tulips, and larkspur are packaged in groups of 10. Pompon chrysanthemums and filler flowers are bunched according to weight.

Table 3–3. Common Bunch Sizes for Major Floral Crops

Bunch Size	Examples
25	Roses, carnations, foliages, such as leatherleaf, palms
10	Bulb crops—tulips, daffodils, irises. Delphinium, larkspur, snapdragons. Standard & Fuji chrysanthemums. Gladioli, lilies (unless noted), liatris. Dendrobium orchids
Variable by weight	Pompon chrysanthemums (usually at least 5 stems). Filler flowers—baby's breath, sea lavender, Monte casino asters
Single	Gerberas, many tropical flowers

From the grower, the flower bunches are packaged in boxes for shipping. Flower heads are usually packaged at both ends of the box to use the space wisely. Wooden supports are secured at one or several places across the box to keep the flowers from shifting. These boxes are quickly **precooled** before shipping and kept cool throughout the shipping process.

3–18. Drypacked flowers are securely packed with flower heads at both ends of the box to use the space wisely and to avoid shifting or damage.

Precooling allows cool air to flow through the box of flowers and quickly replace the warm air. Flowers that are packed in this fashion to the wholesaler and then florist are referred to as being shipped dry or drypacked. Dry pompons chrysanthemums and mini carnations can be kept cool, shipped quickly, and then conditioned by the florist or floral design instructor. Less handling actually insures a less damaged product.

Other flowers, such as gladioli and snapdragons or specialty crops, are packed upright in boxes called hampers. Some crops will also be shipped this way with the stem ends placed in water.

Shipping

Since flowers are perishable, it is important that the product reaches its destination very quickly. Most crops are shipped by air from the grower to the wholesaler. From the wholesaler to the retailer, flowers are shipped in different ways depending on the distance to be traveled. The flowers may again travel by air; however, shipping by truck usually completes the trip.

REVIEWING

MAIN IDEAS

Fresh flowers and foliage can last for days longer by learning about their needs and after-harvest care. Provide cut flowers with high-quality, acidic water, sugars for food, a healthy environment such as clean air and cool storage temperatures, and proper sanitation.

The causes of flower deterioration and death include an inherent genetic life span for each flower, wilting due to excessive water loss or lack of absorption (stem blockage), used food supply, and ethylene gas exposure. To counteract some of these causes, flowers should be harvested at the proper times and conditioned properly.

The steps for conditioning begin with unpacking and inspecting the flowers after receiving them. Sleeves, ties, and lower foliage are removed; the stem ends are recut; and the flowers are placed into a warm floral preservative solution. The flowers should remain at room temperature for two to three hours for efficient uptake of the solution. Flowers may then be placed in a 34 to 38°F cooler. Other special treatments include underwater cutting, treating woody stems or stems exuding milky sap, and reviving roses.

Floral preservatives are very important for increasing longevity of fresh flowers. They have three main ingredients, including a sugar source, an acidifying agent, and a bactericide. Combining the use of floral preservatives with other pretreatments can benefit many different types of flowers. Pretreatments are used to reduce ethylene and for quick hydration. Home remedies that contain citric acid and sugar can be effective (and expensive) as floral preservatives when mixed 1:1 by volume with water.

Floriculture has an international scope. Flowers are grown and shipped all over the world. Individual growers grade, bunch, and package their flowers in an efficient manner so the flowers will arrive at their destination undamaged. Flowers are bunched by specific bunch sizes according to type. Knowledge of bunch size helps when ordering or buying flowers.

QUESTIONS

Answer the following questions using complete sentences and correct spelling.

1. What three factors are important when considering water quality for fresh flowers?

2. What is pH? What pH is recommended for fresh flowers in solution?

3. Why is softened water not recommended for conditioning flowers?

4. What are the proper temperatures (air and water) for conditioning and storing flowers?

5. What length of time should the flowers remain at room temperature? Why?

6. What are some causes of deterioration and death of flowers due to natural aging processes? What are some causes of premature deterioration of flowers?

7. What is ethylene gas? What causes it to form? What effect does it have on flowers?

8. When should the perfect rose be harvested?

9. What are the basic steps to properly condition flowers?

10. Why is underwater cutting recommended?

11. How do you revive a "bent neck" rose?

12. Why should floral preservatives be used for fresh flowers? What are the three main ingredients and their function?

13. Why do some home remedies work reasonably well and others fail miserably? Give examples.

14. What are drypacked flowers? How are they packaged?

EVALUATING

Match the term with the correct definition. Write the letter of the term on the line provided.

a. acidic
b. transpiration
c. phloem
d. turgid

e. green rose
f. highly buffered
g. bactericide
h. pH

i. xylem
j. bent neck rose
k. salinity
l. precool

_____1. Salt content in the water.

_____2. The water-conducting tissue within the stem.

_____3. A rose that is not fully developed.

_____4. Being resistant to change in pH.

_____5. The loss of water from a plant due to high temperatures and low relative humidity.

_____6. Kills bacteria.

_____7. The food-conducting tissue within the plant stem.

_____8. Quickly lowering the temperature.

_____9. Full of water.

_____10. pH of 1 to 6.

_____11. A rose that is prematurely wilted.

_____12. The relative concentration of hydrogen ions in water.

EXPLORING

1. Set up your own floral preservative experiment. Choose five types of soft drinks (diet and non-diet) or mouthwash or lemon juice to compare with a commercial floral preservative as well as tap water. Mix the treatments 1:1 by volume with tap water. Place three to five flowers in each solution. Evaluate the flowers daily or every other day. Record and determine the winner(s).

2. Visit a wholesale florist and watch flowers being conditioned (processed).

3. Test the pH of tap water. Compare it with the pH of several commercial floral preservative solutions mixed according to the directions. Customize your own floral preservative to reach a pH of 3 to 4.5.

CHAPTER 4

The Principles of Design

OBJECTIVES

This chapter is about the principles of design. It has the following objectives:

1 Define floral design.

2 List the principles of design.

3 Explain the concept of proportion.

4 Explain how the concept of balance is applied to floral design.

5 Describe how rhythm is applied to floral work.

6 Explain how the principles of dominance and focal point are used in floral design.

TERMS

asymmetrical balance
balance
center of interest
centering
contrast
counterbalancing
dominance
floral design
focal area

focal point
free, variable rhythm
Golden Mean
physical balance
principles of design
proportion
radiation
regular, repeated rhythm
repetition

rhythm
scale
symmetrical balance
transition
variety
visual balance
visual weight

4–1. The major principles of design are proportion and scale, balance, rhythm, and dominance.

THE principles of design are basic fundamental truths to follow in creating floral arrangements. Although the principles for floral design were first outlined by the English during the Victorian Era, these principles are still valuable to us today. These design principles should not be regarded as mere rules; they are the foundation of every good design despite changing trends and new plant materials.

FLORAL DESIGN DEFINED

Floral design is the art of organizing the design elements inherent in plant materials, container, and accessories according to the principles of design to attain a composition with the objectives of beauty, simplicity, harmony, suitability, and expression. *Flower arranging* is another commonly used term for floral design. However, floral design is the more accurate term because the word *design* implies that the person arranging the plant materials is applying the principles of design.

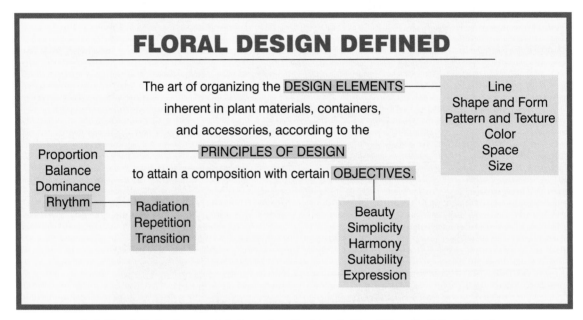

FLORAL DESIGN DEFINED

The art of organizing the DESIGN ELEMENTS
inherent in plant materials, containers,
and accessories, according to the

Line
Shape and Form
Pattern and Texture
Color
Space
Size

Proportion
Balance
Dominance
Rhythm

PRINCIPLES OF DESIGN

to attain a composition with certain OBJECTIVES.

Radiation
Repetition
Transition

Beauty
Simplicity
Harmony
Suitability
Expression

4–2. Floral design is an art that requires the knowledge of the principles of design.

PRINCIPLES OF DESIGN

The **principles of design** (or art) are rules and guidelines to help a floral designer create a beautiful composition. Design principles are fundamental truths used to make accurate floral design decisions. The major principles of design are proportion and scale, balance, rhythm, and dominance. Other minor design principles include radiation, repetition, transition, variation, contrast, and focal point.

Not only learning the principles but also using them well is essential in creating any kind of art, including arranging plant materials. The proper application of each of these principles will lead to artistic and pleasing floral arrangements. Each principle is important and interrelated to the others and can impact the entire arrangement.

PROPORTION

Proportion is the principle of art that is the foundation of all the other principles. Good **proportion** means the pleasing relationship in size and shape among objects or parts of objects. **Scale** is a part of proportion, dealing with relative size only among things, not shapes.

Three aspects of proportion are very important in floral design. These are:

♦ Proper proportion of the ARRANGEMENT to its SURROUNDINGS.

♦ Proper proportion of the FLOWERS AND FOLIAGE to the CONTAINER.

♦ Proper proportion of the FLOWERS AND FOLIAGE to EACH OTHER.

4–3. Proportion is the pleasing relationship in size and shape among the components in a design.

Proportion to Surroundings

The floral design must suit the intended placement in its surroundings. The arrangement should fit the area in size and in shape, as well as in style. Imagine a massive wooden table with a petite rose arrangement placed on top of it. The size of the table would overpower the arrangement, diminishing its visual impact. The small arrangement would be more in proportion in a book shelf niche or on a small table.

Determining proper proportion for flowers that will be carried or worn is

4–4. A floral design that looks too small on a massive table is more in proportion in a small niche.

4–5. These bouquets show the importance of proper proportion. On the left, the bouquet is too small; in the center, the bouquet is overwhelming and too large; on the right, the bouquet is just right.

also very important. The flowers should not overwhelm the person, yet should be large enough for visual impact. Imagine a bride who expects a beautiful bouquet. If the bouquet is either too small or too large, the effect is awkward and out of proportion.

Proportion is very important when designing for any event, whether it is a wedding or a birthday party. Not only should the floral designs be in proper scale to the room, but they should also be suitable and in harmony with the theme and the location. To design an arrangement for an event that has proper proportion as well as harmony and suitability, use the following information:

	For Proper Proportion	For Harmony and Suitability
Room	Size of the room Ceiling height	Style of room furnishings Color of room furnishings
Tables	Size and shape of tables Color of tablecloths	Number of tables
Designs	Centerpieces needed One-sided designs needed Accessories	Colors Theme

Proportion of the Flowers and Foliage to the Container

The Greek's **Golden Mean** (a ratio of 1.6 to 1) and Japanese traditions are used to attain a pleasing proportion between the plant material and the container. Floral designers have learned that proportion will be pleasing if the height of the arrangement is at least 1½ times the height or width of a container, whichever is greatest.

Beginning floral designers often create designs that are too short. The flowers, not the container, should be highlighted. In general, upright arrangements should be taller than they are wide and horizontal centerpieces will be wider than they are tall.

A maximum dimension is not stated however, because that depends on the background, the type of plant material, the theme, the container, and the skill and artistic expression of the designer. If thin, wispy plant materials are used, the arrangement height may be 2 or 2½ times the container height. An arrangement placed on the floor in an entryway may need to be 2½ or 3 times the container height to provide the visual impact and proper scale for the site.

The container plays a significant role in determining the maximum height of a design. Consider four factors of the container when determining the proper proportion of the flowers to the container:

♦ Physical dimensions (height, width, volume)

♦ Color (dark versus light)

♦ Material and texture (pottery, glass, ceramic, wicker)

4–6. The height of an arrangement should be at least 1½ times the container's greatest dimension.—that is, 1.5:1.

4–7. A floral design that is too short makes a beginning designer easy to spot. The container is too prominent in this arrangement.

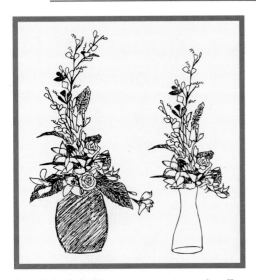

4–8. A dark, bulky pottery vase can visually support a taller, larger floral design than a clear carafe-shaped glass vase of the same height.

4–9. This showy centerpiece with a circus theme is designed to be seen over (the votive candles and round mirror), around (the mirrored column), and under (the flowers).

♦ Shape (ginger jars, carafes, coffee cups)

Containers that are visually heavy, such as a dark, bulky pottery vase, can visually support a taller, larger design than a clear carafe-shaped glass vase. If the same container is available in many colors, the lighter colored or clear ones will support arrangements that are shorter than their darker colored counterparts.

Exceptions

Centerpieces are a major exception to the 1½ times the container height rule. In a dining situation, the centerpiece should not obstruct the view of the people sitting at the table. It is ideal to be able to see over, through (or around), or under a centerpiece. Bud vases or small vase arrangements, placed in the center of a dining table, may also be shortened to allow viewing over them.

Proportion of the Flowers and Foliage to Each Other

The individual flowers and foliage within the floral design should complement each other in size. Variation in sizes of flowers is pleasing and interesting, but huge jumps in size may not be in proper proportion to each other. An arrangement containing only very small flowers, such as baby's breath, and very large flowers, such as Fuji chrysanthemums, does not display proper proportion. Flowers of intermediate size would provide a more pleasing scale relationship within the arrangement.

Steps to Pleasing Proportion—A Checklist

♦ Determine where the arrangement is to be displayed

♦ Select the container (consider shape, color, size, type, and texture)

♦ Select plant material to yield the planned design

- ◆ Establish height
- ◆ Establish width
- ◆ Establish the outermost contour
- ◆ Note changes in proportion that occur as various pieces of plant material are added
- ◆ Make necessary adjustments to yield planned design
- ◆ Prune
- ◆ Add taller material
- ◆ Use less or more of various plant materials as they interact within the design to maintain color, size, shape, pattern, or space balance

BALANCE

Balance is a key part of the beauty of an arrangement. Balance is the physical or visual stability of a floral design. Balance refers to the arrangement's equilibrium or equality in weight, both physical and visual.

Physical balance is the actual stability of plant materials within the container. A design with physical balance has secure mechanics (the foam and the flowers do not move or shift) and can stand on its own in a stable manner and not fall over.

Visual balance refers to the perception of an arrangement being in balance or being equal in weight on both sides of the central axis. A floral design lacking balance is visually unsettling like a crooked picture or a shirt buttoned the wrong way. Poor visual balance in the floral design will overshadow other attractive aspects of the design, such as proper proportion or an effective center of interest.

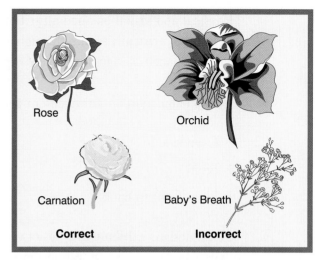

4–10. Avoid large jumps in flower size for pleasing proportion among flowers within an arrangement.

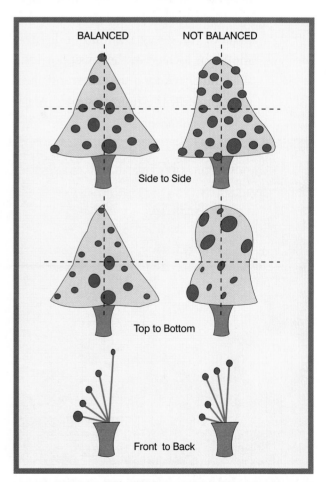

4–11. Check each floral design's visual balance from side to side, top to bottom, and front to back.

Physical and visual balance must both occur for a design to be successful. An arrangement may be physically secure through good mechanics, yet lack visual balance. A beautiful visually balanced design may even topple over during a banquet because the physical balance is poor.

Visual balance in an arrangement should be evident in three views:

♦ From side to side

♦ From top to bottom

♦ From front to back

Floral designs exhibit two types of visual balance. These are symmetrical and asymmetrical balance. To check a floral design for balance, imagine lines dissecting the design into four equal quadrants, vertically and horizontally. Both symmetrical and asymmetrical designs should have equal visual weight on either side of the central axis (side to side). The upper portion of the design (above the imaginary line equally dividing the upper and lower parts of the design) should be lighter in weight. The greater weight of the arrangement should be located in the lower portion, near the container rim. Next, turn the design to the side and check for a smooth transitional flow of flowers from front to back. At the top of the arrangement, the flowers should not be leaning too far forward or too far backward. The outline of the flowers should follow the line of the designer's gently curved hand. The top flowers should not "umbrella" or lean out over the lower flowers.

4–12. Symmetrical balance is formal and dignified. Avoid a mirror image in flower placement, which can be monotonous.

Symmetrical Balance

Symmetrical balance in a floral design occurs when both sides of the design have, or seem to have, the same physical weight. The weight and appearance of the materials on either side of the imaginary central vertical line are similar. Although the design should have equal weight on each side, it should not be an exact mirror image. Symmetrical balance is a European inheritance and is called formal balance. This type of balance is dignified, restful, predictable, and even grand and impressive.

Although symmetrical balance is called formal balance, clever additions can make it interesting and not so predictable. The use of a dynamic center of interest, clever flower placements (groupings), and accessories can "jazz up" this formal design.

A symmetrical arrangement is usually displayed against a symmetrical background and with symmetrically placed accessories. For example, place a pair of candles, one on each side of a symmetrical centerpiece, or have one, two, or three candles centered within the design.

Asymmetrical Balance

Asymmetrical balance is a dynamic, informal balance, which has its roots in Japanese and Chinese flower arranging. The plant material and manner of placement are different on each side of the central vertical axis; however, the arrangement must appear to be in balance. An asymmetrical design achieves balance through compensation or counterbalancing. The combined weight on one side equals that on the other with the differences compensating or counterbalancing visually. This type of balance is active, creative, and stimulating. Suggesting movement, asymmetrical balance strongly attracts and holds attention. Space is very important and contributes to the achievement of balance.

4–13. Accessories and clever flower placements can vary the predictable nature of a symmetrical design.

4–14. Asymmetrical balance is informal, creative, and dynamic.

4–15. An asymmetrical background looks very appropriate for an asymmetrical design.

Asymmetrical designs are usually displayed in a less formal setting. If accessories are used, these are placed in an asymmetrical way; equal amounts of accessories are not used on each side.

Examples of Symmetrical and Asymmetrical Design Styles

Many geometric shapes can be designed as either symmetrical or asymmetrical. For example, a triangle can be designed in a symmetrical way, such as an equilateral (all sides equal) triangle or an isosceles (two sides equal) triangle or in an asymmetrical manner, such as a scalene triangle (all sides unequal). Centerpieces can also be traditionally round or oval or can be varied with asymmetrical placements of branches or flowers.

Symmetrical designs include round or oval centerpieces, topiaries, one-sided styles—oval, round, equilateral or isosceles triangle, inverted T, fan-shaped, and vertical arrangements. Typical asymmetrical styles are crescent, Hogarth curve, scalene or right triangle, diagonal, and vertical.

Table 4–1. Typical Symmetrical and Asymmetrical Design Styles

Symmetrical	Asymmetrical
Oval and round centerpieces	Centerpieces
Topiaries	Topiaries
Vase arrangements	Vase arrangements
One-sided designs:	One-sided designs:
Oval	Crescent
Round	Hogarth curve
Fan	Fan
Triangle—equilateral, isoceles	Triangle—scalene, right
Inverted T	Diagonal
Vertical	Vertical

Understanding Visual Weights

The **visual weight** of a flower or foliage is its perceived lightness or heaviness based on its combined characteristics of color, shape, pattern, etc. An understanding of how to determine visual weights of plant materials is important when balancing a floral design. A good floral designer must learn to judge and place materials of differing visual weights to achieve balance within an arrangement.

Table 4–2. Visual Weights Guideline for Plant Materials

Design Element	Visually Lighter	Visually Heavier
Size	Small	Large
Color		
Hue	Cool	Warm
Value	Light	Dark
Intensity	Dull, grayed	Bright
Shape	Linear	Round
Space		
Single flower description	Airy and open petals	Dense and full petals
Flower placements	Spacious	Clustered
Pattern	Fine	Bold (in size and color)
Texture		
Surface quality	Rough or Hairy	Shiny
Visual quality	Fine	Bold or coarse

Visualize a seesaw at a playground. Two children of equal weight are perfectly balanced on the seesaw; however, a larger, heavier child must move closer to the center of the seesaw to balance the smaller, lighter child at the other end. The same concept applies to placing flowers in a design of differing visual weights. Darker colors appear heavier and are placed lower and closer to the center of an arrangement; lighter colors appear more light in weight and can be placed higher and in the outermost positions. There is a transition

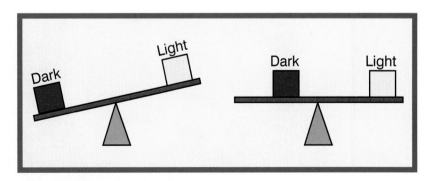

4–16. Dark colors appear heavier and should be placed nearer to the center of an arrangement to achieve visual balance.

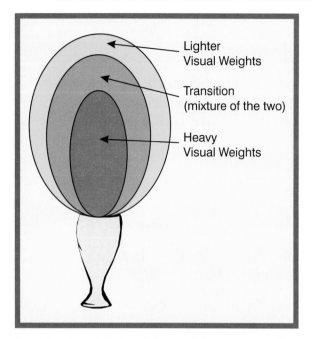

4–17. In a floral design, lighter weights are generally placed higher and in the outermost areas while heavier weights are placed lower and closer to the center of the arrangement.

zone where plant materials of differing visual weights should be subtly combined to create a unified look.

Knowing the specific characteristics of differing visual weights helps a designer to organize and position flowers properly for balance. The following chart can be used as a guideline. Remember that flowers may not have clear-cut characteristics, neither all heavy or all light, so there must be some additional judgment calls made to use the flower properly. For example, a white fully open rose would be heavy because of its size even though its white color is visually light. A dark red rose bud would probably be used higher in the design because of its smaller size, even though it is a dark color. With time and experience, judging visual weights of plant materials will become easier.

Ways to Visually Balance a Design

For both symmetrical and asymmetrical designs, a good designer should learn tips and techniques to visually balance their designs. The keys to beautifully balanced floral designs are centering and counterbalancing.

Centering is the technique of placing dominant plant materials along the central vertical axis. Centering allows heavier plant materials (large, dark, round) to be placed higher in

4–18. Centering dominant and visually heavy plant material is a dramatic and easy way to balance a floral design.

the design. Standard carnations, football mums, bird of paradise, gerbera daisies, and Fuji chrysanthemums can all be centered for a dramatic and beautifully balanced design.

Understanding **counterbalancing** is absolutely necessary for the beginning designer. Counterbalancing means to balance plant materials on one side of a design with visually equal materials on the opposite side. It is essential to the visual stability of the outline of an asymmetrical design, but it is also a valued technique for visually balancing flowers within both symmetrical and asymmetrical designs. Use counterbalancing to avoid making symmetrical designs a mirror image.

For an asymmetrical design, counterbalance a main line (the primary line), positioned in the upper left side of the arrangement, by placing a shorter line (the secondary line) in the lower right side. The secondary line should be approximately one half the length of the primary line.

Visually balancing similar materials within an arrangement uses the technique of counterbalancing with upper left and lower right placements (also upper right and lower left) and the technique of equalizing. The first example is illustrated with the placement of a hot pink mini carnation on the upper left side of a design and counterbalancing it with a similar hot pink mini carnation in the lower right side. Using the equalizing technique, one large red carnation on the lower left side of an arrangement can be counterbalanced by placing two red mini carnations on the upper right side.

Counterbalancing dissimilar materials requires more thought and judgment. Using the visual weight chart will help the decision-making process. For example, a large, bicolor lily on the lower left side of a design can be counterbalanced beautifully with a small pink rose bud and a white unopened tulip on the upper right side. Foliage can also help in counterbalancing each side.

4–19. The main line of an asymmetrical design is counterbalanced with a shorter line (the secondary line) placed low on the opposing side.

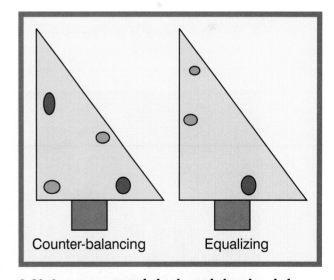

Counter-balancing   Equalizing

4–20. A common counterbalancing technique is to balance a dark flower on the upper left side with one on the lower right. Another technique is to equalize one large flower with two smaller ones placed higher on the opposing side.

RHYTHM

Rhythm is related orderly organization of the design elements to create a dominant visual pathway. The related aspects of the design (colors, shapes) tie the design together and gives it flow. Rhythm is "frozen motion" and suggests movement. A floral design with pleasing rhythm has continuity that invites the eye to view the entire design.

Rhythm can be regular and repeated or free and variable. **Regular, repeated rhythm** is characteristic of a marching band with bold, repetitive beats. In nature, the horizontal branching of the spruce tree or the strong radiating leaves of the yucca plant display regular, repeated rhythm. In floral design, flowers placed at regular intervals from the top to the bottom of the design create the strong regular, repeated type of rhythm. Regular, repeated rhythm is an easy-to-use beginning technique that is strong and compelling but monotonous if overused.

Free, variable rhythm is subtle like the spontaneous chirping of birds in a woodland. In nature, the irregular branching patterns of honey locust and cloud patterns in the sky display free, variable rhythms. In floral design, this subtle flowing style can be used in almost any design including line arrangements, centerpieces, and vase arrangements. The unstructured use of branches, filler flowers, and flowers with multiple florets, such as alstroemeria, lilies, and freesias, add interesting lines and forms to achieve free, variable rhythm.

When the viewer's eye flows smoothly and completely through the parts of an arrangement, the viewer is reacting to the rhythm of the design. When the viewer's eye moves jerkily from one group of unrelated plant materials to another, the design's rhythm is choppy

4–21. Regular, repeated rhythm is strong, predictable, and compelling (left); free, variable rhythm is subtle, unstructured, and flowing (right).

and ineffective. Flowing rhythm can be beautifully created by the use of radiation, repetition, and transition.

Radiation

In floral design, ***radiation*** gives the illusion that all of the flower stems are coming from one point. Radiation gives a strong sense of unity and naturalness to an arrangement because this is the way that plant materials grow in nature. To understand and create radiation in a floral design, ponder the yucca plant. The leaves emerge from a single point and project out from the center; each leaf forms a slightly different angle to consistently fill out the circular shape.

In a floral design, allow the stems to radiate out naturally from the vase or floral foam. From a top view, stems should equally radiate out from the center like the spokes of a wheel or like a daisy's petals. Avoid crossing stems or having too many verticals or horizontals

Front View   Top View

4–22. The yucca plant displays perfect radiation. Floral designers can take tips from this plant and its perfectly radiating leaves when creating floral designs with pleasing radiation.

without transitional angles. Crossing stems will cause the floral design to look unprofessional and messy. Crossing stems, which is a common habit with beginners, also is a very ineffective use of floral foam, leading to crowding and insecure mechanics. The placement of too many verticals or horizontals without the transitional angles will make a design look "flat" and unsatisfactory. A three-dimensional design is the goal.

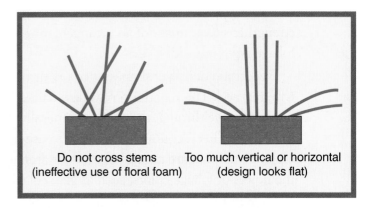

Do not cross stems
(ineffective use of floral foam)

Too much vertical or horizontal
(design looks flat)

4–23. Common radiation mistakes.

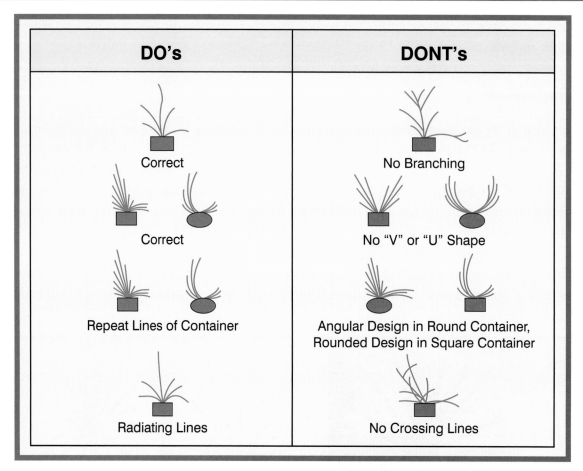

4–24. Examples of repetition of line Do's and Don'ts.

Repetition

Repetition is achieved by the repeated use of one or more of the design elements, such as flower shape, color, space, or line throughout the floral design. Repetition unifies and strengthens the impact of an arrangement but can be boring unless a variety of flowers or foliage types are added.

Repetition of flower shapes or colors throughout the design is an elementary, but effective, method. The repetition of yellow daffodils throughout a design gives it unity and also moves the eye through the design. Generally, the color of the container is repeated within the design. Green containers are easy to use because foliage repeats their color. Some container colors that are neutral or used for dramatic effect are not necessarily repeated within the flower or foliage colors, such as glass, black, or metallic.

Several types of repetition are used in producing effective rhythm. Repetition of line is important for creating rhythm. The main line should end in one direction; a branched line will disrupt the repetitive rhythm of the design. Also, one main rhythm should predominate with opposing lines permitted at the container to continue the line. The viewer should always be able to tell which line is the most important. Exceptions are parallel designs and naturalistic ones. Avoid V-shaped or U-shaped arrangements. The floral design rhythm should repeat the lines of the container; for example, angular lines should be followed with a square container. Place curving ovals or crescent in a rounded container. Avoid crossing lines within the design.

Transition

Transition is a smooth, gradual change from one element to another. Rhythmic change can harmonize and unify an arrangement. The transition from lighter plant materials and placements at the outer areas of a floral design to heavier material and closer groupings near the container and focal point effectively moves the eye smoothly and rhythmically through a design. Rhythmic change in floral design refers to placing small to large flowers, light to dark colors, linear to round shapes, or spacious to more grouped flowers in sequence from the top to the bottom of the design.

A valuable floral design technique to produce rhythm through transition is to vary the flower facings within the arrangement in a systematic way. In general, flowers should face upward at the top, face to the left and right on those respective sides, face forward at the center, and face in logical intermediate placements. Varying flower facings creates a beautifully rhythmic contour to the arrangement and avoids the flat look—that is, as if the design is drawn on a two-dimensional piece of paper.

Transition is important between the arrangement and its container. The foliage and lower flowers should partly conceal or overlap the container rim to provide continuity between the two. The container should not seem separated from the flowers or seem too

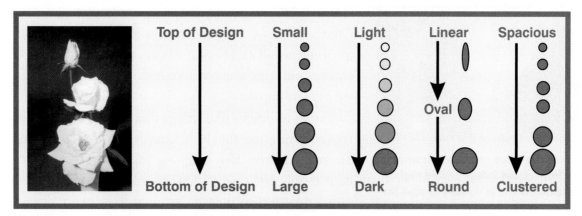

4–25. Rhythmic change through transition refers to grading flowers from small to large, light to dark, linear to oval to round, and from more spacious to more clustered.

4–26. Vary flower facings from upward at the top to outward at the bottom with transitional facings to the left and right sides also.

4–27. This container is too prominent. Transition dictates that flowers and foliage should slightly overlap the container rim to visually connect the floral design and the container.

prominent. There are exceptions to this rule depending on the design style and the value (in dollars or sentiment) of the container.

Variation and Contrast

Variety and contrast are essential to interesting designs and pleasing rhythm. **Variety** refers to a diverse assortment or differing components. Variety focuses our attention and stimulates our interest and imagination. **Contrast** describes objects that have striking differences beyond mere variety or diversity. Contrast takes variety to a higher degree. Too much of anything is dull and boring. However, too much variety can be confusing and chaotic. In floral design, strive for variety within unity.

Try to use more like things than unlike or different things. Using too much repetition can lead to boring designs. An attractive radiating design can be monotonous if only one type of flower is used. Strive for interesting mixtures of flowers, using at least two types for variety; three or more types are even more interesting. Choose differing sizes and shapes of flowers and foliage from linear to round and everything in between. The addition of filler flowers also adds needed variety.

Contrasts that are well planned and controlled make attention-getting and striking designs. Provide contrast in texture and color by placing smooth, shiny, coarse-textured dark green leaves behind a white, spacious, frilly Fuji chrysanthemum. Team linear scotch broom with exotic bicolor lilies, or iris leaves with roses, for contrast in shape. An asymmetrical line mass provides contrast because of its opposing horizontal lines placed at the base of the arrangement.

DOMINANCE AND FOCAL POINT

The effective use of dominance or emphasis lets the viewer know what is most important in the design. **Dominance** in floral design means that one design element or characteristic is more prevalent or noticeable and other elements are subordinate to the main feature. Interest and attention are captured and held if one feature dominates and others are secondary in importance.

One or more methods of developing dominance may be used, but each method should contribute to the unified effect. Dominance may be developed by using dominant plant material; an emphasized design element; a distinctive design style; an idea, theme, or holiday; or a focal point or center of interest.

For example, a vase arrangement of peonies and other flowers shows dominance because of the bold peonies, the dramatic pink and rose colors, and the style of arranging. Three methods have all contributed to the pleasing dominance of this arrangement.

4–28. Dominance is effectively conveyed by the bold use of peonies (plant material) in pink and rose colors (design element) designed as a vase arrangement (design style).

Using an idea or theme is a very easy way to develop dominance. An idea such as a spring fling event would highlight spring flowers in cheerful colors and maybe gardening tools. A circus theme would incorporate bright colors, balloons, clowns, and circus animals. Holidays and special events dictate the types of flowers, colors, and accessories to unify the entire display.

4–29. Develop dominance for floral design and events by targeting an idea, theme, or holiday.

Table 4–3. Ways of Developing Dominance for Floral Events

Method	Examples
Dominant plant material	Abundant garden flowers, tropicals, roses, lilies
An emphasized design element	Shape, space, size, pattern, texture, color
A distinctive design style	Centerpiece, asymmetrical triangle, linear bud vase
An idea, theme, or holiday	Spring fling, birthday, fall, Christmas
A focal point or center of interest	Large flowers, round or special form flowers, dark shades, concentration of plant material, use of framing foliage nearby, strong color contrasts, radiation of the rest of the plant material to the focal area, accessories

Center of Interest (Focal Point or Focal Area)

A center of interest is an important part of many design styles. A **center of interest** (also called **focal point** or **focal area**) visually ties the entire arrangement together. The location of the center of interest is usually centered in the lower part of the arrangement just above the container rim. Some contemporary designs will actually have several focal points.

Although many design styles have a focal area, some floral designs do not. Centerpieces and vase arrangements contain equal flower placements all throughout the arrangement with no single area of focus.

Ways to Develop a Center of Interest

To create the most effective center of interest, always plan this dominant area before beginning the arrangement. In general, the greatest visual weights are concentrated at the center of interest. Consider using some of the following methods of developing a center of interest or focal area:

♦ Large flowers

♦ Round or special-form flowers

♦ Dark shades

♦ Concentration of plant material (greater amounts, less space)

♦ Use of framing foliage nearby

♦ Strong color contrasts

♦ Radiation of the rest of the plant material to the focal area

♦ Accessories

4–30. An effective center of interest may be developed by using several methods, such as concentrating the plant material, using dark, bold red colors (also a strong color contrast of white and red), using framing foliage nearby, and by letting the lines of the design radiate to the center of interest.

Several methods may be used to create a beautiful center of interest that ties the entire design together.

Through dominance and contrast, a design gains both unity and variety. Dominance comes with repetition; contrast comes through change. Each depends on the other to make a successful floral design.

REVIEWING

MAIN IDEAS

Floral design is the art of organizing the design elements that are inherent in plant materials, containers, and accessories according to the principles of design (art) to attain a floral design that has beauty, simplicity, harmony, suitability, and expression.

The principles of design are guidelines to help a floral designer create a pleasing floral design. The design principles are proportion, balance, rhythm (radiation, repetition, transition), and dominance.

Proportion is the art principle that determines the relationship in size and shape among parts of a design. Three aspects of proportion in floral design are very important, including the proper relationship of the arrangement to its surroundings, the proper relationship of the plant material to the container, and the proper proportion of the flowers and foliage to each other. Based on the Golden Mean, the height of an arrangement should be at least 1½ times the container's greatest dimension. The exceptions are centerpieces or small vase arrangements for the dining table that can be shorter to allow for unobstructed views.

Balance is the physical or visual stability of a floral design. A floral design must be balanced both physically and visually. Visual balance should be evident from side to side, top to bottom, and front to back. Symmetrical and asymmetrical balance are two forms that floral designs may take. Symmetrical balance is more traditional and formal but is very pleasing if not designed as an exact mirror image. Asymmetrical balance is informal and dynamic and is achieved through counterbalancing. It is important to understand the visual weights of plant materials to be able to use them successfully to balance arrangements, whether symmetrical or asymmetrical. In general, lighter visual weights, such as linear, light colors, are placed higher and in the outermost areas of a design while heavier visual weights, such as round, dark colors, are placed lower and closer to the center of the arrangement.

Rhythm is the orderly arrangement of design elements within a design used to create a flowing visual pathway. Any design may use two types of rhythm: regular, repeated or free, variable. Radiation, repetition, and transition are three important ways of producing flowing rhythm.

Dominance indicates to the viewer the important feature(s) of an arrangement. Dominance can be developed by emphasizing plant material, a design element, a design style, an idea, theme, or holiday, or developing a dominant area or focal area.

A center of interest or focal area visually ties the entire arrangement together. Create an effective center of interest by using large, round, or special-shaped flowers, dark colors, framing foliage nearby, strong color contrasts, concentration of the plant material, and radiation of the lines of the design to the focal area.

QUESTIONS

Answer the following questions using complete sentences and correct spelling.

1. Why are the principles of design important to floral design?

2. What questions should a floral designer ask when designing arrangements for a specific room? List at least eight.

3. What is the general rule for arrangement height? What are two exceptions to this rule?

4. What determines an arrangement's maximum height?

5. What aspects of containers affect a floral design's height?

6. When designing, how is an arrangement checked for proper visual balance?

7. Should symmetrical balance be an exact mirror image? Why or why not?

8. What are three ways to visually balance a floral design? Be thorough.

9. Why is rhythm important to a floral arrangement?

10. What are important ways to use proper repetition within a floral design?

11. How can a floral designer develop a dominant impact for an event?

12. What is a center of interest? What are other terms for it? Where is it located?

13. What designs do not have a center of interest?

EVALUATING

Match the term with the correct definition. Write the letter of the term on the line provided.

a. Golden Mean   e. asymmetrical balance   i. balance
b. visual weight   f. design principles   j. rhythm
c. transition   g. center of interest
d. proportion   h. radiation

_____1. Visually ties a floral design together.

_____2. A pleasing relationship in size and shape.

_____3. Visual and physical stability.

_____4. A ratio of 1.6 to 1.

_____5. Balanced by compensation or counterbalancing.

_____6. Smooth gradual change.

_____7. Guidelines or rules for floral design.

_____8. Related orderly flow or organization.

_____9. Perceived lightness or heaviness.

_____10. Flower stems appear to emerge from one point.

EXPLORING

1. Visit a furniture store and note the placement of the pictures on the wall in the various display areas. Determine which displays have symmetrical balance and which ones are asymmetrical. Choose your favorite type of balance.

2. Collect three of the same containers and flowers to make arrangements with varying proportion. Make design heights of 1, 2, and 3 times the container's height. Evaluate the Golden Mean for yourself.

3. Design two arrangements with similar materials. Make one a regular, repeated rhythm and the other free, variable rhythm. Which rhythm suits your personality?

CHAPTER 5

Design Elements

TERMS

advancing colors	hue	right triangle
analogous	intensity	scalene triangle
color wheel	inverted T	secondary colors
complementary	isosceles triangle	shade
cool hues	line	shape
crescent	line materials	split complementary
depth	lines of opposition	tertiary colors
design elements	low-visibility colors	texture
equilateral triangle	mass flowers	tint
filler flowers	monochromatic	tone
form	mottled foliage	triad
form flowers	naturalistic	value
free form	pattern	variegated foliage
geometric	polychromatic	warm hues
high-visibility colors	primary colors	
Hogarth curve	receding colors	

THE *design elements* are the physical characteristics of the plant materials that a designer uses in a floral design. Thorough knowledge of the design elements of line and form (shape), space, texture, pattern, and color is so important because floral designers select and organize these "tools"—the design elements—to create beautiful floral designs.

5–1. The beautiful shapes, colors, textures, and patterns of flowers and foliage are fascinating tools for the floral designer.

THE SHAPE OF THINGS— LINE AND FORM

The first design elements to be considered are line and form or shape. In floral design, the beauty of the design may be due to the natural, graceful, flowing lines of the plant material, or to the method of arrangement, or to a combination of both nature and the designer's skill. Good design depends on understanding and effectively using both line and form.

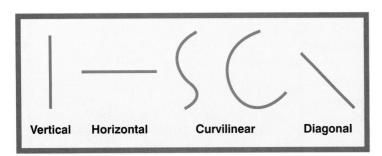

Vertical	**Horizontal**	**Curvilinear**	**Diagonal**

5–2. The four main types of line are vertical, horizontal, curvilinear, and diagonal.

LINE

Line is the prominent feature for several types of arrangements, including line, line-mass, many ikebana or Japanese-style designs, and many contemporary styles. *Line* is the visual movement between two points within a design. The four types of line are vertical, horizontal, curvilinear, and diagonal. All of these lines should appear to radiate from a central part of the design. Lines may be forceful, subtle, continuous, interrupted, or implied.

Line can give a design not only structure but also expressiveness. The emotional significance of each line can add to the expressive quality of any design. The following chart outlines the four major lines and their potential meaning in floral design.

Type of Line		Meanings or Emotional Significance
Vertical	(Like a person standing)	Active, alert, aspiring, inspiring, dramatic, masculine, striking, attentive, formal, dignified
Horizontal	(Like a person sleeping)	Calm, restful, tranquil, peaceful
Curvilinear	(Like a relaxed person)	graceful, playful, flexible, sophisticated, elegant, refined
Diagonal	(Like a person running)	Active, dynamic, strong, on-the-move, restless, violent, or changing (use sparingly)

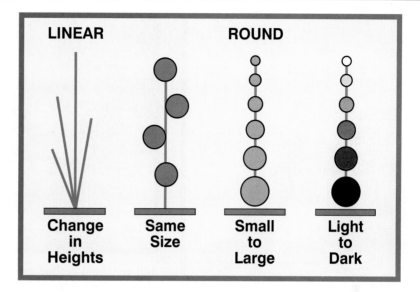

5–3. A line can be created with both linear and round plant materials.

Line can be created not only with linear plant materials but also with round flowers. Place round plant material in a line and in a progression from upward flower facings at the top to outward flower facings near the container. The round flowers can be all the same size and color or can be varied from light to dark, small to large, or dull to bright.

Form and Shape

Line and form are closely related because appropriate lines are needed to create designs with beautiful form. **Form** is the three-dimensional shape of the outline of a floral design. **Shape** is the two-dimensional term for form. Floral design forms or shapes can be either one-sided or all-around (also called free-standing).

THREE CLASSIFICATIONS OF FORM

The three broad classifications of form or shape in floral design are geometric (the largest category), naturalistic, and free form or modern. The three forms can interact within a floral design. Seldom is an arrangement totally or stiffly geometric or completely naturalistic. Free form often incorporates parts of both geometry and nature in its composition.

Naturalistic forms suggest the natural growth of plant material through groupings of flowers and foliage. The floral designer generally uses the plant material as it would appear in nature, that is, branches (trees) placed higher than the grouped flowers with some type of moss for a "ground cover." Naturalistic designs are pleasing both as one-sided designs or all-around centerpieces. As in nature, open spaces are important.

5–4. Naturalistic forms suggest nature and incorporate groupings of flowers and foliage.

5–5. Free form designs are very contemporary and creative, often "bending" the rules.

The *free form* category is a creative "anything goes" form that has very few rules. Free form emphasizes free-flowing lines and outlines and the artistic use of materials (unusual placement, changed color, placed upside down). Many contemporary designs can be classified as free form. It is an advanced design style that "bends" some of the design principles.

GEOMETRIC FORM

Geometric designs mirror the shapes of geometry—the circle, square, triangle, and rectangle. Most geometric designs, however, are based on the circle and the triangle. The three-dimensional terms for circle and triangle are sphere and pyramid. These forms are most commonly referred to as their two-dimensional shapes: circle and triangle. Even though the floral designer uses the two-dimensional terms for these arrangements, the goal is always a pleasing three-dimensional design.

Vertical or Horizontal

Often before beginning a design, the designer must choose whether to create a vertical or horizontal geometric shape. Also, many geometric shapes can be designed as either one-sided arrangements or as all-around designs (centerpieces). The one-sided version will exhibit more vertical orientation and the all-around version will emphasize the horizontal.

Circle

Geometric shapes displaying the spherical or circular shape may be designed as both symmetrical and asymmetrical designs. Symmetrical designs include the circle, oval, and fan or fan-shaped. These shapes are traditional favorites for many occasions and locations in the home.

Asymmetrical circular forms are the crescent and Hogarth curve or S-shaped. The **crescent** is a portion of a circle that resembles a "C" or a new

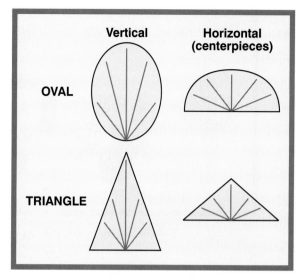

5–6. Most geometric shapes may be designed as either a vertical or a horizontal.

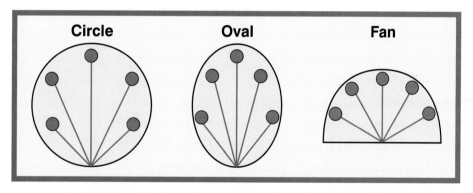

5–7. Symmetrical circular shapes are the circle, oval, and fan.

moon. The **Hogarth curve** resembles an "S" and was created by William Hogarth, an English painter in the eighteenth century. His quote: "A straight line is a line of duty; a curving line is a line of beauty" shows his love for the curvilinear.

Most geometric shapes, including the circle and oval, have many variations in floral designs. These forms may be upright one-sided designs or vase arrangements or they may take the form of rounded centerpieces, the "round mound." Nose-

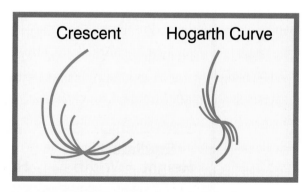

5–8. Asymmetrical circular shapes include the crescent and the Hogarth curve (or S curve).

One-Sided   All-Around   Wreath   Topiary

5–9. Geometric forms, such as the circle or oval, may be designed in many variations.

gays or bouquets for weddings or proms have round, oval, or crescent shapes. Topiaries may have a circular or oval shape as well. Generally, round or curved plant material is used to create these circular shapes. Often, round or circular-shaped containers complement these shapes.

Triangle

Pyramidal (a three-dimensional term) or triangular shapes may also be symmetrical or asymmetrical. Symmetrical triangles are equilateral, isosceles, and inverted "T." All sides are equal in an *equilateral triangle*. An *isosceles triangle* has two equal sides with a narrower width than the equilateral triangle. An *inverted "T"* is a dramatic variation of the isosceles triangle that is very vertical with more space and fewer flowers.

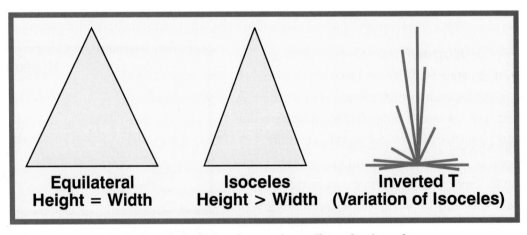

Equilateral
Height = Width

Isoceles
Height > Width

Inverted T
(Variation of Isoceles)

5–10. Symmetrical triangles may be equilateral or isosceles.

5–11. Asymmetrical triangles include right triangles (or L-shaped) and scalene triangles.

Right Triangle
(left and right facing)

Scalene

An asymmetrical triangle is an eye-catching shape because the tallest plant material (height placement) is placed off-center and then counterbalanced on the opposite lower side. Two examples are the right triangle and the scalene triangle. The **right triangle** or "L" shape forms a 90-degree angle near the container and can be left- or right-facing. The **scalene triangle** exhibits three sides of differing length and is dramatic and contemporary.

Combined Forms

A **lines of opposition** design is a high-contrast use of two different design lines or forms, sharing a center of interest to tie the design together. For example, a traditional oval centerpiece, designed with candles placed in the center, is a lines of opposition design—a vertical with a horizontal oval. A wreath with a striking vertical sheaf of wheat placed at the base of the circle beautifully combines a circle and a vertical. An asymmetrical triangle with an opposing diagonal cluster of dried materials also combines two lines or forms—a triangle with a diagonal.

Oval and Vertical

Crescent and Vertical

Circle and Hogarth

Circle and Vertical

Crescent and Vertical

Vertical and Hogarth

5–12. Combining two lines or forms with a shared center of interest creates an eye-catching line of opposition design.

GENERAL FLOWER SHAPES

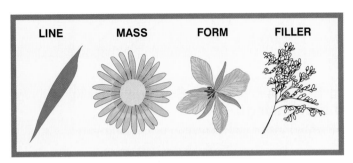

5–13. Plant materials can be classified in four main shapes or forms—line, mass, form, and filler flowers.

Most plant materials can be divided into four general categories based on shape—line materials, form materials, mass materials, or filler flowers or foliage. The combining of these four types of plant shapes or forms lends variety to a design.

LINE

Line materials, such as snapdragons, larkspur, liatris, gladioli, delphinium, heather, or foliage, such as eucalyptus, Scotch broom, or horsetail (equisetum), are ideal to form the outline of an arrangement and direct the eye into the floral design. Linear plant materials are adaptable. Line foliage can be curved, tied, wired, and trimmed to suit the arrangement. Line flowers can be cut into smaller sections to use as fillers or mass flowers.

5–14. On the left, the line flowers (from left to right) of heather, red snapdragons, purple liatris, and green bells of Ireland direct your eye into the arrangement to the mass flowers (lavender lilac, pink gerberas, and pink carnations) and form flowers (yellow-white alstroemeria and pink callas). On the right, the white delphiniums direct your eye to the grouped sweet peas, ranunculus, and roses with white waxflower providing the filler. (Courtesy, California Cut Flower Commission)

FORM

Form flowers, also called special form flowers, are flowers with distinctive shapes, such alstroemerias, freesia, iris, lilies, orchids, open roses, and most tropical flowers, such as bird of paradise, anthuriums, and proteas. Form flowers and materials create a striking center of interest and add uniqueness to a design.

5–15. On the left, the pink lilies are eye-catching form flowers along with the mass flowers of asters and the fillers of ming fern and statice. (Courtesy, California Cut Flower Commission) On the right, the tropical proteas and fully open roses create interesting forms along with the tropical foliages.

MASS

Mass flowers can be classified as round or solid flowers. Although mass types are usually flowers, some dried pods and cones also fit this category. Mass plant materials fill out the shape of a design. Examples of mass flowers or pods are allium, chrysanthemums, carnations, daisies, and lotus pods.

FILLER

Filler plant materials are the fourth category. *Filler flowers* (also called "fillers") are small flowers that are used to add texture, color, and depth as well as fill space between the mass and line flowers in a floral design. Examples are sea lavender, baby's breath, statice, lady's mantle, and golden aster.

5–16. On the left, the round mass flowers of gerberas and slightly opened roses fill out the design with beauty and color; two yellow lilies add variety as a form flower. The yellow solidago, short blue delphinium, and purple statice provide the filler. On the right, the green Kermit chrysanthemums, green hydrangeas, white daisy mums, and large white Queen Anne's lace create fullness and interest with their mass types. The ferns, bells of Ireland, and trailing ivy provide line. (Courtesy, California Cut Flower Commission)

5–17. Note how the filler flowers (sea lavender) blend both designs together. On the left, the form flowers used here are open roses, freesias, tulips, and sweet peas. On the right, the sunflowers are form flowers and delphiniums are line flowers. (Courtesy, California Cut Flower Commission)

FORM, DEPTH, AND THE THIRD DIMENSION

Form is three-dimensional. Height and width are the first and second dimensions. The third dimension, *depth*, allows an arrangement to look natural and full, not flat or pressed. Flowers in a floral design should repeat nature and be full and radiating toward the front. In nature, plants do not naturally grow flat, like an espalier. An espalier is a tree or shrub that is trained to grow in a very narrow space.

Depth is gained by placing the center of interest flower(s) or focal flower(s) to extend beyond the container rim. A pleasing design has a rounded contour, not a stiff, pressed, or flattened one. Achieve pleasing depth by adding flowers or filler within the design at a deeper level than the outermost contour. Depth adds interest and character to a design because the viewer is invited to look within the design. Additional methods for achieving effective depth are listed below.

Methods of Achieving Depth (the Third Dimension) in a Floral Design

1. Vary flower facings: At the top — facing up

   Left side — angle some to the left side

   Right side — angle some to the right side

   Lower front — orient outward

5–18. For depth, allow some plant material to be hidden or "buried" to provide depth and increased interest within an arrangement. Note the "buried" hydrangea, slightly hidden behind the pink ranunculus on the right side of the design and slightly showing in the back on the left side.

2. Radiate plant materials—Avoid too many verticals or horizontals. Consider the yucca plant or the radiating spokes of a wheel.

3. In a one-sided arrangement, (1) finish the back, (2) allow some plant materials to lean back slightly and some to be extended forward.

4. "Bury" some flowers so they are partially hidden by others.

5. Highlight with graded use of color—place light colors (advancing) in front of dark colors (receding); warm colors (advancing) in front of cool colors (receding); try dull colors (receding) behind or in front of bright colors (advancing).

A floral design displaying good depth is the mark of an experienced and talented designer. Beginners tend to make flatter arrangements and seem to fear extending any flower beyond the container or below the arrangement's basic contour.

SPACE IS GOOD TASTE

Another mark of an experienced floral designer is the generous incorporation of effective space within an arrangement. Space is an important design element in every arrangement, adding vitality and life. By creating meaningful spaces, the solids are sharply defined and important and the beauty of separate plant materials can be fully appreciated. Beautiful flowers should be seen clearly without crowding.

Space is inherent within many types of plant materials, such as ferns, iris, and clustered flowers like nerine lilies and alstroemerias. Create space by incorporating branches and lin-

5–19. The effective use of space within a floral design gives it beauty and interest.

ear or unique shapes. Allow plenty of space near these materials for enjoyment of their interesting shapes and spaces.

Most floral designs have more spaciousness at the top with progressively less space toward the center of interest. Learn to plan for effective space at the beginning of the design. Space showcases the good taste of the floral designer.

IN TOUCH WITH TEXTURE AND PATTERN

Texture is the design element that is directly related to the sense of touch. In plant materials, *texture* is determined by both the surface quality (tactile value) and the structure or placement of the plant parts (visual value). Used wisely, interesting textures enhance and increase interest in a design.

Plant materials that have tactile value, that is, texture appealing to the sense of touch, can be described as silky, satiny, feathery, smooth, rough, hairy, furry, woolly, velvety, or prickly. Plants also have many variations in their structure. This visual value can be described as airy or dense, delicate or coarse, lacy or solid.

TIPS WITH TEXTURE

Glossy textures attract attention and should be placed carefully for proper balance. A glossy-textured flower, like an anthurium or the bird of paradise, is more eye-catching than the dull or soft textures of proteas. However, dull, matte surfaces are often easier to use in large quantities than their shiny counterparts.

Although glossy textures attract attention first, varied textures, such as rough, hairy, prickly, or other unique ones will hold the viewer's attention longer. These varied textures are more complex and keep the viewer's interest for a longer time.

The combination and the contrast of shiny with dull, smooth with rough, or polished with velvety can add heightened interest in a design because the plant textures are enhanced and highlighted by their differences. Contrast adds interest yet should be planned and controlled. Huge textural variation among a wide array of plant materials within one arrangement should be avoided.

Plant materials of medium texture can be good blending materials within a design. Foliage often provides this transition. The addition of foliage, such as leatherleaf or Boston fern, provides transition between a soft velvety rose and lacy Queen Anne's lace.

5–20. The textures of the flowers and the container should repeat and enhance each other.

The textures of the flowers and the container should be repeated to enhance each other. A glossy vase can be distracting if the flowers do not repeat the polished, shiny, or glossy texture. The background, fabrics, and accessories should also harmonize with the texture of the arrangement.

POINTERS ABOUT PATTERN

Pattern is determined by the physical characteristics of the plant materials. The arrangement of the leaves and petals create many structural patterns. A fern may have a repeated pattern, expressing precision. Other foliage, such as a saddleleaf philodendron, have an irregular leaf pattern and may seem informal or casual. Many plants have color patterns on their leaves. Pattern is closely tied to texture because leaves with color patterns appear textured or leathery when the surface is actually smooth.

Color patterns in both foliage and flowers add interest to an arrangement. Color patterns are often described as mottled or variegated. Plants with **mottled foliage** have leaves with flecks or areas of a different color. Examples of mottled foliage are mother-in-law's tongue (*Sansevieria*) and galax leaves. Plants with **variegated foliage** have lines, stripes, or areas of another color on the leaves. Examples of variegated leaves are Hosta, prayer plant foliage, and spider plantlets or "babies." Use plant materials with color patterns in small amounts as accents (see Figure 5–1). Overuse of color patterns can create a chaotic look.

MAKING THE MOST OF COLOR

Color is a vital part of our existence. It is all around us in nature, in fashion, and in art. Color can be a compelling entity, creating emotional responses in those who view it.

To many, color is the most noticeable and important element of a floral design. How colors are selected and positioned together will determine whether a floral design is noticed or purchased. Color choice is of the utmost importance to the bride-to-be, the party-giver, the high school student ordering prom flowers, or the interior design-conscious customer. A floral designer's knowledge of color, its properties, expressive qualities, and color schemes should be thorough. With an in-depth understanding of the use and function of color, a floral designer can be more effective and creative.

THE COLOR WHEEL

In the seventeenth century, Sir Isaac Newton illustrated the theory of color. He passed white light through a prism, causing the light to separate into a rainbow of colors—RED, ORANGE, YELLOW, GREEN, BLUE, VIOLET—all with varying wavelengths. He developed the color wheel by bending the spectrum of six colors into a circle.

In nature, the color wheel appears naturally in a rainbow or when light passes through a waterfall to create miniature rainbows. Those colors are the full spectrum colors of the color wheel. The **color wheel** that floral designers use today is a circle that divides colors into primary, secondary, and tertiary colors and includes the tints and shades of each color. The **primary colors** are red, yellow, and blue and are called the foundation colors since all other colors are created from these three. The **secondary colors** are orange, green, and violet and are a mixture of the two adjacent primary colors. For example, a mixture of yellow and blue creates green. The six **tertiary colors** have hyphenated names such as red-orange and blue-green and are created by mixing the adjacent primary and secondary colors.

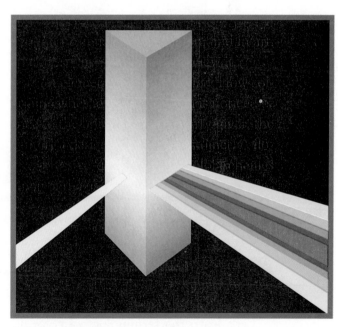

5–21. Sir Isaac Newton passed white light through a prism to discover a rainbow of colors.

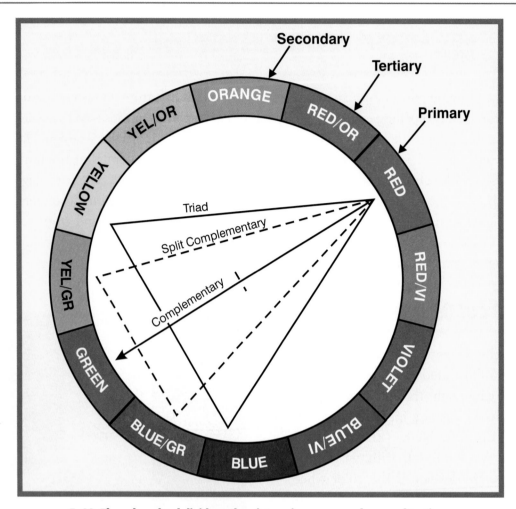

5–22. The color wheel divides colors into primary, secondary, and tertiary.

COLOR VOCABULARY

Let's learn the terminology of color. Color has three important qualities that a floral designer should know—hue, value, and intensity (or chroma).

The Qualities of Color

Hue is the name of a color. The hue or name of the color stays the same even though it may be lighter, darker, or grayer. Two major exceptions are pink, which is light red, and tan and brown, which are the light and dark values of orange.

Warm hues are red, orange, and yellow and the tints, shades, and tones of those hues. These colors evoke cheerful, warm feelings and are associated with warm or hot things like fire, heat, or the sun. These hues are considered ***advancing colors***, which means that flowers, containers, and accessories in warm colors look larger and seem to advance or move toward the viewer. Warm colors are focusing and stimulating and are good choices for a design that is seen from a distance. Beware though, because some people find an excess amount of warm colors irritating.

Cool hues are blue (sometimes violet) and its tints, shades, and tones. These hues evoke thoughts of ice and cool mountain streams. These hues are considered ***receding colors*** and are not highly visible from a distance. These hues are great for intimate, up close arrangements or as accents in designs with warm colors or white.

5–23. Warm colors are red, orange, and yellow and bring thoughts of heat and sunshine. Cool colors are blue and sometimes violet and evoke thoughts of the sky and calm, cool, icy mountain streams.

White, black, and gray are considered neutral hues. Static hues are those hues between warm and cool hues, mostly green and violet. Violet is an interesting hue because it is variable, that is, it can be cool or warm depending on its proximity with other colors, the lighting, or its background.

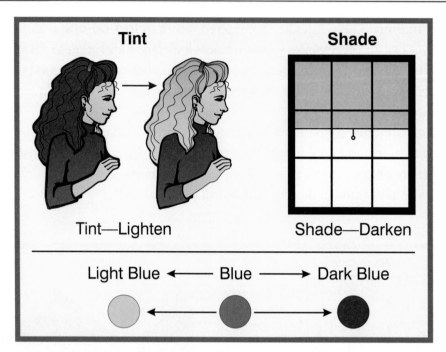

5–24. A tint is a light value, a hue with white added. A shade is a dark value, a hue with black added.

Value is the lightness or darkness of a hue. A **tint** is the light value of a hue, that is, the hue with white added. Think of a person tinting or lightening their hair to remember that a tint of a hue is a lighter form of the full spectrum hue. A tint of blue is light blue; a tint of red is called pink instead of light red; light violet is usually called lavender; a tint of orange may be peach to tan. A **shade** is the dark value of a hue, that is, the hue with black added. A person pulling a shade in a room darkens the room. Adding the word *dark* to the hue or name will identify a value for most hues, such as green (dark green), blue (dark blue), violet (dark violet or purple), yellow (dark yellow), and orange (dark orange). Some values are more commonly called by other names. Dark blue may be called navy; dark orange may be called burnt orange, rust, or brown (if dark enough); dark yellow may be called gold.

Intensity (or chroma) is the relative brightness or dullness of a hue. The full spectrum hues have full intensity and purity because of the absence of white, black, or gray. The colors of a rainbow after a summer rain display the bright, pure, full intensity colors. Flowers with reduced intensity (dullness) have either a mixture of gray or another color added to the full spectrum hues. A **tone** is a color that has been subdued by the addition of gray. Tone is a good word for this concept because it gives the idea of being toned down.

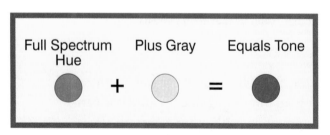

5–25. A tone is a grayed hue.

To determine if a flower is a full spectrum hue or a tint, shade, or tone, use the color wheel to compare it. If a color wheel is not available, think of the pure rainbow colors as a starting point.

Color Force

The combination of hue, value, and intensity all contribute to determine the visibility or color force of the flowers within an arrangement. For example, an arrangement for a large area should be designed with a majority of flowers that are highly visible and advancing. *High-visibility colors* are warm hues, light values (tints), and bright intensities. These colors are effectively used as the framework of a design for proper proportion as well as balance well throughout the interior of the design. *Low-visibility colors* are cool hues, dark values (shades), and dull intensities. When used as the framework of a design, these colors will not be eye-catching and may make the arrangement appear too short or unimpressive. Low-visibility colors are excellent in arrangements viewed at close range or for use within an arrangement placed at a distance to provide contrast and depth.

5–26. Note that the yellow lilies in this centerpiece are much more eye-catching and highly visible that the light-blue sea holly (*Eryngium amethystinum*) filler. Although both colors of lilies are warm and advancing, yellow is more highly visible than orange.

The Expressiveness of Colors

Through the ages, color has been used to express messages and ideas. We respond emotionally to colors. Let's discover some of the qualities and emotion-producing characteristics of each color.

Red, the color of fire and blood, is a very showy, warm, advancing color and a powerful, strong hue. It conveys a wide range of contrasting emotions, such as love or hate, anger or passion, excitement or danger. Red is forceful and bold and can be placed in designs seen from a distance. Red is the most pleasing in warm color schemes, not cool ones, except in an analogous scheme with purple or with blue and white for patriotic themes. A design tip is to allow adequate space for red in a design. Red can overpower other colors so don't crowd it. Pink, a tint of red, suggests spring, lightness, and femininity. Maroon and other dark values can indicate power and maturity but may not be as visible from a distance as standard red.

Orange is attention-getting and stimulating but not as visually overpowering as red or as eye-catching as yellow. Orange gives warmth and radiance to a design and expresses festive, energetic, vivacious, outgoing, and friendly emotions. Generally, only small amounts of orange are used within a design, but light values (tan, peach, salmon) or dark values (rust, copper) of orange can be used in greater amounts without overwhelming the viewer. Orange is typically used in the autumn but can be used in small amounts throughout the year to give a cheerful radiance and depth to any design. Brown, a dark value of orange (sometimes, yellow), expresses mellow, down-to-earth, tranquil feelings. It is a favorite in fall arrangements, dried arrangements, and for a container color.

Yellow is a highly visible, attention-getting, warm color that conveys cheerful, happy, vibrant feelings, or cowardly, irritating ones. Yellow reflects more light than the other colors and can be placed into a design to brighten a design and add highlights. Yellow is very versatile with many colors and can be added in small amounts to add "life" and brighten dark colors. Add yellow when designing for a dark location or for low lighting conditions.

Green is a fresh, soothing, restful hue that provides a natural background for all of the other colors. Green also conveys quietness, peace and tranquility, and "green with envy." Use green as a blending and softening effect. Green is a great choice for a container color.

Blue is a cool receding color that is not highly visible from a distance. Blue conveys cool, calm, serene, and dignified feelings or sad, private, or boyish messages. It also expresses loyalty and truth, as in "true blue." Light blue can seem joyful, youthful, and playful. Dark blue may convey more somber or depressing emotions. Combine blue with brighter warmer colors for visibility and highlights. Different lighting can also affect its appearance.

Violet (or purple) suggests royalty, splendor, and refinement. It can be gentle, mysterious, and even sad. Violet will seem warm or cool depending on the background, proximity of other colors, and the lighting. Violet adds depth to a design when in combination with warm colors.

Color Schemes Used in Floral Design

The study of color use in floral design is challenging but also rewarding. Knowledge of color schemes can help even a novice designer to design more eye-catching and pleasing arrangements. Typically, for pleasing balance and proportion, one color should be more prominent to unify the design.

Color schemes are based on either related or unrelated color schemes. The two related color schemes are monochromatic and analogous. The unrelated color harmonies are complementary, split complementary, triad, contrast, and polychromatic.

Related	Unrelated
Monochromatic	Complementary
Analogous	Split complementary
Triad	Contrast
Polychromatic	

A *monochromatic* color scheme includes only one hue and its tints, shades, and tones. This color harmony is very pleasing to the eye and unifying. An easy-to-spot monochromatic design would include light lavender asters, medium purple mums, and deep purple delphinium. Some monochromatic designs are trickier to identify, such as one in the orange family—beige gerbera daisies, bright orange safflowers, burnt orange chrysanthemums, and brown autumn leaves. Usually, green foliage and other neutral colors are considered the background of a design and not taken into consideration in determining the color

5–27. Color schemes can be related (all yellow) or unrelated (yellow, blue, purple) color harmonies.

5–28. A monochromatic color scheme may have only one hue in its design but may include tints and shades.

harmony. Exceptions would be Christmas arrangements or other striking use of greens. To spice up a monochromatic color scheme, use varying textures and patterns.

Analogous color schemes incorporate colors of two or three adjacent hues on the color wheel, usually either warm or cool. Different values and intensities may be used. This color harmony is pleasing because of the rhythmic related color flow and the variety. A design with red tulips, orange gerbera daisies, and yellow daffodils, freesias, and forsythia is an analogous color scheme of warm colors. An analogous color scheme using cool colors is blue iris, violet-blue statice, light lavender freesia, and deep purple delphinium.

A **complementary** color harmony (also called direct complementary) combines two colors that are directly opposite each other on the color wheel. Tints and shades are also included. Complementary colors intensify and enhance each other's color, provide very strong contrast, and make bold, eye-catching statements. The direct complements are orange and blue, red and green, and violet and yellow. One of the pair should be used in a greater amount in the design, including light, medium, and dark values.

5–29. An analogous color harmony includes adjacent families on the color wheel, such as yellow, orange, and red. This analogous color scheme displays all warm colors.

5–30. Complementary color schemes are bold and showy.

The **_split complementary_** color scheme consists of one hue combined with the two hues that are on each side of its direct complement on the color wheel. This color harmony is a more subtle contrast than the direct complementary but is still interesting and eye-catching. Examples of the split complementary color scheme are

1. Yellow with blue-violet and red-violet.
2. Red with blue-green and yellow-green.
3. Green with orange-red and red-violet.

A **_triad_** color harmony is a combination of three hues equally spaced on the color wheel. A triad may consist of the three primary colors (red, yellow, blue) or the secondary colors (violet, green, orange) as well as any tints and shades. This exciting color harmony is effective when one color dominates the other two that are used in smaller amounts. The primary color triad appeals to all ages and genders.

5–31. A split complementary color scheme is eye-catching and incorporates one key hue and the two adjoining hues of its direct complement.

5–32. A triad of primary colors—red, yellow, and blue—is exciting and appeals to all ages and genders.

The **polychromatic** color scheme uses a wide range of colors, both warm and cool. Generally, one color will be more prominent. This color scheme is common in spring mixtures and very festive and pleasing to the eye.

5–33. A polychromatic color scheme includes a wide range of colors and is very lively and festive.

REVIEWING

MAIN IDEAS

A floral designer selects and organizes flowers and foliage according to their physical characteristics, the design elements. The design elements are line and form (also referred to as shape), space, pattern, texture, and color.

Line is the visual movement between two points within a design. The four types of line are vertical, horizontal, curvilinear, and diagonal. In floral design, specific lines can be chosen for the meanings and ideas that each conveys, such as alert or inspiring emotions for a vertical line or dynamic, restless feelings when using a diagonal line.

Form and line are closely related; lines are used to create the three-dimensional shape of a floral design outline. The three broad categories of form or shape are geometric, naturalistic, and free form. Naturalistic designs suggest the natural growth of plants in nature through groupings and the use of space and other aspects of nature, such as moss and branches. Free form is a creative, contemporary type of advanced design in which some of the rules are "broken."

Geometric designs mirror the shapes of geometry. Most floral design shapes are based on the circle and triangle. Geometric designs may be vertical, horizontal, circular, or triangular. Examples of symmetrical circular forms or shapes are the circle, oval, and fan; asymmetrical circular forms include the crescent and the Hogarth curve. Symmetrical triangles may be equilateral or isosceles. Examples of asymmetrical triangles are right triangles (or L-shaped) and scalene triangles. Lines of opposition designs combine two high contrast design lines or forms, tied together with a strong center of interest.

The forms of plant materials can be divided into four general categories—line, form, mass, and filler.

Depth, or the third dimension, is a very important aspect of form. Depth creates a natural and full look, not a flat or pressed appearance. Methods for achieving depth include varying the flower facings, radiating plant materials, finishing the arrangement in the back of a one-sided design and allowing some plant materials to lean back slightly with others extending forward, "burying" some flowers (flowers are partially hidden), and highlighting with graded use of color.

Another design element is space. The effective use of space within a floral design gives an arrangement beauty and added interest.

Texture, another design element, describes the surface quality and the appearance and placement of the plant parts. Glossy textures attract attention first but do not hold the viewer's attention. Varied textures, such as rough, hairy, or woolly, hold the viewer's attention and keep it longer. Contrast in textures within a design adds variety and interest.

Pattern is a design element that is determined by the physical characteristics of the plant material. Plants have both structural and color patterns. Color patterns, used in small amounts, add interest to a design.

Color may be the most noticeable of the design elements. Colors are formed as light passes through a prism, separating into the rainbow of colors—red, orange, yellow, green, blue, and violet.

Color has three important qualities: hue, value, and intensity. Hue is the name of a color; colors are warm hues (red, orange, yellow) or cool hues (blue and sometimes violet). Value is the lightness (tint) or darkness (shade) of a color. Intensity is the relative brightness or dullness of a hue. A tone is a grayed hue. Highly visible colors are warm hues, light values, and bright intensities and are effective in designs to be viewed from a distance.

A floral designer can use color to express emotions and ideas. Color schemes can be related (monochromatic and analogous) or unrelated (complementary, split complementary, triad, and polychromatic). Monochromatic schemes include only one hue and its tints, shades, and tones. Analogous color schemes incorporate two or three adjacent hues on the color wheel with varying tints and shades. Complementary color harmonies are the high-contrast use of two colors that are direct opposites on the color wheel. Split complementary schemes consist of one hue and the two hues of each side of its direct complement on the color wheel. A triad color scheme is a combination of three equally spaced hues on the color wheel. Polychromatic color schemes use a wide range of hues both warm and cool.

QUESTIONS

Answer the following questions using complete sentences and correct spelling.

1. What are the six design elements?

2. What are four major lines used in floral design? List two expressive meanings for each one.

3. How are form and shape different?

4. What are the three broad categories of form?

5. Who developed the S curve and why?

6. What are typical shapes (forms) for most geometric designs? List two symmetrical and two asymmetrical examples for each shape.

7. What are the four types or shapes of plant materials? How do these shapes combine in a design to complete the composition?

8. What floral design techniques can be used to create depth within a design? Be thorough.

9. Why is space important within a design?

10. What is the value of using both glossy and varied (hairy, rough, prickly) textures within an arrangement?

11. Which hues are advancing colors and which ones are receding? Discuss the appropriate selection of colors for a large design to be displayed on a stage at graduation.

12. Name the colors of the color wheel in order and give characteristics and emotional meanings for each hue.

EVALUATING

Match the term with the correct definition. Write the letter of the term on the line provided.

a. triad
b. tint
c. tone
d. scalene triangle

e. shade
f. complementary color scheme
g. isosceles triangle
h. texture

i. intensity
j. secondary colors

_____1. Relative brightness or dullness.

_____2. Using two hues that are directly opposite each other on the color wheel.

_____3. The light value of a hue.

_____4. The dark value of a hue.

_____5. An asymmetrical triangle with three unequal sides.

_____6. The surface quality and the placement of the plant parts.

_____7. Using three equally spaced hues on the color wheel.

_____8. A grayed hue.

_____9. Colors formed by mixing two primary hues.

_____10. A symmetrical triangle with two equal sides.

EXPLORING

1. Create two floral designs. Choose one related and one unrelated color scheme. Gather flowers, foliage, containers, accessories, and fabrics in the appropriate colors, including tints, shades, and tones. Take a photograph of each design. Critique the use of color for proper proportion, balance, rhythm, and dominance (center of interest).

2. Plan, sketch, and then design an expressive arrangement with a dominant line. Identify the major line and its emotional or expressive significance. Note the evolution of the design. Did the design turn out as originally visualized or planned?

3. Visit a florist to determine which form wins the "favorite shape contest." List each featured form or shape and tally the number shown, both in the cooler and on display in the shop. Were you surprised at the results?

4. Design two arrangements using the same number and kinds of flowers. Design the first one with a flat pressed look; create depth within the second one, using as many methods as possible. Compare.

CHAPTER 6

Designing Corsages and Boutonnieres

OBJECTIVES

This chapter is about the design of corsages and boutonnieres. It has the following objectives:

1 Identify and describe the supplies needed.

2 Describe design mechanics and techniques.

3 Identify and describe styles of corsages and boutonnieres.

4 Discuss proper placement and pinning of corsages and boutonnieres.

TERMS

chenille stem
combination method
daisy hook method
design mechanics
dip dyes
feathering
finishing dips or sprays

floral spray
floral tint
gauge
glamellia
hairpin method
nestled boutonniere
pierce method

staging the bow
stem dyes
stitch method
tip spraying
tulle
wrap around method
wrist corsage

6–1. A corsage can show recognition during a special occasion.

FOR special occasions, many people add a festive touch to their attire by wearing floral accents. A woman may wear a shoulder or wrist corsage. A man may wear a boutonniere on his lapel. These special flowers show appreciation and recognition of an achievement or special event.

Special events for wearing flowers include weddings, proms, birthdays, anniversaries, school events like homecoming or "big games," holidays like Christmas, Valentine's Day, St. Patrick's Day (a green one, of course), Easter, Mother's Day, and many other occasions.

CORSAGE SUPPLIES AND THEIR EFFECTIVE USE

Corsages and boutonnieres require some specialized and unique supplies compared to other aspects of floral design. Knowledge of the proper supplies and their effective design use is a good foundation for beautiful floral work.

BASIC CORSAGE SUPPLIES

The basic supplies for creating corsages and boutonnieres are floral tape, wire in several gauges, and ribbon.

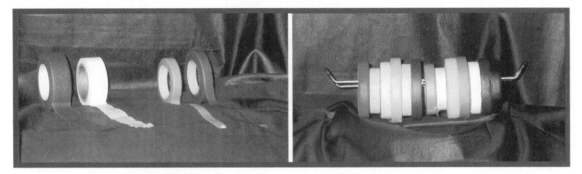

6–2. Floral tape is available in two widths and many colors.

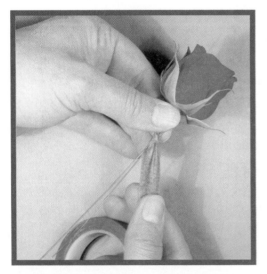

6–3. To adhere securely to itself, floral tape must be stretched and pulled tightly.

Floral tape is made of paraffin-coated paper and is used to cover wires and stems in a unobtrusive way. Floral tape does not feel sticky to human hands; only when the floral tape is stretched and pulled tightly will it adhere to itself. A beginning floral designer may find that prestretching the tape will help the taping to be more secure. Floral tape comes in two widths—½ inch and 1 inch. The narrower width is commonly used for corsage work; the wider width may be used for bouquets, wreaths, or other design work. Floral tape comes in a wide array of colors, including light and dark green, tan, white, gray, pink, yellow, and red. Generally, most corsage work is completed with light or dark green depending on the

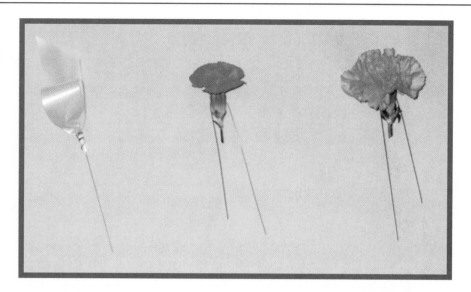

6–4. Remember, the smaller the wire gauge number, the thicker the wire. Use thinner gauge wire for bows and thicker gauges for flowers. Use a #24 gauge wire for mini carnations and a #22 gauge wire for a standard carnation.

flower stem color, but other colors can be selected depending on the flower color and the occasion.

Florist wire is sold in 18 inch lengths by the gauge. Wires are easier to use in 9 inch lengths; wedding bouquet work may require 18 inch lengths. The **gauge** of a wire describes its thickness or thinness. A tip to remember is that the smaller the gauge number, the thicker the wire. Commonly used gauges for corsage work are #26 for bows; #24 for medium-weight flowers such as mini carnations, spray chrysanthemums, or daisies; and #22 for heavier flowers, such as standard carnations, roses, or a fully open lily. Filler flowers may be wired with #28 wire.

Ribbon also has its own terminology and differing widths. Ribbon is typically sold as #1, #1½, #3, #5, #9, and #40. A thinner pixie ribbon is also offered. Thinner ribbons, including #1, #1½, and #3, are most commonly incorporated into corsage work. Ribbons #5 and #9 are used for potted plants, while #40 is used for bows on funeral sprays. Regular and wired-edge ribbon may come in satin, cotton, silk, sheer, paper, or burlap. Satin ribbon will have a shiny side and a matte or dull side. Some of the ribbons, including printed cotton, will have a definite front side and underside. Curling ribbon is another type but is usually used for tying packaged floral designs.

COLOR CHANGING SUPPLIES

Floral sprays and tints give the designer a great tool for changing the natural color of a flower to match a fabric swatch of a special dress or shirt. **Floral sprays** are opaque paints that will completely cover any flower color. **Floral tints** are translucent paints that allow some color underneath to show. Glitter sprays add a touch of glittery, metallic color.

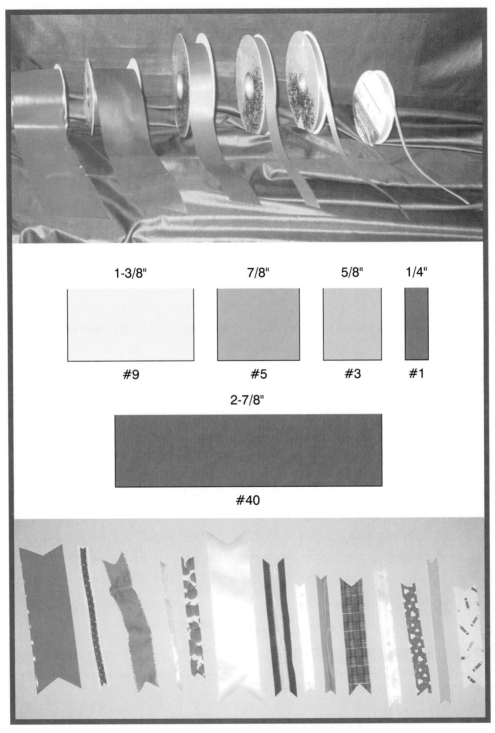

6–5. Ribbon comes in many widths and materials.

When using floral sprays, go outdoors if possible or find a well-ventilated room. Cover adjacent areas with newspaper or spray into a large shipping box or trash can. The methods to apply sprays, tints, or glitter are:

6–6. Floral sprays are great color tools for the floral designer. Color was applied to a carnation in the normal way (right side) and with the tip spraying technique (left side).

♦ Shake the can thoroughly to mix the paint.

♦ Check the paint flow on a box lid or trash can first.

♦ Hold the nozzle approximately 10 to 12 inches away from the flower or other item.

♦ Press the nozzle down in quick bursts while moving the can side to side, starting just before the flower (or item) and going just beyond it.

♦ For fresh or silk flowers, apply a single light coat. Some foliage, containers, or other accessories may benefit from several light coats for better coverage. Light sprays of glitter spray are more attractive than one heavy coat.

♦ Let the sprayed material dry thoroughly. Place the just-sprayed flower upright in floral preservative solution for even drying rather than on the counter or table. Remember, just-sprayed flowers will stain a table surface.

♦ Before storing, turn the spray can upside down and press the nozzle until only air is released. Performing this practice after each use will keep the spray can from becoming plugged with dried paint.

For a varied look, try a special spray technique that applies color to only the edges of the petals, known as tipping or ***tip spraying***. Tip spraying works well for carnations.

♦ Wire and tape the stem.

♦ Place the flower through the center of a paper towel, newspaper page, or corsage bag to protect hands from the paint.

♦ Gather the paper or bag around the flower head and hold tightly, exposing just a small amount of the flower edges.

♦ Spray a light coat of paint. The process can be repeated to darken it or add another color.

◆ Allow flower to dry thoroughly

Stem dyes and dip dyes are also available. **Stem dyes** are color solutions that are transported through the flower's xylem in the stem to change the flower's color. Green St. Patrick's Day flowers are a common example of this technique. Usually, flowers are ordered and shipped directly from the wholesaler already dyed, but this method can be done as an interesting lab experiment. Flowers can be stem dyed using the following steps:

1. Mix the stem dye according to the instructions. Use warm water (90 to 100º F) for the best results.

2. Use fresh, white or light-colored flowers that have been shipped "dry" or have been set out of the cooler for 2 hours. Room temperature flowers give better and quicker results.

3. Remove the lower foliage and place the freshly recut flower stems into the stem dye solution.

4. Allow 15 to 30 minutes for the stem dye to be absorbed through the xylem. Watch the flowers carefully. Remove from the solution when the following occurs:

   a. For short-stemmed flowers—flower color is just lighter than desired

   b. For long-stemmed flowers—flower color has just appeared in the lower petals (color will continue to darken when the dye within the xylem is absorbed.).

5. Rinse and recut the stems. Place the flowers in warm preservative solution and let the flowers remain at room temperature until the coloring is completed (usually one to two hours).

Dip dyes are semi-transparent colors that change the flower's color by directly dipping the flower head in a color solution. Use fresh, white or light-colored, flowers for the best results. After dipping the flower head, gently shake off any excess dye. Rinse the flower in water and shake gently again to remove excess water and speed the drying process. Dry the flower thoroughly before using it to avoid staining.

GLUES AND ADHESIVES

Floral glue and adhesives can be used to directly attach small flowers to leaves or ribbons. Using glues can be quite a time-saver in constructing corsages and floral hairpieces. A low-temperature glue gun can be used to attach silk or fresh durable leaves and flowers to combs or to a wired corsage with care being taken that the heat of the glue does not discolor the plant material surface. Pan melt glue is formulated as small pieces to be melted using an electric skillet or frying pan set at 275º F. Materials or wires are placed into the pan to apply the glue. When not in use, the pan should be turned off and stored once cooled. Many companies now offer floral adhesives that are effective in attaching plant materials to many surfaces. Floral adhesives require more time to dry compared to glue guns or pan melt glues.

OTHER SUPPLIES AND ACCESSORIES

Cotton balls can be used to extend the life of certain special flowers used in corsages and boutonnieres. A small piece of moistened cotton is placed at the cut end of the flower after wiring but just before taping. This extra needed moisture is helpful for roses, orchids, lilies, and gardenias.

Silk leaves can be substituted for fresh foliage in a corsage. Silk leaves may suggest rose leaves, ferns, or simple oval shapes and are available in many tints and shades of green, white, and occasionally other colors. **Tulle** is florist netting that adds color, texture, and support for some flowers. It comes in many colors and finishes. Tulle can be wired using #26 wire and added to corsages as needed. Other

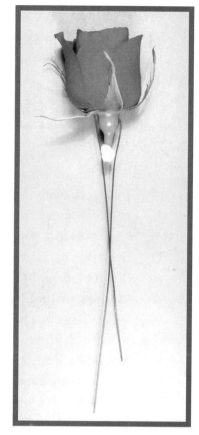

6–7. Cotton can provide extra needed moisture for some special corsage flowers.

6–8. Other corsage supplies include silk leaves, tulle, and pearl spray accessories.

accessories for corsages include pearl sprays, rhinestones, and novelty items, such as footballs, chenille letters, butterflies, or bees. The accessories with wired stems can be taped directly to the corsage; other items can also be glued in place as needed.

PACKAGING SUPPLIES

Proper packaging is very important to keep the corsage or boutonniere in a state of high humidity. Moisture loss as well as warm temperatures will cause the rapid deterioration of a corsage. Common packaging supplies include finishing dips or sprays, a mist bottle, corsage and boutonniere bags and pins, and cardboard or clear boxes.

Finishing dips or sprays are applied to the finished corsage to seal the stomata of the flowers and minimize water loss. The stomata (or pores on the undersides of a leaf) of a flower close naturally to prevent water loss; this process is mimicked with the application of finishing solutions. Finishing sprays should always be allowed to dry thoroughly before packaging to prevent discoloration of the petals. Examples of finishing sprays include Design Master Clear Life and Floralife. Crowning Glory™ may be used as either a dip or a spray. Read the directions carefully before using.

Corsage and boutonniere bags are available in plastic or cellophane in several sizes. A mist bottle can be used to spray a small amount of water into the fully open corsage bag before placing the corsage into it. Always avoid getting the bow wet. To close the bag, repleat the sides and fold two or three times, allowing air to be trapped inside the bag. Some designers blow into the bag to provide an extra air cushion (and added carbon dioxide). Seal the corsage or boutonniere bag with a single corsage or boutonniere pin. A corsage will have a second pin attached directly to it in the bag. For added protection and attractive presentation, the sealed bags may be placed into a cardboard or clear box.

6–9. Corsage and boutonniere packaging supplies should include bags, pins, boxes, and a mist bottle.

DESIGN MECHANICS

Good design mechanics are very important to the quality of any floral design. The **design mechanics** are the techniques and devices that hold a corsage or an arrangement together in a secure way. Knowledge of the proper supplies and their effective design use is a good foundation for beautiful floral work and secure design mechanics.

Proper wiring, taping, and bow making techniques are crucial to making a "well-designed corsage or boutonniere." A beautiful creation that falls apart will always be remembered as a poor design. Mechanics are important!

WIRING TECHNIQUES

Flowers are wired to remove the bulky stem and allow the flower head to be easily positioned. Flowers and foliage require different wiring techniques, depending on the structure of the plant material. The main methods are the pierce method, the daisy hook or hook method, the hairpin method, the wrap-around or clutch method, and the stitch method.

An important practice to note before wiring any flower is that the wire becomes the stem and the flower's stem must be removed except for a thumb's width, approximately 3/4 inch.

6–10. Flower stems are removed to reduce bulk and allow for easy positioning. Leave a "thumb's width" (about 3/4 inch) of stem.

Pierce Method

The **pierce method** involves inserting a wire through the calyx of a flower to wire for corsage work. It is effective for flowers that have a thick calyx just below the flower head. Flower examples are roses and carnations.

1. Pierce through the flower calyx. Use #24 or #22 wire depending on the weight of the flower.

2. Bend the wires down parallel to the stem. Do not wrap the two wires around each other.

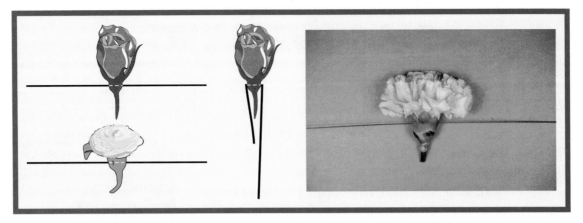

6–11. Flowers with a thick calyx, such as roses and carnations, are wired with the pierce method.

3. Start taping at the calyx, covering the pierced area and tape the entire length of the wire. Always cover the wires, the "mechanics" holding your corsage together.

Double Pierce Method

The double piercing technique is effective to give additional support for some flowers that have a thick stem and heavy flowers, such as orchids or lilies. Other delicate flowers, such as alstroemeria or Peruvian lily, can be double pierced with two thinner gauge wires (#26) to give extra support for the flower yet not damage the delicate stem.

1. Pierce through the calyx or stem, just below the flower head, with the first wire. Use #24 wire.

6–12. The double pierce method works well for alstroemeria, which is a delicate flower and stem yet has a thick calyx. This method gives added support.

2. With the second wire, position it at a 90-degree angle and slightly lower than the first wire and pierce through the calyx or stem.

3. Cover all wires as the stem is taped.

Daisy Hook Method

The **daisy hook method** (or hook method) is a technique of inserting a wire through a flower stem and the flower itself and making a hook at the end of the wire and pulling it down into the flower. This technique will securely wire flowers that have a hard central disc without a prominent calyx, such as daisies and chrysanthemums. Other individual florets of delphinium, dendrobium orchids, and hyacinths can also be wired in this manner, using thinner gauge wire (#26 gauge).

1. Place a #24 wire either through or next to the stem and push the wire through the flower head until it emerges.

2. Bend the wire into a small hook, approximately ½ inch long. For the best support within the flower, both sides of the hook should be parallel with each other; avoid bending the hook too far (almost closed) or not far enough (wide open).

3. Tape the stem, starting near the flower head, being sure to tape the end of the hook as well.

6–13. Use the daisy hook method for daisies and chrysanthemums that have a hard central disc without a prominent calyx.

6–14. The wrap around method securely holds together clusters or groups of filler flowers or foliage.

Wrap Around Method

The *wrap around method* is effective in wiring little bunches or clusters of filler flowers, such as waxflowers or baby's breath, by encircling the stems with wire and bending the wire downward to form a new stem. Fine textured foliage, such as plumosa fern, tree fern or ming fern, can also be held together effectively with this technique.

1. Trim stems of flowers or foliage to a 1 inch length.
2. Position the middle of the #24 or #26 wire alongside the stems and wrap the other wire half around the stems and the supporting wire.
3. Bend the wire parallel to the stems and tape, always covering any wires.

Hairpin Method

The *hairpin method* works well to wire ferns or other compound leaves and multi-flowered stems. The technique is to bend a wire in half (like a hairpin) and place it through a leaflet or frond to provide support high up the stem or to allow the plant material to be bent, curved, or positioned more easily. Boston ferns, flat ferns, and eucalyptus may be wired with this technique; freesias, larkspur, or dendrobium orchids may also be wired in this way. The hairpin method can be used to wire ribbon loops or ribbon loops with tails.

1. Bend a #24 wire in half to form a hairpin.
2. Place the wires through the leaflets or florets at the point where support is needed.
3. Pull the wire through until the curved part of the hairpin rests on the stem.
4. Place the wire parallel to the stem.
5. Gently wrap one wire around the stem and the other wire below the lowest leaflets or florets on the stem. Hold the top part of the hairpin firmly when wiring to avoid stripping off leaves or florets.
6. Tape the wire at the end of the stem.

6–15. Ferns or freesias may be wired with the hairpin method for added support and ease in positioning. Ribbon loops are also effectively wired with this technique.

Stitch Method

The **stitch method** is a foliage wiring technique, used on solid or wide leaves, such as salal (lemon leaf), Ti leaves, ivy, or individual leaflets of holly or silver dollar eucalyptus. Leaves wired with this method can be shaped and curved to fit the style and shape of corsage or boutonniere. This technique involves sewing, that is, making a small stitch or insertion through the back midrib of a leaf, pulling the wire through, bending the wires down, and wrapping one wire around the stem and other wire.

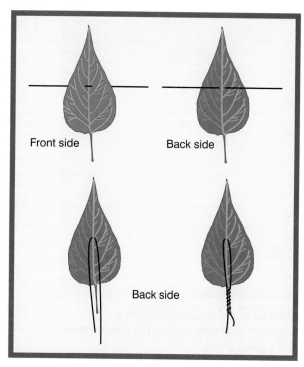

6–16. The stitch method provides good support and ease in positioning for many types of leaves or leaflets.

1. Cut a 1 inch stem or ½ inch petiole (if possible) on the leaf or leaflet.

2. Pierce through the center midrib with a #24 wire at or just above the halfway point of the leaf length. (If the leaf is wired too low, the leaf will not be supported. If the wire is positioned too high, the wire will show.)

3. Push the wire through until equal wire lengths appear on both sides of the stitch.

4. Bend the ends of the wire down.

5. Wrap one wire around the leaf stem and the other wire.

6. Tape the stem, covering the lower wires.

SPECIAL WIRING TECHNIQUES

Orchids and gardenias often require special wiring techniques because of their unusual shape and delicate nature. Manufactured stems can be effective in corsages for flowers such as stephanotis. Carnations can be made into smaller sizes by using a process known as feathering. Silk flowers also require a special technique before use in corsage work.

6–17. An orchid can be wired with a combination of both an inserted chenille stem and a pierced wire.

Combination Method

Although orchids and gardenias can be wired with the pierce method, another technique can also be used with good results. This **combination method** employs a chenille stem inserted into the 1 inch stem of the flower. (The calyx of the gardenia is removed.) A **chenille stem** is a wire that is covered with soft, fuzzy chenille fibers, also known as a pipe cleaner. The stem is then pierced with a #24 wire. The stem is taped, starting at the top to cover the pierced area and continuing all the way down to cover both the wire and chenille stem.

Another combination method is wiring a football mum with a daisy hook (or simple insertion of a wire through the stem) and a pierce. The weight and type of flower may lead to the employment of a combination of wiring techniques.

Non-piercing Method

Phalaenopsis orchids are extremely delicate and should be carefully wired to give support but not damage the flower. It is important to note that the wires are positioned around and through the flower petals but are not piercing any part of the phalaenopsis orchid.

1. Tape the center of a #26 or #28 wire with white tape. A chenille stem may be substituted for the taped wire.

6–18. A phalaenopsis orchid is wired without piercing any flower parts. The taped wire is rested against the central membrane with the wire ends taped securely to the flower stem.

2. Bend the wire in half to form a U shape.

3. Place each end of the wire on either side of the narrow membrane that connects the lip to the rest of the flower.

4. Pull the wire until the taped center is resting against the membrane. The wire will extend through the flower between the petals and will not pierce any part of the orchid. The wire may need to be bent at this stage.

5. Position the wires alongside the stem.

6. Wrap the first wire around the stem and the second wire and tape completely.

Gardenia Tips

Gardenia are wonderfully fragrant and beautiful, yet fragile and easily bruised. Avoid touching the gardenia petals during the corsage-making process. Buy tailored gardenias, which have a collar of leaves already in place to keep bruising to a minimum. Another tip for working with gardenias is to cover the finished gardenia corsage with wet tissue to keep it fresh and unblemished.

Manufactured Stems

Stephanotis flowers have a lovely tubular shape that needs special treatment to prevent wilting. Special stems have been manufactured to help with this situation. Before using them, condition the flowers in cool water so each one will be firm and fully turgid.

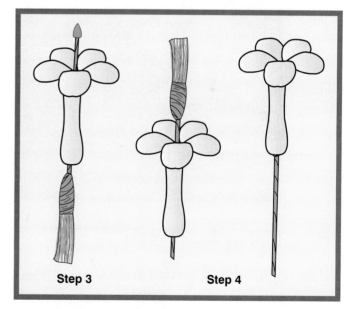

Step 3   Step 4

6–19. A moistened manufactured stem provides needed moisture and support for a stephanotis flower.

1. Place the cotton portion of the manufactured stem upside down in water to thoroughly moisten it.

2. Gently pull the flower stem and green sepals away from the stephanotis flower.

3. With the end of the manufactured stem positioned under the flower, push out the flower parts (the ovary, etc.) through the center of the flower.

4. Insert the end of the moistened manufactured stem through the flower opening and pull it gently into the tube until it fills the tubular part of the flower. The stem can be used as is or can be taped.

Feathering a Carnation

Feathering is the process of making smaller flowers from a larger carnation. Depending on the design use, a carnation can be divided into various portions to make any desired carnation size. This technique gives a designer greater flexibility in corsage work with fewer flowers in stock.

1. Remove the stem below the calyx.
2. Hold the calyx firmly and pinch (or cut apart) the carnation into halves, thirds, or quarters, depending on the desired size of the feathered carnations.
3. Separate the carnation pieces, keeping the calyx attached.
4. Tightly tape the new smaller flower, letting the calyx enclose the petals.
5. Pierce the newly created flower with a #24 wire and tape the entire stem.

6–20. A carnation is feathered by dividing it into smaller sections, taping each part tightly, and pierce-wiring each section before taping each stem.

Rolling Rose Petals

Outer rose petals that are removed from a rose can form a delightful little rose bud accent in a corsage or boutonniere. A single petal can be used or two or three petals to provide a fuller looking rose accent.

1. Trim a small circular area from the base of the petal.
2. Roll the petal from side to side.
3. Tape the petal to keep it rolled. Low temperature glue will also secure it.
4. Add a second or third petal as desired. Tape or glue each petal.

5. With a #24 or #26 wire, pierce the petal(s) just above the tape and bend the ends downward.

6. Tape the entire length of the wire.

Wiring Silk Flowers and Foliage

Silk flowers and foliage can be used to create attractive corsages and boutonnieres Silks may be added to fresh corsages to provide a needed color or an out-of-season flower or can comprise the entire corsage. Flowers with a plastic calyx may be wired with the "hot wire" method. Heat a #24 gauge wire in a candle flame and pierce through the plastic calyx. The stems of silk plant materials may be too thick or not wired at all so a simple wiring technique is useful for silks.

1. Remove all but ½ to ¾ inch of the stem.

2. Dip the end of a #24 (#22 if heavy) wire into pan melt glue, applying a fine line or bead of glue.

3. Position the glued wire along the stem of the flower or leaf.

4. Allow ample time for the glue to dry.

5. Tape tightly from the base of the flower or leaf, continuing until the stem is completely covered.

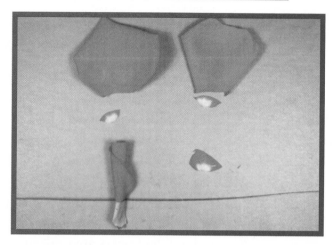

6–21. Rose petals can be rolled to make charming rose bud accents in corsages.

6–22. A plastic calyx may be pierced with a heated #24 gauge wire (left side). Silk plant materials may be used in corsage work by gluing a wire to the shortened stem of the flower or leaf (right).

BOW MAKING

Bows are a fundamental part of creating corsages. On the other hand, boutonnieres should not be designed with a bow although occasionally a small ribbon treatment may be added to signify school spirit or highlight other significant colors.

Most people (customers) perceive that a corsage is not finished until a bow is added. However, some corsages can be creatively designed and not need a bow at all. Besides their addition to corsages, bows are also added to bud vases, vase arrangements, some floral designs, such as holiday ones, and on potted plants.

Basic Bow Making Tips

Take note of the following tips for the beginning bow-maker:

1. Most ribbon has two sides, shiny and matte (or dull). The finished bow should be entirely shiny or entirely matte.

2. A bow being constructed is held in place with the thumb, index finger, and middle finger. The thumb is on top, positioned inside the center loop. The index and middle fingers are underneath the bow, stabilizing and acting like a shuttle on the underneath side.

3. The opposite hand (usually the "writing hand") feeds the ribbon and makes the loops and twists.

4. The twist is an important part of bow-making success. All of the twists should be small, straight across, and aligned exactly on top of each other. A thin wire ties the bow together exactly at the point of the twists. If the twists are elongated or not made at the same spot, the bow will appear messy and crinkled in the middle with loops of differing lengths that will not position properly. "It's all in the twist!"

5. Making bows is not easy. Practice, practice, practice.

6. Avoid making bows with large, floppy loops, which are out of proportion to the design, crush easily, and flatten and lose their shape quickly.

7. Bows may be wired with chenille stems, taped wire, regular wire, or narrow, matching ribbon (listed in order of easiest to more challenging).

8. Make the bow directly off the bolt to ensure the proper ribbon length.

9. Streamers or ribbon tails may be added to the bow. Sometimes, a streamer is added at the beginning of the construction; often, the streamers are created at the end. The ribbon length depends on the design. For example, short streamers are appropriate for corsages and longer tail lengths for bud vases or vase arrangements.

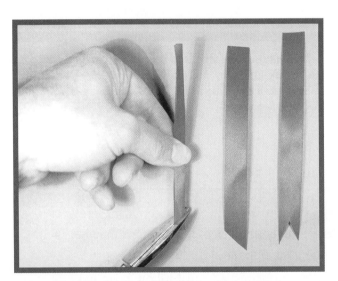

6–23. Diagonal or bow tie finishes for ribbon tails or streamers add that last finishing touch.

10. Streamers or ribbon tails can be trimmed as a diagonal or a bow tie finish. A blunt cut hints that the designer does not have the proper "attention to detail."

The Steps—Bow Making 101

A bow with a center loop is the most common type of bow. The center loop makes the bow appear finished and masks the area where the wire is holding the bow together.

1. Decide if the bow will be shiny or matte finish. Let's choose shiny for this explanation.

2. Hold the ribbon with the dull side touching the thumb. Loop the ribbon over the thumb, make the small center loop, and hold in place with the index and middle finger. The shiny side of the ribbon should be showing.

3. Twist the ribbon to reveal the desired finish.

4. Make a loop of modest proportions, 1½ or 2 inches long, increasing the length for larger designs. Twist the ribbon so the shiny side is visible.

5. In the opposite direction, make another loop of the same size. Twist to reveal the shiny side.

6. Continue making loops on each side of the center loop with an equal amount of loops on each side. A little corsage might only have six loops (three on each side); a larger one may have eight loops (four on each side) or more.

7. To make streamers, make one last twist to reveal the shiny side. Determine the desired length of ribbon tail. Grasp the shiny side of the ribbon at a point twice the ribbon streamer length (for two ribbon tails) and place the ribbon (shiny side up) directly underneath the first streamer. To add a streamer on the opposite side, determine the desired length and cut the ribbon at that spot from the bolt.

8. Place a #26 wire through the center loop with equal amounts of wire on each side. Slide the wire under the thumb and bring the ends underneath the bow between the index and middle fingers. Twist the wire, pulling tightly to gather the ribbon twists securely into place. The wire in the middle of the bow should not show. Pull the wire tighter in the center if the wire is apparent.

9. The last step—staging the bow. ***Staging the bow*** means to arrange the bow loops so the bow appears balanced and full or rounded. To effectively stage it, place the thumb back into the center loop and apply pressure with the thumb and index finger pinching together. With the index finger of the other hand, position the loops in an alternating fashion around the center loop, that is, pull the first loop to the left, the second loop to the right, and alternate with the remaining loops. Be sure to place the finger into the loop to move it; do not crease the loop by grabbing it by the tip.

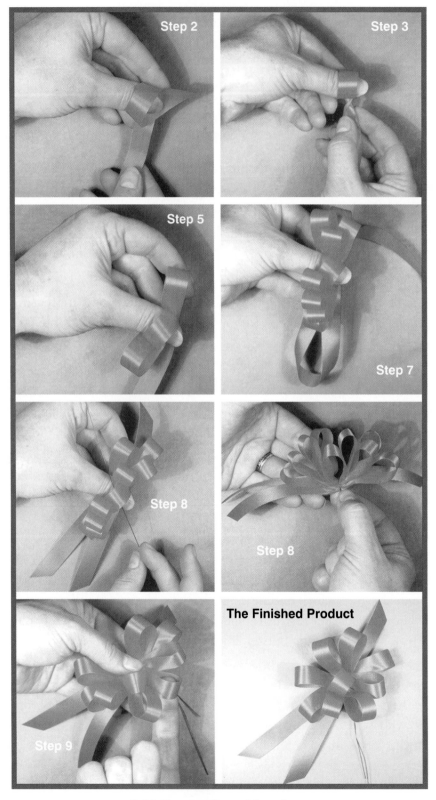

6–24. The steps for making a bow.

STYLES OF FLOWERS TO WEAR

The styles of boutonnieres and corsages have changed over the decades and centuries. Corsages worn in the 1800s and early 1900s were much larger and more grandiose. Current styles tend to feature more petite versions.

Proportion is an important principle to remember in designing today's corsages and boutonnieres. The size of the corsage should fit the person's size; children and petite women should wear smaller corsages. The component parts of the corsages and boutonnieres should be the same relative scale to each other. The foliage should not be too long and overwhelm the flowers. Likewise, the bow should be in proportion to the flowers and foliage chosen. A beautiful corsage with an over-sized bow will be distracting and not pleasing in proportion.

Balance and focal point are also important. Choose symmetrically or asymmetrically balanced styles depending on the occasion or attire. Often, a combination of the bow and a unique or larger flower will create an obvious and pleasing focal area.

STEM FINISHES FOR BOUTONNIERES AND CORSAGES

The stem ends for boutonnieres and corsages are usually visible and can be finished in a variety of ways. These tips will help the beginning designer.

1. At the beginning of construction, always tape the entire length of wire.

2. The stem ends should be in alignment with the top flower or foliage. A poorly aligned stem will cause a corsage to be pinned on at an angle and look poorly designed.

3. The stem finish should always allow the corsage to lay flat and should not interfere with the attachment of the corsage or boutonniere.

4. At the end of construction, another finishing touch is to pull the floral tape over any exposed wire ends after the stem finish has been completed.

The simplest finish is the straight stem. A curled stem can offer a unique variation yet it is quick and simple to do. Variations of the curled stem include a simple roll to

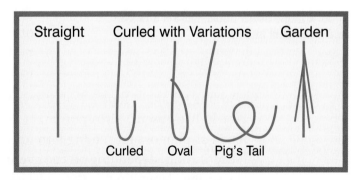

6–25. A variety of stem finishes add uniqueness and style to both boutonnieres and corsages.

the side, an oval loop with the end curled around the main stem as a stylized touch, or a "pig's tail" curl, fashioned by rolling the stem around a pen.

The garden finish is a natural, "gardeny" look, keeping the taped wires separate. The corsage stems are taped only at the top to secure them. The individual wires are separated and cut at slightly varying lengths.

Boutonnieres

Boutonnieres may be designed with a single flower or several small flowers. The overall design should be attractive and tasteful and not too large or overpowering. Although roses and carnations are common boutonniere flowers, a wide variety of suitable flowers may appropriately be selected. Foliage, used individually or in combination, can add an attractive green framework to feature the flower.

6–26. A single flower boutonniere is a classic and traditional favorite.

Single Flower Boutonniere

A single flower boutonniere is a classic and popular boutonniere choice for weddings, proms, and many special events. A medium-sized flower is a common selection, along with filler and foliage. Avoid large flowers, such as orchids, because of the similarity to a corsage size. Mechanics, particularly smooth, tight taping, are important for a boutonniere because the stem is prominent and not covered by the bow as in a corsage.

1. Remove all but 1 inch of the stem on the chosen flower (rose, carnation, alstroemeria). Wire and tape it.

2. Adding filler, if desired—Add a sprig (or two) of baby's breath, positioned around the flower to accent it, not overshadow it. Tape the filler to the taped flower stem.

3. Adding foliage—Tape a leaflet (or two) of leatherleaf to the back of the flower (or Italian ruscus, pittosporum, or other small leaf). Fine textured, lacy foliage, such as plumosa fern, ming fern, or tree fern, may be used in combination or in substitution, depending on the event. Some leaves may need additional support by wiring, depending on their placement in the corsage and their size. *With experience, the filler and foliage can be taped to the stem at the same time.*

4. Stem finish—Choose the desired stem finish and cut the stem accordingly. Pull the floral tape to cover the exposed wires or add a small extra piece and tape over the ends, working from bottom to top. Add a boutonniere pin.

Multiple Flower Boutonniere

For a very special or festive touch, multiple flower boutonnieres are a nice choice. A multiple flower boutonniere is designed with smaller flowers, along with foliage (and filler—optional). If a garden look stem finish is desired, leave the stems separate during the construction steps and tape only at the top to hold the composition in place.

Table 6–1. Popular and Appropriate Boutonniere Flowers and Foliage

Flowers	Foliage
Roses (all types)	Leatherleaf
Carnations (miniature and standard)	Plumosa fern
Chrysanthemums (sprays, not standards)	Tree fern
Alstroemeria	Ivy
Stephanotis	Pittosporum
Freesia	Ming fern
Asters (Matsumoto types)	Italian ruscus
Florets—Dendrobium orchids, delphinium	Evergreens (seasonal)
Linear accent flowers— grape hyacinths, lily of the valley, heather	Boxwood
Numerous filler flowers	Huckleberry

1. Wire and tape two or three small flowers or florets. (Be sure to remove all but ¾ inch of the stem.)

2. Adding foliage—Tape a small leaf or leaflet to the back of each taped flower.

3. Positioning—Place the smallest flower at the top, with the second flower lower and slightly to the right (zigzag pattern). A third flower is positioned lower than the middle flower and slightly to the left. Tape to hold in place. *The second and third flowers are angled slightly forward.*

4. Adding filler (optional)—Add a cluster or two of filler flowers as needed.

5. Another leaf or two can be taped behind the flowers, if needed.

6. Stem finish—Complete the stem finish, cover exposed wire ends, and add a pin.

6–27. A multiple flower boutonniere is comprised of smaller flowers.

6–28. A nestled boutonniere is a small flower inserted into the center of a carnation.

Nestled Boutonniere

A nestled boutonniere is a popular choice to showcase school colors or to add a festive touch to any event. Corsages can also be designed with nestled flowers. A **nestled boutonniere** is a boutonniere designed with a smaller flower, such as a sweetheart rose or small cluster of a filler flower, like statice or waxflower, inserted or "nestled" into the center of a carnation. The technique is the most effective when the two flowers are different colors that blend or contrast well.

1. Wire (#22 wire) but do not tape a small flower (leave only a ¼ inch stem).

2. Choose a carnation with a different color. Remove the pistil (the central female organ of a flower—ovary, style, and stigma) inside the carnation to allow the smaller flower to be nestled lower into the carnation. Remove all but ¾ inch of the stem below the calyx.

3. Insert the small flower into the carnation with the wires emerging at the base of the carnation calyx. Position the small flower in the carnation center.

4. Pierce (#24 wire) the calyx of the carnation and bend the wire ends parallel with the other wires. Tape the wires completely to the ends.

5. Add filler and foliage as desired. Tape, complete the stem finish, and add a pin.

CORSAGES

Corsages add wonderful touches of color, vibrancy, and meaning to any special event, including birthdays, weddings, anniversaries, award programs, dances, parties, and any social events. For proms and weddings, the corsage colors are very important and often swatches of fabric are needed for the designer to carefully match the color of the dress.

The flower choices for corsages are nearly limitless. Small, medium, and large flowers can be used with a variety of fillers and foliage. Wilt-prone flowers should be wired and taped with a moist piece of cotton or can be avoided altogether.

Single Flower Corsage

A single flower corsage is a showy corsage when designed with larger flowers, such as an orchid or lily. This corsage is very popular for holidays, anniversaries, and at weddings for the mothers or grandmothers of the bride or groom. This corsage can also be designed with a medium-sized flower, just like a single flower boutonniere with a bow added. This smaller single flower corsage is suitable at weddings for younger girls and for those who help at the cake table, gift table, and guest book.

1. Wire and tape an orchid with a 1 inch stem, using the double pierce method or the combination method.

2. Prepare foliage—Wire and tape three leaves.

3. Assemble the corsage—Place the foliage at the top and sides of the orchid. Tape.

4. Add the bow. Tape, covering the length of the stem ends.

5. Stem finish—Complete the stem finish. Add two corsage pins. The pins should be placed just into the stem and not through it (Ouch!).

Small Beginner's Corsage with Two Flowers

Many girls and ladies prefer a small corsage. A small two-flower corsage is very similar to a multiple flower boutonniere except that a corsage almost always has a bow. Here are the steps for a beginner's first multiple flower corsage.

Table 6–2. Popular Corsage Flowers and Foliage

Flowers	Foliage
Roses (all types)	Ivy
Carnations (miniature and standard)	Ming fern
Chrysanthemums (sprays and football)	Tree fern
Alstroemeria	Plumosa fern
Stephanotis	Pittosporum (all)
Freesia	Leatherleaf
Gladioli florets	Ruscus (all)
Gardenias	Salal or lemonleaf
Orchids—Cattleya, Cymbidium, Dendrobium, Phalaenopsis, Vanda	Evergreens (seasonal)
Asters	Camellia leaves
Lilies, Lily of the Valley	Boxwood
Florets—hyacinth, delphinium, larkspur	Bear grass (looped)
Grape hyacinths	Holly
Numerous fillers	

6–29. A single flower corsage can be fashioned with a larger flower that creates a showy and special look for the wearer.

6–30. A two-flower corsage is a simple multiple flower corsage for a beginner.

1. Select two carnations and remove all but ¾ inch of the stem. Pierce with a #24 wire and tape down the entire length of the wire.

2. Adding filler, if desired—Add a sprig (or two) of sea lavender or baby's breath, positioned around each flower to accent it, not overwhelm it. Tape the filler to each taped flower stem.

3. Adding foliage—Tape a leaflet (or two) of leatherleaf or ivy to the back of the flower. Fine textured, lacy foliage, such as plumosa fern or tree fern, can be added in combination. Additional leaves can be added at the end of construction, if needed. *The filler and foliage can be taped to the stem at the same time to save a taping step and keep the stem thinner.*

4. Positioning—Place the smallest flower at the top, with the second flower lower and slightly to the right (zigzag pattern). The two flowers should not form "eyes," instead, one should be higher than the other. The lower flower should angle slightly forward.

5. Stem finish—Complete the stem finish, cover exposed wire ends, and add a corsage pin.

Multiple Flower Corsage

A multiple flower corsage can be quite showy and relates a sense of appreciation and recognition to the wearer. This type can be worn for numerous special occasions and holidays.

A multiple flower corsage can be designed with many types of flowers and foliage with accessories, such as tulle tufts and ribbon loops as a well as a bow. This type of corsage gives the designer much flexibility and creativity; the corsage can be symmetrical or asymmetrical with vertical, rounded, crescent, or triangular shapes.

1. Select five flowers (three to seven), ranging from buds to fully open. Wire by piercing with a #24 wire.

2. Choose foliage and fillers to add to the flowers. Position leaves and sprigs of filler of the proper proportion and tape to the flowers.

3. Placement—Place the smallest bud or flower at the top. Position a partially open or larger flower lower and to the right side. Continue the zigzag pattern by placing the third and largest flower lower and to the left. Bow loops or additional filler can also be added at this time. Tape once or twice around the stem. *The first flower is the vertical center of the corsage and lays flat. The second and third flower are angled slightly off vertical and angle slightly forward.*

4. Position the fourth and fifth flower in a downward fashion so the wire is attached at the same joining point as the other three flowers. Add bow loops or filler as needed. Trim any excess wire before taping to reduce bulk.

5. Position the bow within the flowers to form a focal area near the largest flowers.

6. Additional leaves can be added behind the corsage, if needed, to frame the flowers, complete the desired shape, or add artistic flair.

7. Determine the stem finish, tape, and trim the stems accordingly. Add two corsage pins.

8. Be sure that the corsage lays flat. "Try it on before packaging."

6–31. The lower flowers in a multiple flower corsage are positioned in a downward fashion to keep the corsage a manageable size and well balanced.

Wrist Corsage

A **wrist corsage** is a lightweight corsage designed to be attached to a wristband for wearing on the wrist. Sometimes, a wrist corsage is preferred for dances or for attaching to strapless gowns or dresses of very lightweight material.

A well-constructed multiple flower corsage can be worn as a wrist corsage by attaching to an elasticized band, a plastic latch-type band, a plastic empty floral tape roll, or by tying on the corsage with ribbon tubing. The corsage should always be tied or taped (or both) very securely.

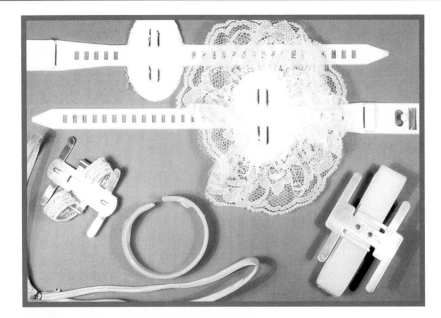

6–32. A lightweight corsage can be worn as a wrist corsage by using some of the pictured tricks of the trade.

6–33. A football mum corsage is a great way to show school spirit.

Football Mum Corsage

In some areas of the country, football mum corsages are traditional favorites at football games, especially homecoming events, at the high school and college level. A basic football mum corsage is designed with one mum, foliage, and a bow, but many additions can give uniqueness to the design, such as trailing ribbons, accessories—footballs, school letters and megaphones, and two or three football mums used instead of one.

1. Leave 1 inch of stem on the flower. Wire the football mum with a combination method, in this case, both a daisy hook (#22 wire) and a pierce (#22 wire).

2. Wire five salal leaves or other broad foliage with a stitch method and tape.

3. Bend the leaves to frame the football mum in a symmetrical fashion. Tape.

4. Add a bow. Accessories may also be added.

5. Finish the stem and add pins.

Glamellia Corsage

A variation of the single flower corsage is the unique glamellia corsage. A *glamellia* is a composite flower that is comprised of gladiolus florets, made to resemble a camellia, that is, a gladiolus camellia (gla + mellia = glamellia). Many parts of the gladiolus in various stages of opening are used, including buds and partially- to fully-open florets.

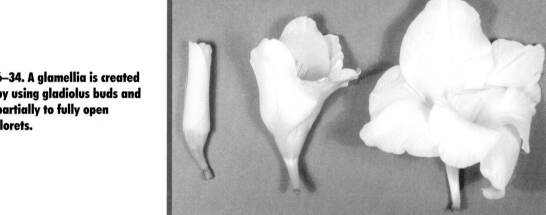

6–34. A glamellia is created by using gladiolus buds and partially to fully open florets.

Key tips for making a glamellia:

♦ Selection of buds and florets—Select gladiolus buds and florets in various sizes.

♦ Preparation of florets—Each floret chosen is cut at the base of the floret. The central flower parts will fall out (or can be pulled out), but the petals will remain together.

♦ Placement of florets—Each floret is placed to form a rounded composite flower. The added floret is trimmed on the appropriate side to fill in the round shape.

♦ Floral adhesives—Floral adhesives can also be used to attach additional florets instead of or in addition to wiring.

♦ Size—Glamellias may be created from only three or four buds and florets or may be much larger and showier, using five or six buds and florets with a collar of gladiolus petals underneath it.

6–35. Gladiolus florets are wired and taped together to form a showy composite flower called a glamellia.

The steps in designing a glamellia are as follows:

1. Select a bud, removing the green sepals and all but 1 inch of stem. Wire by piercing and tape.

2. Slip the wired and taped bud into a partially open bud until the bases of the florets meet. Pierce with a #26 wire and bend the wire ends down. Tape.

3. Slip the two wired buds into a partially open floret and pierce with a #26 wire. Bend the wire ends down. Tape.

4. Cut open a nearly open floret on the appropriate side and position it around the three wired florets. Wire as before and tape. Use glue if necessary.

5. Continue adding florets, making a rounded, symmetrical shape until the desired size is reached.

6. Add salal or other bold foliage to support the delicate new flower. Add other foliage as desired.

7. Add filler, if desired, complete the stem finish, and insert two corsage pins just into the stem.

PROPER PLACEMENT AND ATTACHMENT OF FLOWERS TO WEAR

Corsages and boutonnieres are worn on the left shoulder because of the Victorian practice of placing them "over the heart." Place flowers "over the heart" on the left side; place name tags on the right side as an extension of the hand-shaking arm.

Boutonnieres are worn near the buttonhole of a jacket lapel. One pin should be sufficient to provide secure placement. Boutonniere pins are shorter than corsage pins and have a smaller head in black, gray, or white colors. An effective technique is the "hidden pin method." Pin the flower so the pin is hidden underneath the lapel. From underneath, pin through a small amount of the fabric, pierce through the stem, and pin another small amount of fabric on the other side. With this technique, only the flower and stem will show. If pinning from the front side, match the boutonniere pin to the jacket color.

Corsages should be placed higher on the shoulder and pinned securely with two pins. One pin is placed through the corsage stems with another one positioned higher, through the flowers, to keep the corsage from shifting or falling forward. The hidden pin method works well for jackets and vests. When pinning corsages on dresses or blouses made of delicate materials, added support is needed to support the weight of the corsage. Position a small folded tissue or lightweight piece of fabric underneath the area to be pinned. Pinning through a bra strap will also give security to the attachment. Most corsage pins are white or pearl-headed.

Wrist corsages are worn on the left wrist although some left-handed persons may prefer to wear them on the other side. A wrist corsage should be small enough to be comfortable wearing and should not be worn too high on the forearm away from the wrist.

A corsage or boutonniere should always be constructed in a secure way so the person wearing it enjoys the experience. Mechanics and other details of design should not be apparent; the beauty and suitability of the design should be the most obvious features.

REVIEWING

MAIN IDEAS

Corsages and boutonnieres are special designs worn by ladies and gentlemen for holidays, weddings, and numerous special occasions. Knowledge of the necessary supplies and their use, proper design mechanics, appropriate styles of boutonnieres and corsages, and their proper placement are all important factors to know to be a good designer of flowers-to-wear.

The basic corsage and boutonniere supplies are floral tape, wire, and ribbon. Floral tape is a paraffin-coated paper that is self-adhering when stretched. Wire is available in different gauges or thickness and is used to replace the natural stem of flowers or foliage. Ribbon is available in many widths and finishes. Other important supplies are floral sprays, tints, stem dyes, and dip dyes for changing the color of flowers or foliage. Floral glue and adhesives are great time-saving tools for the designer in creating corsages and boutonnieres. Small pieces of a cotton ball can be a device to add moisture to the cut stem of a flower before wiring and taping. Other supplies include silk leaves, tulle, and accessories, such as pearl sprays, footballs, or school letters. Packaging supplies are finishing dips or sprays, corsage and boutonniere bags, boxes, pins, and a mist bottle.

Basic design mechanics are vital to a well-constructed corsage or boutonniere. Design mechanics are the techniques and tools that hold a design together securely. Proper wiring, taping, and bow making techniques are important design mechanics. Important wiring techniques for corsage and boutonniere making are the pierce, double pierce, daisy hook, wrap around, hairpin, stitch, and other special techniques, such as combination wiring, the non-piercing method, and using manufactured stems. Tips for working with gardenias, feathering a carnation, rolling rose petals, and wiring silk plant materials are also included in the design mechanics section.

Bows are a fundamental part for creating most corsages. The steps for creating a bow include making a twist after each loop, beginning with the center loop and each succeeding loop on either side of the center loop. Streamers or ribbon tails can be added at the completion of the bow loops. The bow is then wired securely and staged (or positioned).

The stem ends of corsages and boutonnieres may be finished in several ways, including the straight stem, the curled stem with a very curly "pig's tail" variation, and the garden look with separate taped wires cut at varying lengths.

The common boutonniere styles are the single flower and multiple flower types. A nestled boutonniere is a specialty type that has a small flower (sweetheart rose, for example) inserted into a carnation of a different color.

Popular corsage styles are the showy single flower type, a beginner's two-flower corsage, and the multiple flower style. A wrist corsage can be adapted from a small corsage, which is attached by a variety of bands or other techniques to be worn at the wrist. Stylized corsages include the football mum corsage and the glamellia corsage.

Proper placement and attachment of the flowers to be worn is also important. A boutonniere is worn slightly lower than a corsage's placement. Both types should be pinned on securely on the left side. Wrist corsages should be worn at the wrist and not on the forearm.

QUESTIONS

Answer the following questions using complete sentences and correct spelling.

1. Why does a person wear flowers?

2. What does it mean to "cover your mechanics"? Give two examples.

3. What are some basic supplies needed to design a corsage? Be thorough.

4. Why are stems removed when making boutonnieres and corsages?

5. How is a boutonniere different from a corsage? How does the placement of a boutonniere differ from that of a corsage?

6. What are the different ways to wire foliage? List and give examples for each method.

7. What is a chenille stem and how is it used in corsage work?

8. How have corsage styles changed over the years?

9. What are different methods for wiring flowers? List the methods and specific flower types.

10. What are three important tips for successful bow making? What are the steps of making a bow with a center loop?

EVALUATING

Match the term with the correct definition. Write the letter of the term on the line provided.

a. nestled boutonniere

b. hairpin method

c. glamellia

d. stitch method

e. stomata

f. pistil

g. finishing dips and sprays

h. dip dyes

i. gauge

j. feathering

_____1. The thickness or thinness of a wire.

_____2. Adding florets to make a bigger composite flower.

_____3. Dividing a flower to make smaller sizes.

_____4. Adding a smaller flower within a larger one.

_____5. A sealant to prevent water loss.

_____6. Ovary, style, and stigma—the female parts of a flower.

_____7. To change color by immersing the flower head in a color solution.

_____8. The pores on the undersides of a leaf.

_____9. Inserting a wire through the midrib of the underside of a leaf, bending the wires down, wrapping around the petiole.

_____10. Bending a wire in half and inserting through leaflets or parts of a flower to give support or modify the shape, then wrapping the wire around the stem and other wire.

EXPLORING

1. When attending a dance, prom, or wedding, make note of the styles of flowers that are worn or carried. Determine which style is the most popular. If possible, casually interview a few people to find out why that style was chosen.

2. Feather a standard carnation. Make a range of sizes and incorporate five to seven flowers within a corsage.

3. Make a multiple flower corsage and a multiple flower boutonniere to match. Use five different wiring techniques. Complete each design with a garden stem finish.

4. Experiment with color. Try all of the color changing methods using white carnations. Compare the colors produced and the time involved for each method.

CHAPTER 7

Designing Basic Floral Work

OBJECTIVES

This chapter is about basic floral design. It has the following objectives:

1 Identify and describe supplies and tools needed.

2 Explain how to design bud vases and vase arrangements.

3 Explain how to construct basic geometric designs.

4 Define naturalistic design.

5 Describe how to foil a potted plant.

TERMS

anchor pin
brick
contour
floral foam
florist shears
foliage grid

greening pin
grid
grouping
hyacinth stake
needlepoint holder
poly foil

pruning shears
rosette
tape grid
water tube

7–1. Learning basic design skills is a good framework for the beginning floral designer.

FLORAL designers may choose many types of designs to create. Before creating more difficult floral work, a designer must master basic designs and styles. Knowing and using the correct tools and supplies is essential for a floral designer. The effective use of floral foam, as well as other foundation mechanics, makes a floral designer more flexible and artistic.

Learning and mastering many styles, such as vase arrangements, geometric, and naturalistic designs, is an exciting challenge for the beginning designer. The proper choice of a design style will depend on the place, the occasion, and the designer's skill.

DESIGN TOOLS AND SUPPLIES

Knowing and using the correct tools and supplies is very important to the floral designer. Since new products and supplies are constantly being developed, a designer needs to stay current and look for new items that may make the job even easier.

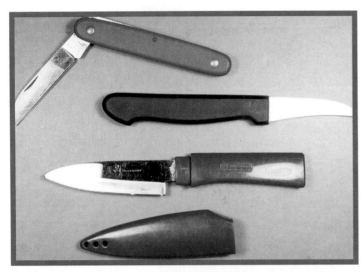

7–2. A knife is an efficient tool for any floral designer. Folding or paring-type knives are chosen depending on the designer's preference.

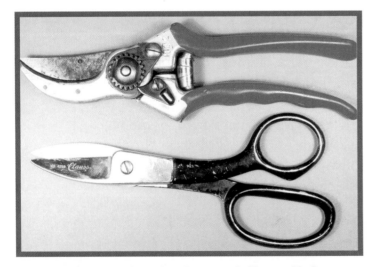

7–3. Florist shears and pruning shears are indispensable for cutting thick and woody stems.

CUTTING TOOLS

Knives

With experience, a floral designer will learn that a knife is the fastest and most efficient cutting tool to use. Any type of knife can be chosen depending on the designer's preference. Pocket knives are convenient because they can be folded; knives that resemble paring knives are another option. Always keep the knife sharp for the best results.

In the beginning, using a knife may result in an injured thumb or fingers. Hold the stem in one hand and the knife in the other. Cut the stem with a diagonal cut while pulling the stem upward with the other hand. Avoid placing any fingers or a thumb in the way. Using a knife may be awkward at first but will become quite natural with practice.

Shears and Pruning Shears

Florist shears are a cutting tool with short, serrated blades for cutting thick or woody stems. Some tropical flowers and small branches can be easily cut with shears rather that a knife or scissors. Florist shears are preferable over ordinary scissors for cutting plant material because the blades will not pinch the stem.

Pruning shears will cut very thick or tough branches with a smooth cut. Often, florist shears may not be able to cleanly cut through a big branch. When selecting pruning shears, be sure to select a type with a sharp cutting blade; always avoid the anvil-type, which cuts the stem by pinching it.

Scissors

Both ribbon scissors and utility scissors will be useful for a designer. Ribbon scissors are cutting tools with long sharp blades designed for cutting ribbon, netting, or fabric. To maintain their sharpness, these scissors should not be used to cut anything else, including plant materials. Utility scissors are scissors that can be used for trimming leaves, paper, or other materials. Having a pair of utility scissors will allow the ribbon scissors to be used only for their intended purpose.

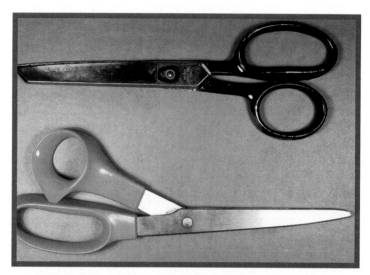

7–4. Utility scissors can be used for trimming foliage or cutting paper or other materials. Ribbon scissors should be used only for ribbon, netting, or fabric.

SUPPLIES AND THEIR USE

Floral Foam

Floral foam is a porous material designed to hold water and provide stability for stems within a floral design. Flower stems can be held at any angle when inserted into a block of floral foam. Floral foam comes in two formulations for both fresh and dry plant materials. The dry foam will be discussed in Chapter 11. The fresh foam is green and commonly available as a brick or a block. A *brick* of foam is approximately the size of a fireplace brick.

7–5. Floral foam is porous and easy to cut with a knife. Floral foam is available as a brick.

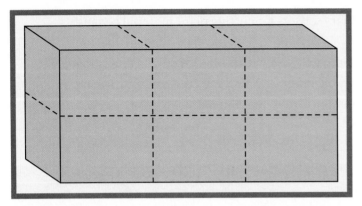

7–6. To avoid waste, cut the foam brick into the fraction of the brick needed. For a one-sixth brick, cut into thirds and then in half lengthwise.

Because of its porous nature, floral foam can be easily cut to any size or shape, depending on the container size. A simple butter knife, florist knife, or a heavy-gauge wire can be used to cut the foam.

To avoid waste, cut the foam into the fraction of a brick needed. For example, green plastic design bowls can be fitted with either a quarter (small to medium centerpiece) or a third (larger centerpiece) of a brick. Turn the foam to the side and cut the brick into thirds or quarters. For a smaller container, one-sixth of a brick may be needed. In this case, the foam is first cut into thirds and then half lengthwise. The foam may be cut before or after saturating with water.

The floral foam should be properly and thoroughly soaked with water before use. The correct method is to place the foam into warm preservative water and let it sink into the water at its own rate. Never quickly force a block of foam under water. Air pockets may be trapped in the foam. When properly and fully saturated with water, the foam provides adequate moisture to the flowers and foliage. Do not reuse floral foam because rewetted foam is not an efficient water-holder.

7–7. To ensure proper soaking, let the floral foam naturally take up water at its own rate. Never hold dry foam under water because air pockets will form inside the foam.

Placing Foam in the Container

The foam should be placed into the container with some of the foam extending above the rim of the container. Some stems may be placed into this top area of the foam. If the foam is too short, stem placements will look awkward and too upward; if the foam is too tall, the top portion will dry out too quickly. For small arrangements, leave a ½-inch foam area; for larger designs, one or two inches of foam can extend above the container.

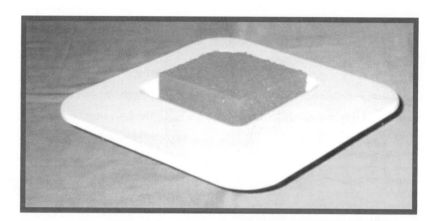

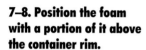
7–8. Position the foam with a portion of it above the container rim.

For foam placed into glass containers, the green foam can be camouflaged with silver foil or the appropriate color of cellophane. Corsage bags or other plastic can also be used to downplay the green color showing through the crystal vase.

Always provide a small area to add water to the arrangement. For round containers, the square or rectangular foam will not totally fill the space so that makes watering the arrangement easy. In square or rectangular containers, the foam may completely fill the container so a triangular piece of the foam should be trimmed out from the back of the foam to provide a spot to water the arrangement without excessive spilling.

7–9. Foil or colorful cellophane can camouflage green foam placed into glass containers.

Attaching the Foam to the Container

Foam can be secured to a container with waterproof tape, an anchor pin, or pan melt glue.

The moistened foam should be attached to the container. The foam should fit snugly into the container,

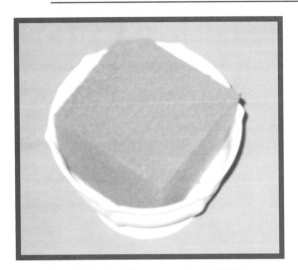

7–10. The foam should not completely fill the container. Always allow an area for watering the arrangement.

but can be further secured with tape. Foam can be taped to the container with waterproof tape. The tape is available in two widths, ¼ and ½ inch, and also in three colors—white, green, and clear.

An anchor pin is an effective way to secure foam in a low bowl. An **anchor pin** is a plastic, four-pronged design mechanic that is attached to a container with floral clay (and sometimes, glue). The anchor pin allows the designer to use a smaller piece of foam positioned anywhere within the container. However, if a large piece of foam is used, several anchor pins may be needed to secure it.

Glue can be used to attach foam to a plastic container or liner. The foam must be dry for this tech-

7–11. Foam can be secured to a container with tape (left) or an anchor pin (right).

nique to work. The foam is dipped into the pan melt glue, covered with a thin layer of glue, and then immediately placed into the plastic container or liner. The glue should be allowed to cool and then the foam and container are both placed in the preservative water to wet the foam. Tip the container slightly to the side to allow the foam to take up water gradually. The advantage of this method is being able to prepare the container and foam ahead of time for a large event or party.

Other Foundations

Needlepoint holders are also useful in creating designs. A **needlepoint holder** is a design mechanic that has a heavy metal base with many sharp, closely spaced, upright metal pins. These holders, also called pin holders or frogs, are available in different shapes (round, oval) and sizes and are attached to a container with floral clay. Needlepoints are used for line designs or designs with just a few flowers. Except for designs created for the shop or an exhibition, florists do not use this mechanic because of the expense of each needlepoint and the difficulty in delivering the design.

Wire mesh, also called chicken wire or poultry netting, can also provide a support mechanic for designs. Chicken wire can be used both in vases as the only foundation or in combination with foam. The wire mesh covering the foam gives added support, especially for designs with thick or heavy stems.

Other Supplies

Other supplies that may be needed in design work are greening pins, water tubes, and wooden picks or hyacinth stakes. *Greening pins* look like hairpins with an "S" or flat top and are used to secure moss or foliage in a design. Short pieces of wire can also be bent in half to secure moss if greening pins are not available.

Water tubes are small, rubbercapped, plastic tubes used for holding

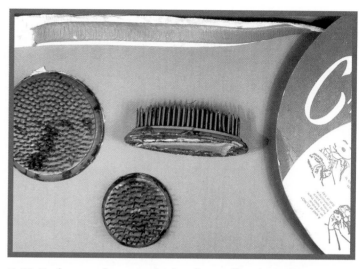

7–12. Designs can be created using the needlepoint holder as a design mechanic. The needlepoint holder is attached with floral clay.

7–13. Wire mesh or chicken wire can provide support in vases and as a covering over foam.

water and a single flower or a small cluster of filler flowers. A flower stem is placed through the small opening in the rubber cap and into the small reservoir of the water tube. Since the water tube holds only a small amount of water, the water level should be frequently checked. Water tubes come in various sizes, in green or clear colors, and are rounded or pointed. The rounded tubes may be used for boxed or packaged flowers that may be out of water for a while; the pointed water tubes are ideal for placing into floral foam. To extend the stem

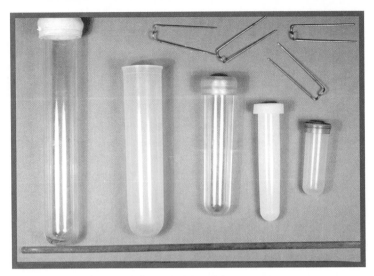

7–14. Water tubes, hyacinth stakes, and greening pins are common supplies that a floral designer may use.

length of a flower in a design, a pointed water tube may be used alone to add a small amount of additional stem length. For greater stem length needs in a tall arrangement, the water tube can be wired to a wooden pick or attached to a hyacinth stake. Some water tubes are made to fit over a hyacinth stake; other water tubes can be wired, taped, or both to a hyacinth stake.

A *hyacinth stake* is a long green wooden stick that is commonly used to support heavy flowers, such as hyacinths, in a flowering pot. Hyacinth stakes can also add height and give support to accessories in an arrangement.

BEGINNING WITH THE BASICS—BUD VASES AND VASE ARRANGEMENTS

Learning the basic design styles will help build the skill and confidence for a floral designer to tackle more difficult styles. Some of the basic design styles include bud vases, vase arrangements, basic geometric shapes, and wrapping a potted plant. A variety of vases and containers can be used to create basic designs. Glass, pottery, plastic, ceramic, metals, and baskets can all provide an interesting foundation for basic designs. Bud vases are quite slender; vases for vase arrangements are taller and wider; basic geometric designs can be created in a multitude of sizes and shapes.

BUD VASES

A bud vase design is a simple and versatile design style of one or several flowers as well as foliage. A bud vase arrangement is usually one-sided, but can also be designed as an all-around arrangement for a small dining table. Bud vases can brighten a spot on a desk, table, counter, or other small area.

7–15. A variety of vases and containers are suitable for basic design styles.

Containers for a bud vase design are typically called bud vases and are commonly available in 6- and 9-inch heights. Other smaller vases make quite intimate and charming designs; taller bud vases make dramatic statements. Be sure to check if the bud vase opening is large enough to insert more than one or two stems. The vase itself may be quite beautiful but can be totally impractical for flower arranging. Bud vases can be made of glass, crystal, plastic, or metal in straight and flared shapes.

The flowers for a bud vase should be at least one and a half times the vase height. For a dining situation, the flowers can be slightly shorter to allow viewing over the flowers. Choose a shorter vase for a table centerpiece.

Suitable flowers for bud vases are small- to medium-sized flowers that would be in proportion with the thin vase. Examples are roses, carnations, irises, tulips, daffodils, alstroemerias, chrysanthemums, tropical flowers, such as small anthuriums and heliconias, and all filler flowers. Foliage that is suitable for a bud vase would be all types of ferns, galax leaves, myrtle, ivy, pittosporum, ruscus (all types), small-leaved eucalyptus, euonymus, and evergreens. Large leaves, such as palms, tropical foliage, and even salal, may be too overwhelming for a small bud vase.

Bud vases may have one to three flowers or multiple smaller flowers. Most bud vases have a bow added for color, but may be designed without one depending on the flowers used and the skill of the floral designer. The bow should be designed with green enameled wire, which resists rusting.

The bow is located in the lower part of the design, sometimes slightly overlapping the rim of the bud vase. The bow can shorten the visual height of a bud vase if the flowers are slightly short for the vase. Once the location of the bow is determined, the bow wires may be merely placed into the vase. For a more secure attachment, gently wrap the wire around the stems and twist them together in the back. The loose wire ends can be trimmed or positioned to overlap the stems a second time. For a very finished look, cover the wire with matching ribbon and tie in a knot. These secure bud vase flowers can be easily delivered or can be given

7–16. A single flower bud vase can be a simple yet elegant way to express appreciation or love.

away at the end of a banquet or other event. This tying technique is one way to make a small presentation bouquet.

A Bud Vase with a Single Flower

A bud vase with a single flower can be a simple yet elegant expression of love or appreciation. Any flower that is proportionate to the bud vase can be chosen.

1. Select the bud vase and fill it to within an inch of the top with floral preservative solution.

2. Select and position the foliage to form a framework for the flowers. The foliage may vary in height from one times the vase height to one and one-half times the vase height (1:1 or 1½:1). Remove any leaves that will be in the vase solution.

3. Place the single flower in the center and just slightly lower than the tip by ½ inch. If designing with a rose, be sure to remove any bruised or irregularly colored outer petals.

4. Add additional foliage near the bud vase rim to give stability to the flower.

5. Add filler flowers if desired.

6. Make a bow and place it in the center beneath the flowers near the vase rim.

7. Check the vase solution for debris or leaves. Hold the flowers firmly and lift them out of the vase. Flush out any debris by adding more preservative solution. Remove any leaves in the vase solution.

A Bud Vase with Three Flowers

A bud vase with three flowers is a traditional favorite. The three flowers are usually all the same kind of flower but can also be a tasteful mixture. The three flowers should have varied heights and placements, forming a zigzag pattern. A linear arrangement of flowers will also work if filler flowers are used to add variety.

1. Select a bud vase and fill it with floral preservative solution. Leave an inch space at the top.

2. Choose three flowers. Start with the tallest one and place it at the necessary height for proper proportion (1½:1 or 1:1). Center it in the vase.

3. Vary the height by cutting the second flower shorter. Place it to the left or right of the first flower. This second flower should "zig" compared to the first one.

4. Place the third flower lower and on the opposite side of the second flower. The third flower should "zag." The lower two flowers will zigzag compared to the top flower.

5. Add linear foliage to accent the flowers. Place foliage at the container rim to add texture and stabilize the flowers. (Note: The foliage can also be added at the beginning.)

6. Add filler and a bow if desired. The bow may be placed off-center if the design warrants it.

Multiple Flowers in a Bud Vase

For a showy bud vase that expresses emotions, such as the joy of spring or the beauty of the Christmas season, several flowers and foliage can be arranged in a bud vase. The bud vase should be carefully selected with a wide enough opening to allow space for multiple flow-

7–17. Vary the heights and placement of three flowers designed in a bud vase.

7–18. Multiple flowers in a bud vase are colorful, cheerful designs. Note: The lavender and pink bud vase has a double bow made with both lavender and pink ribbon. The red and white bud vase does not have a bow at all.

ers. The technique is similar to the three flower bud vase with varied heights and placements of flower. A bow may be included or deemed unnecessary depending on the design.

VASE ARRANGEMENTS

The Italians were the first to arrange flowers from the garden in a vase. Vase arrangements are a classic way for gardeners to display and feature their garden flowers indoors. Vase arrangements may be one-sided or all-around designs. The containers for this style can be various shapes and sizes, available in ceramic, glass, pottery, or plastic. Avoid extremely wide openings on some vases (some low bubble bowls) because the flowers tend to fall out easily. Vase arrangements can be designed as one-sided arrangements or to be viewed from all sides (all-around).

7–19. Vase arrangements can be designed to be viewed from one side only (left) or from all sides (right).

Tips and Techniques

Many beginning designers become frustrated when designing in vases because the flowers all fall to the outside edge. There are tips and techniques to help avoid the dilemma of the "doughnut arrangement" (a circle of flowers with a big hole in the center). Grids can be used to give some support to the flowers. A *grid* is a framework of materials at the top of a vase that provide support for flowers in a vase arrangement. Grids may be formed with foliage, tape, or wire mesh.

7–20. Grids, made with either foliage (left) or tape (right), form a framework to provide some control in placing flowers in a vase arrangement. (Note that a glass vase would be taped with clear tape. The green tape allows the technique to be clearly seen.)

The most natural type of grid that does not require additional materials is the ***foliage grid***. The designer places the foliage, such as leatherleaf or Italian ruscus, into the top of the vase in a radiating pattern. The overlap of the stems forms a natural framework that will allow some control in the placement of the flowers.

The ***tape grid*** is achieved by placing tape across the opening of the vase at 90-degree angles to form a support grid. The ends of the tape are secured with an additional piece of tape around the outside rim of the vase. The tape color should be chosen to match the vase if possible, for example, clear tape with glass vases, green tape for dark-green or black vases, and white tape for white or light-colored vases. The clear tape can be used for any other vase colors.

Marbles and gemstones (somewhat flattened, rounded glass pieces) can also be used in both bud vases and vases to provide color, texture, and weight, if necessary. Match the color of the marbles and gemstones to the color of the flowers or foliage.

Traditional Vase Arrangement of a Dozen Roses

Who wouldn't want to receive a beautiful vase of a dozen roses? A dozen roses symbolizes love and romance and is a very important design style to learn.

Both the one-sided and all-around styles are appropriate for a dozen roses.

Designing a One-Sided Design with Twelve Roses

A traditional one-sided arrangement of a dozen roses looks very full and colorful. A one-sided design of twelve roses may be triangular or rounded in outline.

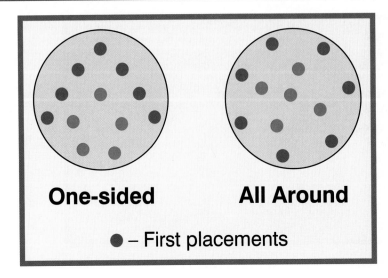

One-sided   **All Around**

● – First placements

7–21. The comparison of stem placements for arranging a dozen roses in a one-sided versus an all-around arrangement.

1. Select an appropriate vase.

2. Create a taped grid over the opening of the vase, using clear tape.

3. Position 8 to 10 stems of leatherleaf in a radiating pattern.

4. Remove all thorns on the roses and any leaves that will be below the water line. Remove damaged or discolored "guard" petals on the roses.

5. Position the tallest rose in the center of the back of the vase. Additional foliage may be needed to lend support. The height of the rose should be approximately 1½ times the container's height.

6. The next roses are cut slightly shorter (½ inch) and positioned to the left and right of the first rose. Add the next slightly shorter pair of roses to the left and right sides of the previous pair. The third pair of roses is cut ½ inch shorter and placed as the outermost roses on both the left and right.

7. Position the last five roses in front of the back row or "V". Center one of the roses in front of and shorter than the first rose placement. Space the last four roses to fill the remaining area, leaving room for a #9 bow, if desired.

8. Make a #9 bow in an appropriate color, attach the wire to a hyacinth stake or unused stem, and insert the stake or stem into the design.

9. Check the vase solution for debris, flushing it out if found. Fill (don't over-fill) the vase with preservative solution.

7–22. A dozen roses can be designed as a one-sided arrangement (left) or as an all-around arrangement (right).

Designing an All-Around Arrangement with Twelve Roses

An all-around arrangement may be the preferred choice for arranging a dozen roses depending on the site, perhaps in the center of a room or in the center of a table. The outline of the arrangement may appear triangular or rounded.

1. Select an appropriate vase. Fill with preservative solution to within an inch of the vase rim.

2. Create a foliage grid by positioning 8 to 10 stems of leatherleaf (or other foliage).

3. Remove all thorns and any foliage that will be in the vase solution. Remove any damaged or discolored "guard" petals from the roses.

4. Determine the height of the design, using the tallest, prettiest, or straightest rose as the guide. Trim the rose to the correct height, but do not place it into the vase yet. Trim four roses ½-inch shorter and seven roses approximately 1-inch shorter than the tallest one. Lengths will vary depending on the shape of the vase.

5. Start by positioning the seven shortest roses to form the outer ring of flowers. Place the stems into the vase in an angled manner, not vertically. The angled placement will allow the rose to extend outward.

6. Continue by adding four roses in the inner ring. These roses should be taller than the first ones and placed more vertically.

7. Place the tallest rose in the center, forming a 1½:1 ratio of flowers to vase. The rose length may dictate a slightly shorter arrangement height.

8. Add additional foliage, filler, and a bow as desired. Check the vase solution for debris, flush any debris, and fill with preservative solution.

The traditional arrangement of a dozen roses can be varied by cutting the stems at slightly differing lengths to create a casual bouquet. One-sided or all-around vase arrangements can be designed with many different kinds and mixtures of flowers and foliage. Vase arrangements are versatile designs, adapting to a variety of locations, occasions, colors, and flowers.

7–23. Vase arrangements can be so versatile! The smaller one-sided design mirrors the larger design of lilies, roses, and alstroemeria. A lemonade pitcher has a colorful burst of lilies and crocosmia with a few slices of lemons and oranges in the vase solution to add to the theme. (The citrus slices contribute additional citric acid, but should be changed frequently.)

DESIGNING BASIC GEOMETRIC SHAPES USING FLORAL FOAM

The most common geometric shapes are based on the vertical, triangle, and circle. These shapes may be symmetrical or asymmetrical, traditional or casual, formal or informal depending on the occasion, the flowers chosen, and the designer's preference. This part of the chapter will discuss the one-sided basic geometric shapes that are designed in floral

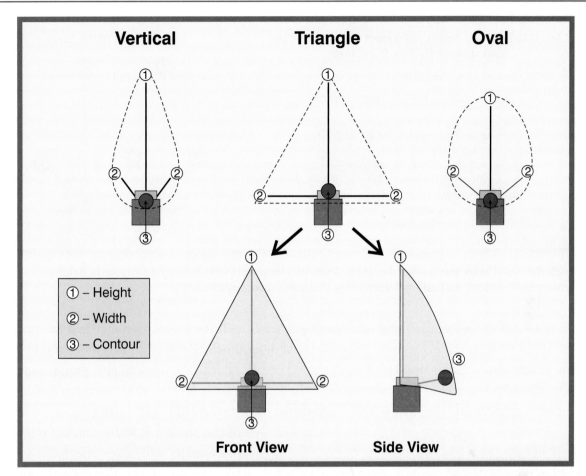

7–24. Beginning designers can follow a pattern of placement—height, width, and contour. The framework, created with foliage or flowers (or both), helps novices to visualize the appropriate design shape.

foam; chapter 8 will cover all-around designs, or centerpieces, in the different geometric shapes.

A beginning designer should visualize the shape before and during the design process, making adjustments if the actual shape does not match the desired goal. A simple guideline for designing is to start with the height placement, then add the width placement(s), and next determine the outermost contour. In other words, design with a plan in mind—height, width, and contour. **Contour** is the three-dimensional radiation in a gradual way from the vertical height placement to horizontal, as viewed from the side. The contour of an arrangement, viewed from the side, should be gently rounded, not steep or flat nor puffed out or pregnant-looking. These placements, in foliage or flowers, or both, create the basic shape or framework. Once the designer is more experienced, the steps become automatic and can be varied without losing track of the desired design results.

Floral foam is a great tool and should be used in a wise manner. Position the initial foliage and flowers, establishing the arrangement height, in the back one-third of the foam to allow

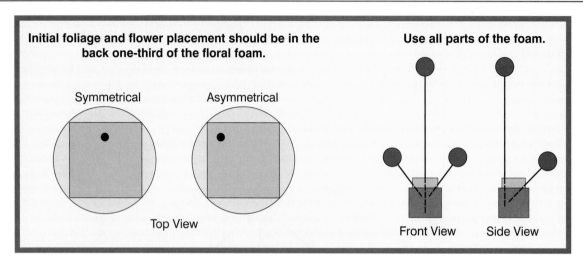

Initial foliage and flower placement should be in the back one-third of the floral foam.

Symmetrical

Asymmetrical

Top View

Use all parts of the foam.

Front View   Side View

7–25. Use floral foam wisely when designing. Strategic placements will enable the designer to finish an arrangement without the foam self-destructing (the Swiss cheese syndrome).

proper support and to facilitate additional placements, if necessary. Symmetrical designs should have centered placements; asymmetrical designs will be placed to the left or right of the exact center. Adequate stem length should be placed into the foam to give proper support. Do not cross stems; use the left side of the foam for flowers appearing in the left side of the arrangement and the right side of the foam for those flowers to be placed in the right side of the design. Equally spacing stem placements will allow the foam to support all of the flowers without falling apart. Beginning designers often experience the Swiss cheese syndrome—lots of holes and not much support.

Vertical Designs

Vertical designs are very eye-catching and bold. Branches, line flowers, or form flowers placed in a linear fashion form a strong vertical statement. The width placements should be secondary to the height. Vertical designs are suitable for desks, tables, or counters with a small amount of space. Bud vases

7–26. Vertical designs are eye-catching and great for limited table space or for placing on the floor.

are typically vertical designs. Tall rounded containers, as well as low bowls, can be used to create vertical arrangements.

1. Select a container and place the floral foam securely within it. The floral foam should be ½-inch above the rim of the container.

2. Place two snapdragons or three roses or bird of paradise in a vertical fashion into the foam. These flowers should be vertical or slightly leaning backward.

3. Add corkscrew willow to emphasize the height.

4. Green up the design with linear myrtle and leatherleaf.

5. Create a center of interest.

6. Add mass flowers, if needed or desired, to fill in the shape. Do not widen the arrangement too much.

7. Add framing foliage, if desired.

8. Cover foam with moss or foliage. Green up the back of the design. Add floral preservative solution to the vase.

TRIANGULAR DESIGNS

The triangular design is a popular one for all types of occasions. It is a distinctive shape for small hospital designs, as well as large altar pieces for weddings, church services, or funerals. Triangles can be symmetrical designs (equilateral or isosceles) or asymmetrical designs (right triangle or scalene triangle). The inverted T, which can be either symmetrical or asymmetrical, is a type of isosceles triangle with a strong vertical emphasis.

Symmetrical Triangles—Equilateral and Isosceles

The equilateral triangle is a symmetrical triangle with three equal sides. The symmetrical isosceles triangle has two equal sides with greater height than width. The choice of either the equilateral or the isosceles triangle would be the designer's preference.

The steps in designing the two types of symmetrical triangles are similar.

1. Select a container and position moistened floral foam with at least ½-inch above the rim. Tape the foam to secure it.

2. Green up the triangular shape.

3. Position the height flower at least 1½ to 2 times the height of the container.

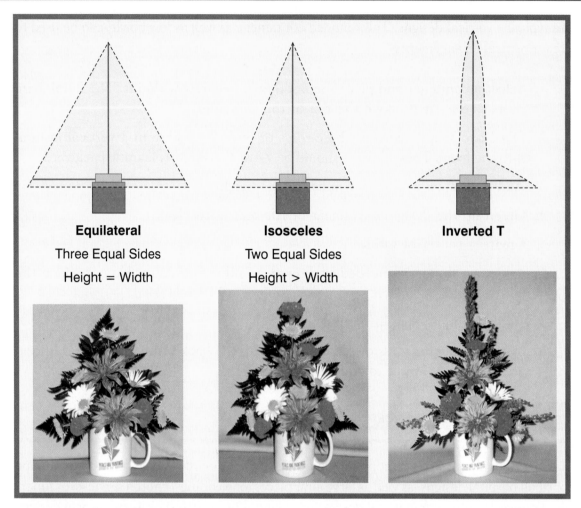

Equilateral	Isosceles	Inverted T
Three Equal Sides	Two Equal Sides	
Height = Width	Height > Width	

7–27. Outline of the equilateral triangle, the isosceles triangle, and the inverted T. Equilateral and isosceles triangles are two variations of a symmetrical triangle. An inverted T is a type of isosceles triangle.

4. Add the width placements. Position the width placements in the side of the foam near the back with the stems angling slightly forward.

   a. For an equilateral triangle, each width placement should be just less than one-half the height. For an isosceles triangle, each width placement is approximately one-third the height.

   b. For an inverted T, the width varies from one-third to one-half the height.

5. The contour flower may be added now (also later). From the side, determine a gentle curved contour for this arrangement. Curve the hand slightly to help in the visualization. Position this outermost flower in the front of the foam. The focal area can be completed now.

6. Next, add mass flowers to fill in the shape of the triangle. Strive for smoothly transitional flower facings. For the inverted T, the outline is not filled in. The vertical and horizontal placements are featured along with the focal area. The arrangement looks like an upside down T.

7. Add filler and additional foliage for texture as desired.

8. Green up the back of the arrangement and add floral preservative solution to the container.

Asymmetrical Triangles—Right Triangle and Scalene Triangle

A right triangle and a scalene triangle are both asymmetrical designs. Another name for a right triangle is an L-form or L pattern arrangement. Asymmetrical triangles may be created with the vertical height on the right or the left side. Asymmetrical triangles may be displayed in a more formal setting by creating one left-sided design and one right-sided design. The complementary pairs can be placed to face toward or away from a painting or other important feature.

The asymmetrical triangles have unequal materials, yet equal visual weight on each side of the vertical axis. It is important to visually balance the materials used in these designs. Begin by counterbalancing the height and width placements. The width placement of an asymmetrical triangle is approximately one-half the height. If the width placement is positioned at a 90-degree angle, this triangle is called a right triangle or L pattern. If the width placement is positioned diagonally, the triangle is an asymmetrical scalene triangle.

7–28. The width placement is positioned differently for a right triangle and a scalene triangle.

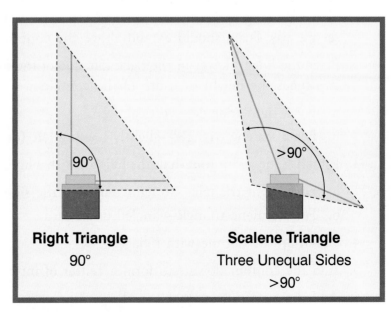

Right Triangle
90°

Scalene Triangle
Three Unequal Sides
>90°

7–29. A right triangle (left) and a scalene triangle (right) are two types of asymmetrical triangles.

A right triangle may be designed in a low or tall container depending on the occasion and location. Because of a width placement that angles downward, a scalene triangle should be designed in a tall container. If designed in a lower container, it should be placed on a base or pedestal that allows room for the width placement to flow downward.

The designing steps are similar for both asymmetrical triangles. A right-sided triangle (high on the left and low on the right) will be described.

1. Select the appropriate container and tape moistened floral foam into it in a secure way. Foam should extend above the container rim.

2. Place the linear flower in the back left side of the foam. The height should be two times the height or width of the container.

   a. For a right triangle—vertical
   b. For a scalene triangle—slightly leaning left (or right)

3. Establish the width (one-half the height) with a linear flower, filler, or foliage.

   a. For a right triangle—straight out from the side at a 90-degree angle
   b. For a scalene triangle—angled downward

4. Green up the outline with foliage.

5. Add the contour flowers to form a center of interest or focal point.

6. Add the mass flowers to fill in the outline of the shape.

7. Place filler and additional foliage to cover the floral foam.

8. Green up the back of the design. Add floral preservative solution to the container.

CIRCULAR DESIGNS

An oval design, a crescent, and a Hogarth (or S-curve) are all one-sided circular designs. Circular designs are a diverse group of arrangements that may be one-sided or all-around. The circular centerpieces will be covered in the next chapter.

Oval Designs

Oval or egg-shaped designs are appropriate as small informal designs or large formal designs. An arrangement may also be designed as a round shape, although the oval shape is the more common style. The symmetrical oval and triangle should be constructed in differing ways so that they do not resemble each other. For example, the width placements vary in that the triangle has horizontal placements and the oval has an upturned, rounded placement instead of the width placements. The front contour varies also because the triangle forms a straight line across the front and the oval has a rounded shape.

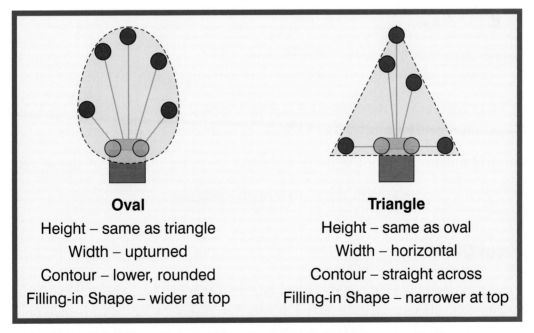

Oval	Triangle
Height – same as triangle	Height – same as oval
Width – upturned	Width – horizontal
Contour – lower, rounded	Contour – straight across
Filling-in Shape – wider at top	Filling-in Shape – narrower at top

7–30. Take note of the differences in width and contour placements for the oval and the triangle. An oval also has wider flower placements at the top of the design.

7–31. An oval design can be a cheerful arrangement, suitable for formal or informal occasions depending on the flowers selected.

Designing a Symmetrical One-sided Oval Arrangement

1. Select a container and position moistened floral foam in a secure way. Allow floral foam to extend above the container rim. Tape it in.

2. Green up the outline, judging the proper proportion for the container. Add height, width, and contour foliage. Fill in the center of the foam with foliage as desired.

3. Place the tallest flower centered in the back of the floral foam. The height should be 1½ to 2 times the vase height. The flower should be positioned vertically or slightly leaning backward.

4. Position the width flowers in an upward fashion extending from the center of the side of the foam. There should be no horizontal placements in an oval design.

5. Add the outermost contour flowers to form the rounded outline at the bottom of the design.

6. Fill in the outline starting from the top. Add flowers, such as round shapes like daisies or carnations, to widen the top of the arrangement to make it round.

7. Add round mass flowers and fillers to complete the oval design. Look at the arrangement from the side to check for a smooth curved contour.

8. Add foliage to mask the floral foam and green up the back of the design.

9. Fill the container with floral preservative solution.

Crescent Design

A crescent design is a curving C-shaped line mass that can be a cheerful expression of spring with daffodils and pussy willow or a dignified arrangement for the Christmas holidays with evergreens and holly. This design can be informal or formal and can be successfully combined with accessories like candles or hurricane lanterns. Some wedding bouquets are designed as an inverted crescent shape. A crescent arrangement is usually designed in a low container or bowl.

Finding curving material to use for a crescent arrangement can be challenging. Some branches or other foliage may curve naturally and can be easily used. Other materials, such as eucalyptus, scotch broom, ferns, Italian ruscus, and myrtle can be curved by shaping with the hands or wiring. The wiring should be inconspicuous. Flowers may also be wired to follow the curved lines within a crescent.

Designing a Crescent Arrangement

1. Select a low bowl and add foam that extends slightly above the rim. Tape to secure the floral foam.

2. Position a curving branch in the upper left side of the design. The height should be at least 1½ times the width of the container.

7–32. A crescent design is a flowing C-shaped arrangement.

3. Counterbalance the height with a curving width placement in the lower right side. The width placement should be one-half the height.

4. Add foliage as a framework for the flowers. Do not widen the arrangement beyond the C shape.

5. Position the flowers in the height, width, and contour placements.

6. Fill in with flowers and fillers to finish the C shape.

7. Add foliage and moss to cover the floral foam.

8. Finish the back of the design with foliage. Add floral preservative solution to the container.

Hogarth Curve

A Hogarth curve is an S-shaped line mass design. This geometric shape is named for William Hogarth, an eighteenth-century painter, who said: "A straight line is a line of duty; a curving line is a line of beauty." The S curve is a serpentine or gently undulating S, not a bold rounded S. The Hogarth curve is an elegant design style that can be used for formal occasions. The upright Hogarth is much more common than the horizontal style.

Designing a Hogarth Curve

1. Select a tall container and position moistened floral foam with at least an inch extending above the rim. Tape the foam to the container.

2. Select Scotch broom, sea lavender, or a leptospermum branch and work it into a gentle curve. The material can be carefully massaged into a curved shape while blowing hot air on it with your breath.

3. Position the curving material in the center of the back of the floral foam. The line should curve just like an S.

4. Counterbalance the height placement with a downward placement of the same material, placed in the center and front of the foam.

5. Use ferns and galax leaves to green up the serpentine shape of the S curve. Place additional sea lavender, Scotch broom, or leptospermum throughout the outer framework.

6. Position roses or carnations—first the height placement, then the repeating downward placement.

7. Add a fully open rose or large carnation at the center of interest. Group other mass flowers nearby to emphasize the focal area.

8. Position other flowers in a transitional way from the height and downward placement toward the center of interest.

9. Add foliage and filler as needed to fill and to cover the foam.

10. Finish the back of the design. Fill container with floral preservative solution.

7–33. A Hogarth curve is a line mass design that is shaped like a slim S.

NATURALISTIC DESIGN

A naturalistic design draws on nature and the garden for its inspiration and incorporates the grouping of flower and foliage and the use of natural materials, such as branches, stones, moss, bulbs, fruit, or seedpods. *Grouping* means to place flowers and foliage in units or sections of just one type as if they were growing that way in nature. A designer who understands how plants grow and knows the plants' relative heights to each other can add a realistic touch to the design. Think of this design as a "little niche of nature" or a miniature landscape. The possibilities and combinations are endless. A design could represent the spring woodland, the summer garden, or the autumn roadside. The designs can be designed with all fresh-cut flowers, fresh and dried materials, or a combination of fresh flowers and potted plants.

7–34. Floral designers can use nature and the garden for their inspiration when creating naturalistic designs. A naturalistic design is a miniature landscape with grouped flowers and foliage.

The containers used to design naturalistic arrangements vary from low baskets and bowls to saucers and trays. Moistened green sheet moss masks the floral foam and is allowed to show, giving a realistic landscape look to the arrangement. Foliage can be placed into the designs in *rosettes* with the stems all emerging from one place as if it were growing in the woodland. The rosette technique mimics the growth of ferns and other plants and is very natural looking. Use longer leaflets on the outer ring and progressively shorter leaflets toward the middle of the rosette.

Accessories, such as realistic purchased birds, nests, butterflies, and even insects, can add interest and realism to the design. Do not overdo the accessories, rather, let the plant materials be the most important part of the design.

Designing a Naturalistic Arrangement

1. Select a basket or appropriate low container. Use a liner or make one from poly foil.

2. Position moistened floral foam in the container with just a small amount extending above the rim. For some designs, the foam can be even with the top of the container.

3. Gather sheet moss and slightly moisten for ease in using it. (Before using it, place the sheet moss in a plastic bag and spray with water or furniture dusting spray to make it pliable and less dusty.)

4. Fill in the edges of the container with moss to cover the liner. Additional moss will be used after the flowers are positioned.

5. Place line flowers, such as snapdragons or liatris, in a grouping with varied heights and angles.

6. Position a second grouping of lilies, sunflowers, or other interesting flowers. Use varied heights. One grouping is usually taller and more dominant than the other grouping.

7. Position additional mass flowers in groupings as needed. Place ferns in rosettes with all of the stems emerging from one "growing point."

8. Add fruit, seedpods, birds, nests, or other accessories in appropriate amounts. Accessories can be placed at the base of the container for repetition.

9. Cover the floral foam with sheet moss. Add floral preservative solution.

WRAPPING A POTTED PLANT

Learning to decorate a potted plant is an important basic skill for a floral designer. A beautifully decorated plant can be a welcome gift or display feature. There are several ways to decorate blooming and foliage plants. The pot can be hidden by inserting it into baskets, containers, and preformed pot covers that look like upside-down hats and by wrapping the pot with foil or cellophane or both. Decorated pots can be adorned with ribbons, birds and nests, branches, or seasonal items, such as hearts or shamrock accessories.

Foil is available as two types—lightweight foil and poly foil. The lightweight foil is colorful on one side and silver on the other. *Poly foil* is a thicker foil with a thin plastic covering on the silver side. In addition to wrapping potted plants, poly foil is useful as a liner in baskets or containers with drainage holes or as a protective liner for containers that need be protected from moisture (metal containers). Foil is available in many colors and patterns. The designer may choose which colorful side to display.

STEPS IN WRAPPING POTTED PLANTS

1. Cut a square of poly foil to fit the size of the pot. Smaller pots will need a smaller square with some of the foil trimmed away. Fold one corner of the foil across to the opposing side to determine a smaller square. The sides of the foil should extend beyond the rim of a centered pot. If not, the piece of foil is too small and should be re-cut.

2. Fold the cut edges over to present a more attractive look.

3. Place the plant in the center of the foil.

7–35. The steps of wrapping potted plants.

4. Holding the foil in the center of the opposing sides, bring the foil up to the pot rim and tuck a small portion into the rim of the pot.

5. Bring the other two sides up to tuck into the pot rim. The points of the foil should project smoothly upward and slightly outward from the pot.

6. Smooth the foil gently around the potted plant.

7–35 (Continued)

7. Determine the front and most attractive side of the plant. Near the edge of the pot, insert a wooden pick (or half of a hyacinth stake) through the foil and into the pot.

8. Wrap a length of #9 ribbon (#5 for smaller pots) around the pot to hold the foil in place. Tie the ribbon with a knot around the wooden pick (or stake).

9. Attach the bow to the pick (or stake).

7–35 (Continued)

REVIEWING

MAIN IDEAS

A floral designer should learn the proper tools, supplies, and basic design styles to provide a strong framework of knowledge in flower arranging. The tools that a floral designer will use include a knife, florist shears, pruning shears, ribbon scissors, and utility scissors. With practice and experience, a sharp knife can help the designer to become an efficient and fast designer. Shears are useful for thicker stems; pruning shears provide needed strength for cutting thick branches or tough stems. Ribbon scissors should not be used to cut plant materials but should be reserved for only ribbon, netting, or fabric. Utility scissors find many uses in trimming leaves, paper, or other materials.

Floral foam is an important design mechanic for the floral designer. Floral foam is a porous material, designed to hold water and give support to stems in design work. It is available in bricks and can be trimmed to any size to fit any container. To avoid waste, cut the foam brick into the portion needed. Floral foam should be soaked thoroughly before using. Always allow it to take up water at its own rate. The foam should be placed into the container with some of the foam extending above the rim of the container and with a small open area in the back for watering the arrangement. To provide stability, the foam can be secured to a container with waterproof tape, anchor pins, or pan melt glue.

Other foundations for arranging flowers are needlepoint holders and wire mesh. Other supplies that floral designers may use include greening pins, water tubes, wooden picks, and hyacinth stakes.

Learning the basic design styles will help a floral designer to build skill and confidence to be able to tackle more difficult styles. The basics of floral arranging include learning to design flowers in vases from small designs, such as bud vases, to larger ones called vase arrangements. Bud vases may have one to three flowers or multiple smaller flowers.

Vase arrangements can be designed with the help of a few tips and techniques, such as using a grid to avoid the "doughnut arrangement" (a circle of flowers with a big hole in the center). Grids give some support to the flowers. The types of grids are the foliage grid or a tape grid. Marbles and gemstones can be used in the vases to provide color, texture, and weight. The traditional vase arrangement is a dozen flowers, such as roses, designed in either a one-sided or all-around arrangement. Vase arrangements are very versatile and can be designed with many types of flowers and foliage.

The basic geometric shapes designed using floral foam are vertical, triangle, and circle. These shapes may be symmetrical or asymmetrical. Beginning designers should keep the shape in mind while placing the starting framework of height, width, and contour placements in foliage and flowers.

A vertical design has greatly reduced width placements and is a dramatic design for limited table area or to place on the floor. The symmetrical triangles are equilateral and isosceles triangles. An inverted T is a type of isosceles triangle. The height should equal the width for an equilateral triangle. The height is greater than the width for both the isosceles triangle and the inverted T. Two types of asymmetrical triangles are the right triangle and the scalene triangle. The height placements for all asymmetrical triangles are placed to the left or right of center. A right triangle has a 90-degree angle width placement compared to the height; a scalene triangle has a downward width placement and, therefore, forms a larger than 90-degree angle.

One-sided circular designs include the oval, crescent, and the Hogarth curve. The width placements of the oval design are placed in an upward fashion to create a rounded shape. A crescent is a C-shaped design that employs curving materials (naturally or wired) to successfully design it. A Hogarth curve is a slim S shape (serpentine shape) that is an elegant type of design.

Naturalistic designs are a little niche of nature or a miniature landscape. Plant materials are placed in groupings and rosettes and accessories, such as stones, nests, branches, birds, and moss, are welcome additions to create the naturalistic look.

Knowing how to attractively wrap a potted plant is an important skill for a beginning designer. Potted plants may be placed in baskets or containers or wrapped with cellophane or foil or both.

QUESTIONS

Answer the following questions using complete sentences and correct spelling.

1. What are five basic cutting tools needed for the floral designer and what function do they each serve?

2. What is the proper way to size, position, and secure floral foam into a container?

3. Why is it important to learn the basic design styles?

4. What is a doughnut arrangement and how do you avoid making one?

5. How do you position a dozen flowers to create a) a one-sided vase arrangement, and b) an all-around vase arrangement?

6. What are the guidelines or steps when designing any basic geometric shape?

7. What are the differences in designing an equilateral triangle, an isosceles triangle, and an inverted T?

8. How are the scalene triangle and right triangle different? What container choices would you make for each type?

9. Which circular design is your favorite? Discuss its construction.

10. What is a naturalistic design? What are some design techniques used in this style that are not used in geometric designs?

EVALUATING

Match the term with the correct definition. Write the letter of the term on the line provided.

a. poly foil
b. anchor pin
c. contour
d. needlepoint holder

e. foliage grid
f. floral foam
g. water tube
h. hyacinth stake

i. florist shears
j. pruning shears

_____1. Small, plastic, rubber-capped container for holding a single flower in a floral preservative solution.

_____2. A cutting tool with short, serrated blades for cutting thicker stems.

_____3. Positioning leaves in an overlapping, radiating fashion to provide support of flowers.

_____4. Wrapping material with a thin plastic covering on the silver side to hold water.

_____5. Cutting tool with a sharp cutting blade for cutting very tough or extremely thick stems.

_____6. Side view of an arrangement showing a gradual, gently rounded, three-dimensional radiation from vertical to horizontal.

_____7. Porous material that provides support for stems and holds water.

_____8. A long green wooden stick that supports flowers and adds height to the accessories in an arrangement.

_____9. A weighted, metallic base with upright metal pins for supporting flowers.

_____10. A four-pronged plastic holder attached to a container to secure floral foam.

EXPLORING

1. Obtain three potted plants of different pot sizes (4-inch, 6-inch, etc.). Select appropriate foil and ribbons and gather wooden picks or hyacinth stakes and seasonal accessories, such as birds or holiday picks. Decorate each potted plant in an attractive and different way.

2. Gather the materials to design three asymmetrical triangles—a right triangle, a scalene triangle, and an inverted T with branches or other asymmetrically placed materials. Determine occasions and locations where each design would be appropriate. Which design is your favorite and why?

3. Create two vase arrangements of garden flowers. Try making one vase arrangement without using any grids. Was a doughnut arrangement the result? Then, use the foliage grid for one vase and a tape grid for the other one. Decide which grid was the most successful for you.

4. Gather moss, branches, and stones, as well as some flowers, leaves, and a low container for designing a naturalistic arrangement. Determine if you will design a woodland walk or spring garden or fall landscape and create a little niche of nature.

CHAPTER 8

Designing Centerpieces and Holiday Arrangements

OBJECTIVES

This chapter is about designing centerpieces and holiday arrangements. It has the following objectives:

1 Identify types of centerpieces.

2 Explain how to properly design a centerpiece.

3 Learn how to take a centerpiece order.

4 Describe floral arrangements for holidays and themes.

TERMS

binding
candleholders
conical centerpiece
contemporary design
cornucopia

novelty design
paddle wire
pavé
pillowing
plush animals

raffia
terracing
votive candles

8–1. Centerpieces and floral arrangements can add a beautiful and festive flair when entertaining.

FLOWERS make a beautiful impression at a social event. Designing floral arrangements for parties, holidays, and other events is a creative challenge for a floral designer. The flowers should convey the theme and the formality or informality of the event as well as be attractive and suitable for the location. Both centerpieces and one-sided designs are appropriate for social events, depending on where the design is placed.

For an event with a definite theme, suitable accessories can add to the expression of the design. Many holidays and events, such as birthdays, anniversaries, and going-away parties, can rely on the clever use of accessories to enhance the flowers and design styles.

TYPES OF CENTERPIECES

Centerpieces have been a traditional favorite for entertaining since the English first developed them in the eighteenth century. Centerpieces add a colorful splash in the center of a dining table, coffee table, or banquet table. They may be formal or informal styles, traditional or contemporary, vase arrangements or arrangements designed in floral foam. Centerpieces are also called all-around arrangements because the design is colorful and attractive on every side.

THE PROPER DESIGN OF A CENTERPIECE

Traditional centerpieces are designed to allow people to see each other across the dining table. The centerpiece should not obstruct the view at eye level. Contemporary centerpieces are designed to allow viewing over the centerpiece as well as through or under it. Topiaries and other contemporary designs may have splashes of color below and above eye level.

All-around centerpieces and one-sided designs can be created for the same event. For instance, all-around centerpieces would be used to beautify tables, and a one-sided arrange-

8–2. Centerpieces add color and interest to a table. Centerpieces are designed to allow viewing over, under, and through the flowers or accessories. Note the two diverse styles—traditional (left) and contemporary or high style (right).

ment would be suitable for a buffet table that is along one side of a room. The two styles would be designed to coordinate in color, flowers, and feeling.

The shape and style of the centerpiece will depend on the dining area where the centerpiece will be placed. Round or rectangular tables are the most common choices for a dining room or banquet room. In general, round centerpieces are placed on round tables and oval centerpieces are designed for rectangular or oval tables. Centerpieces may be simple bud vases, small vase arrangements, or round or oval designs created with floral foam as the design mechanic.

Bud Vases

Bud vase designs are well suited for use on a small dining table or for placing several along a rectangular table. The designs should be fashioned in an all-around style. For an informal teacher's reception, small asymmetrical bud vases were positioned equally along the rows of three rectangular tables. Curling ribbon was used in each bud vase to create the bow and provide long streamers. Some streamers were curled and arranged on the table, and some long streamers were tied to apples. The apples were placed in one's and two's informally along the tables.

Small clusters of bud vases of different types of flowers in each vase can make a unique centerpiece. Tie the grouping together with a round mirror placed underneath them. Small individual vases could also be placed at each person's place at the table.

Small Vase Arrangements

Small vase arrangements can replace the traditional round centerpieces designed in floral foam. The vase arrangements should be designed in short vases with a 1:1 proportion to

8–3. Small vase arrangements are great for table centerpieces.

allow people to see each other across the table. Vase arrangements are very colorful and emphasize flowers more than bud vase designs. Symmetrical or asymmetrical styles may be chosen according to the theme and formality of the event.

ROUND CENTERPIECES

A round centerpiece is perfectly suited to a round table. It is a popular style and can be designed with one type of flower or a colorful mixture. The size of the centerpiece should be appropriate to the table size, amount of people, and table furnishings. The round centerpiece has a similar appearance when viewed from any direction in a room.

Choose a low rounded container that suits the theme. The choices include low plastic utility containers, small wicker baskets (lined) with or without a handle, low pottery bowls, or metal containers with liners. For some centerpieces, the container may not be noticeable when the arrangement is completed.

A round centerpiece is round when viewed from above, however, from a side view, a round centerpiece may be either rounded or triangular in contour. The type of plant material and designer's preference will determine which outline is chosen.

Designing a Round Centerpiece

1. Select a low container with a large diameter opening to allow an adequate piece of floral foam.

8–4. A round centerpiece is round when viewed from above. A round centerpiece may be either rounded or triangular in outline when viewed from the side.

2. Position a moistened piece of floral foam into the container with ½ to 1 inch of foam extending above the container rim. Trim off the corners of the foam at a 45-degree angle. The angled corner allows easier stem placements into the foam and is easier to mask with foliage (covering the mechanics). Secure the foam to the container.

3. Green up the container by placing leatherleaf (or other thin-stemmed foliage) around the rim of the container. Place the leaves so the tips angle slightly downward. (Do not overdo it or there will no room for flowers.) The foliage should extend an equal distance away from the container to form the round shape. The size of the finished arrangement will dictate the length of the first leaf placements.

4. Add more leatherleaf in the center of the foam to give a rounded or triangular outline and to mask the floral foam.

5. Place the tallest flowers (daisies or cushion chrysanthemums) to establish the height. This placement should not extend above eye level when a person is seated at a table (under 12 inches).

6. Position additional chrysanthemums (five to six) to form the width of the centerpiece. Place these flowers equally around the container rim and the same distance from the center of the arrangement. Stop and look at the design from above to check for the round shape.

7. Position three to five additional chrysanthemums to begin filling in the shape. Watch for appropriate flower facings.

8. Using mini carnations, begin filling the width and contour of the design. Do not crowd the flowers. Allow space between each flower. Place a few carnations

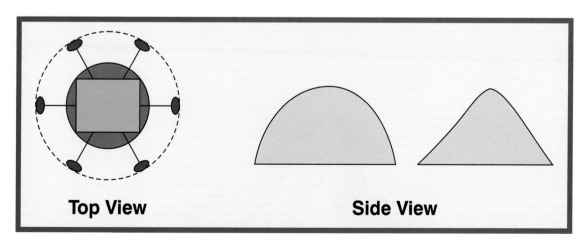

Top View   **Side View**

8–5. The top view reveals equal width placements around the container rim and equidistant placements from the center of the design (and from the container, too). The side view reveals the effect of varied width and height placements—rounded or triangular outlines.

deeper within the arrangement to add depth and fullness of color without crowding.

9. Look for gaps in the outline and fill in with a third type of flower or a filler flower.

10. Cover any noticeable floral foam with foliage, if necessary. Add more foliage, if needed, in the center of the design. A second type of foliage can also be added.

8–6. The steps of making a centerpiece.

OVAL CENTERPIECES

An oval centerpiece is an attractive horizontal style to adorn oval and triangular tables. Oval centerpieces may be created as a garden mixture, a traditional formal design with candles, or an asymmetrical informal design.

Appropriate containers to use are low containers that are round, oval, square, or rectangular. The container should match the theme and formality of the event although the foliage tends to mask the container in most cases.

The oval centerpiece is oval in shape when viewed from above. A low centerpiece may also be diamond-shaped from the top view. Linear plant materials are positioned at the width and outermost contour placements to create the diamond shape.

Like the round centerpiece, an oval centerpiece may also be rounded or triangular in outline. When viewed from the side, the contour can be either rounded or triangular due to the designer's preference or the types of plant materials.

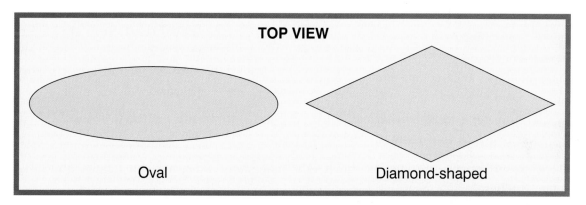

TOP VIEW

Oval   Diamond-shaped

8–7. Low horizontal centerpieces may be oval or diamond-shaped from the top view.

8–8. An oval centerpiece was designed with a triangular outline. The heather was removed from the top and sides to create a rounded outline.

8–9. An oval centerpiece can add beauty and color to the center of an oval or rectangular table.

Designing an Oval Centerpiece

1. Choose a low plastic utility design bowl, add 1/3 brick of moistened floral foam, sculpt the foam edges by cutting at an angle, and tape the foam to the bowl with 1/8-inch green waterproof tape.

2. Green up the centerpiece by inserting two matching longer pieces of leatherleaf on each side. Green up the narrow sides of the oval by placing shorter pieces of leatherleaf and sprengeri fern. Check the shape from above before adding any flowers.

3. Add ming fern, leatherleaf, and sprengeri fern in the center to form the oval framework and to mask the floral foam.

4. Insert purple statice for the height placement, keeping the height under 12 inches.

5. Add lily buds for the elongated width placements, one on each end.

6. Place alstroemeria to form the contour on the narrow side of the oval.

7. Position a lily and bud and two peonies on each side and fill in the shape with alstroemeria and purple statice.

8. Insert ming fern and sprengeri fern to cover the foam.

CONICAL CENTERPIECES

Conical centerpieces are cone-shaped or three-dimensional isosceles triangles. Cone-shaped designs originated after the historical period of the Greeks and Romans and before the Middle Ages during the Byzantine period. Designs were symmetrical, conical, and formal. Although this style is not highly prevalent, the cone design is a perfect shape for

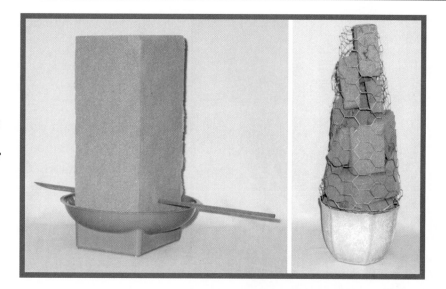

8–10. Conical designs can be created using either a floral foam foundation or a chicken wire base.

a tabletop Christmas tree centerpiece or a Colonial Williamsburg design with fruit, foliage, and flowers.

Conical centerpieces are too tall to be placed in the center of a dining table but make an attractive centerpiece for a buffet table or corner table. A pair of conical centerpieces would effectively enhance each end of a large serving table or fireplace mantle.

The mechanics of a cone-shaped design should be carefully constructed. There are two ways to make the floral foam foundation.

1. Sculpt a brick of floral foam by trimming the top corners away at an angle. (The floral foam does not have to be cone-shaped because the plant materials can be trimmed to appropriate lengths to create the cone shape.) The moistened foam is placed upright in a plastic design bowl, ceramic container, or basket and secured by placing a hyacinth stake horizontally through the foam at the level of the container rim and taping or gluing (or both) that stake to the container. The excess length of hyacinth stake is removed.

2. Wrap chicken wire or wire mesh around moistened pieces of floral foam to form a cone or pyramidal shape. Waxed string or paddle wire can be used to hold the form together. The framework is securely positioned into a container and then covered with a thin layer of moss, held in place with a few greening pins. This mechanic works well for inserting heavy placements, such as fruit.

For Christmas tree designs, use evergreens that are available in the area or your yard or purchase "trimmed off" branches from a Christmas tree grower. Outstanding choices are boxwood, yew, spruce, pine, cedar, and arborvitae used singly or mixed. Color schemes should enhance the setting, ranging from traditional red and green; red, white, and green;

8–11. Conical designs make an eye-catching tabletop Christmas tree.

red and gold; burgundy and pink; silver and blue; to mixed colors. The style may be formal with elegant accessories and containers of gold or silver, child-oriented with toys and lots of bright mixed primary colors, or contemporary with unusual colors and accessories.

For a charming conical buffet piece for any time of the year, form the foliage framework with salal, huckleberry, ruscus, Italian ruscus, philodendron leaves, and ivy. Moss may be used to cover any foam that shows. Add whole fruits, such as grapes, apples, oranges, lemons, limes, and kiwis, as well as cutting some of the long-lasting citrus and kiwis in halves. The original Byzantine designs, shown in paintings, used a pineapple at the top of the design. Vegetables can be added if the theme is suitable.

Designing a Conical Centerpiece

1. Gather evergreens, pine cones, flowers, ribbon or netting, accessories, and the container prepared with a moistened brick of sculpted floral foam.

2. Begin with the framework of evergreen foliage, adding 6- to 8-inch height placement and 3- to 4-inch width placements. Smaller or longer pieces can be used depending on the desired size of the finished tabletop tree. Optional, a string of lights (50 or 75 lights) can be wound loosely around the foam at this stage.

3. Continue adding evergreens to fill in the shape. Step back from the design to evaluate the shape, adjusting as necessary.

4. When the greens are 2/3 finished, add wired pine cones, appropriate accessories, and flowers, such as carnations, roses, star of Bethlehem, lilies, or fillers, such as sea lavender (to give a frosty or snowy appearance) or white Monte Casino asters (for a more casual look).

5. Fill in with additional greens if needed. Moss may be added if desired and appropriate to the theme.

6. Adorn with ribbon, bows, or tulle, if desired.

7. Place in the chosen setting with fabrics draped underneath or behind as needed. Position suitable accessories at the base of the tree.

8. Fill the container with floral preservative solution.

ADDING ACCESSORIES

Accessories can add flair and an expressive touch to centerpieces and holiday designs. However, the accessories should be in harmony, necessary, and properly placed to be effective. Do not overdo the addition of accessories. Always ask yourself these simple questions before using any accessories.

♦ Does the accessory go with the theme? Is it in harmony with the style and feelings of the design?

♦ Is the accessory necessary? Does it form a center of interest, convey an idea, or provide a needed color or texture?

♦ Is the accessory properly placed?
  • For symmetrical designs—centered or placed on either side.
  • For asymmetrical designs—off center or something tall on one side with a counterbalancing smaller object on the other side.

♦ Have I used too many accessories? Could the design be improved with fewer items near it?

What are some typical accessories? Let's explore the choices and the methods of placing each one into an arrangement.

Candles Add Class to a Design

Taper candles are lovely additions to centerpieces. Taper candles come in many colors and sizes from 5 to 18 inches long. The 10-, 12-, 15-, and 18-inch lengths are most often used in centerpieces. Choose candle lengths that will keep the flame above or below eye level. Pillar candles also come in many colors and in 2- and 3-inch diameters in lengths of 6, 9, and 12 inches.

The mechanic used to securely insert candles into a design is called a candleholder. **Candleholders** are green plastic devices with a round fitted top to secure a candle and a pronged base to insert into the floral foam. Candleholders come in varying sizes to fit the

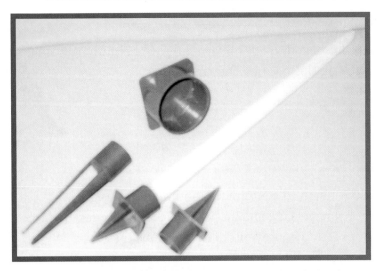

8–12. Green plastic candleholders provide a secure foundation for candles used in centerpieces.

candle diameter being used. When designing with candleholders, hot glue moss or position leaves to cover the mechanics of the candleholders.

When using more than one taper candle in a design, be sure to place them two finger widths apart, approximately 1 inch. Candles placed closer than this will heat up and burn very fast. Candles that are chilled in the cooler or refrigerator for several hours will burn more slowly.

If candleholders are not available, taper candles may be slightly carved to form a taper at the bottom and deeply inserted into the foam. This method leaves less foam for the flower placements. If the taper is not securely positioned in the foam, it may result in a wobbly candle. Pillar candles may be firmly placed into a design without candleholders by attaching five or six wood picks taped to the bottom of the candle with waterproof tape. Securely tape the tops of the 4-inch wood picks to the candle base. The wood picks are inserted into the foam and the pillar candle rests on top of the foam. The picks can be trimmed to a shorter length if needed.

Other Accessories

Wholesale florists and craft stores offer a wide array of seasonal and holiday accessories to place into a design. These accessories are usually attached to a wire stem for ease in adding to a design. Choose accessories that add to the theme. Examples are birds, hearts, shamrocks, Easter eggs and bunnies, flags, Christmas presents, and other novelties. Some accessories will need to be wired before adding to a design. Natural materials, such as the cones of spruce, Douglas fir, and pine, are perfect additions to a Christmas centerpiece. Each of these cones can be wired with heavy

8–13. Make a stem to insert a cone by slipping a heavy gauge wire around the base of the cone. Twist the wire tightly to form a stem. The cone may be added to centerpieces and wreaths.

gauge wire to form a stem. Take a #22-gauge wire and bend in half around the base of the cone. Twist the wire tightly to form a stem for it.

Fruit provides an interesting addition to suitable designs. A variety of choices are colorful and unique for adding mass, providing a center of interest, adding to a topiary or conical design, and attracting attention in a design. Fruit can be added to a design by placing the sharp end of a wood pick or hyacinth stake into the fruit and inserting the other end into the design. For heavy fruit, add a second pick and a bead of hot glue where the pick and the fruit join. For grapes, use greening pins and/or #22-gauge hairpin wire placed between the stems. Oranges, lemons, limes, pineapples, or kiwis can be cut in half and placed into a design with the wood pick method. Position fruit near the container as was common for Dutch Flemish designs. Check the fruit frequently and replace as needed.

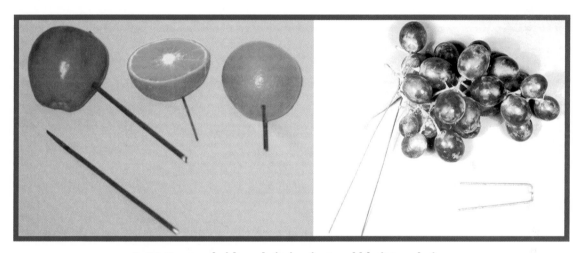

8–14. Use wood picks or hairpin wire to add fruit to a design.

Balloons add festive and eye-catching excitement to an arrangement. The balloon color and message should coordinate with the flowers and the theme. Balloons may be filled with air or helium but should always be securely attached to a flower arrangement. One, two, three, or several balloons can be added to a design. Add balloons to a design using the following steps:

1. Wrap the wire of a wood pick around the ribbon ends of the balloons.

2. Loop the ribbon ends back around to the wood pick.

3. Wrap the wire around the ribbon ends a second time.

4. Insert the wood pick completely into the floral foam. The wood pick will swell slightly in the moist floral foam and securely hold the balloon ribbons in place.

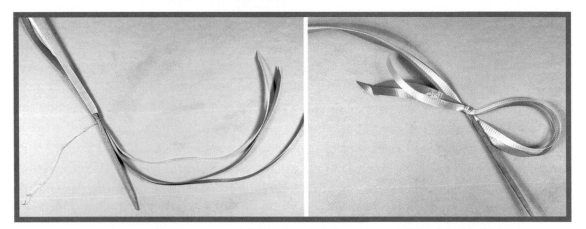

8–15. Attach balloons to a design using a wood pick and a double wiring method.

TAKING AN ORDER FOR AN EVENT

If someone asks you to design flowers for an event, do not take this responsibility lightly. Much information should be gathered to ensure the appropriate flower designs are provided. Remember, a beginning designer can always say "No" until more experience and skills are gained.

The following checklist is helpful in learning as much about the event as possible.

♦ WHEN is the event? Date? Time of day? How much time to set up?

♦ WHERE is the location of the event? Size of room? Ceiling height?

♦ WHAT is the style of the room?

♦ What is the color scheme of the room?

♦ What is the preferred style of the event? Formal or informal? Traditional, elegant, casual, or contemporary?

♦ What is the color scheme? Theme? (Avoid specifying flowers, if possible.)

♦ HOW MANY tables will need centerpieces? Table shape? Size of table? (Ask how many people will be seated at each table.)

♦ What is the color of the tablecloths and napkins?

♦ How many additional centerpieces or one-sided designs will be needed? (Centerpieces could also be used on serving tables and head tables. One-sided designs could adorn an entryway, a buffet table near a wall, or a head table with a tabletop lectern.)

♦ What is the budget?

The location should be visited in person if it is an unfamiliar one. Sketch the room shape and general placement of the tables, including the head table, if any. Sometimes, large hotels and banquet halls have mirrors and votive candles available for patrons to use. Ask about reserving these items if it is appropriate to the theme.

DESIGNING SEASONAL AND HOLIDAY ARRANGEMENTS

Flowers can play a pleasing, integral part of every season and many major holidays.

- Spring holidays include Valentine's Day, St. Patrick's Day, Easter, Professional Secretaries' Week (last week in April), and Mother's Day.

- Summer floral holidays include Memorial Day, Father's Day, Independence Day (Fourth of July), and many local festivals and fairs.

- Fall holidays include Grandparents Day (first Sunday in September after Labor Day), Sweetest Day (third Saturday in October), Halloween, and Thanksgiving.

- Winter brings the Christmas season and New Year's Eve celebrations.

VALENTINE'S DAY

Valentine's Day and flowers are inseparable. Nothing conveys love and romance like flowers. Red, pink, and white are traditional colors, but mixed colors of flowers can also convey a springy mood as well as a romantic feeling. Typical design styles are the ever-popular dozen roses in a vase, other vase arrangements, bud vases, and mixed bouquets designed in floral foam. Popular containers are bud vases, crystal vases, ceramic or metallic containers, baskets,

8–16. Hearts and flowers make a great duo for a Valentine's Day celebration.

mugs, and anything red or heart-shaped. Hearts, ribbons, candy, and balloons are all typical Valentine's Day accessories.

Designing a Sweetheart Bouquet

1. Select a red or hot pink basket with a handle. Fit it with a liner or line it with a double thickness of poly foil.

2. Cut a piece of foam to extend 1 inch above the container rim. Moisten the foam and securely position it in the basket. With a preformed liner, tape the foam securely to it. Use moss to cover the liner edges. With a foil liner, add a small amount of moss along the edges to cover the foil and wire the foam to the basket. The wire is inserted through a small amount of the woven material on the basket edge. Twist-tie the wire. Bring the other end of the wire across the moss and foam (the moss keeps the wire from cutting through the floral foam) to the other side and repeat the process. Remove any excess wire. Trim off the pointed corners of the foam.

8–17. A sweetheart bouquet speaks of love in red and pink colors.

3. Green up the basket with red huckleberry, galax leaves, and leatherleaf to form a triangular (isosceles) design.

4. Position three red roses; the top one forms the height of the design along with the tallest red huckleberry branch. Place the other two roses in a vertical line below the tallest rose in a slightly zigzag fashion.

5. Fill in the width and contour placements with genistra and mini carnations in pink and light-pink colors.

6. Position four tulips, two on each side of the handle. Do not position them as a mirror image, rather counterbalance them. Note: Tulips will continue to elongate after being added to a design. (Note, the tulip in the center of the right side—it has realigned itself upward, moving away from its original spot, which is now open just below it and to the right.)

7. Add hot pink carnations lower in the design and on the opposite side of the roses.

8. Fill out the design with genistra and carnations, also using the carnation buds.

9. Cover any floral foam that shows with leatherleaf, moss, or red huckleberry.

10. Green up the back of the design. Add floral preservative solution.

11. A heart accessory and a card with a message can be added before delivery.

EASTER AND SPRING THEMES

Easter and springtime themes go together so well. Easter designs can be either whimsical with Easter bunny themes or spiritual with Resurrection Sunday themes. Typical color schemes would be mixed spring colors using both pastel and bright colors. Appropriate designs and styles would be decorated Easter lilies or other spring plants; mixed flowers in vase arrangements; geometric shapes in baskets, pots, or vases; and novelty designs. Suitable Easter containers would be baskets, ceramic containers of all shapes, crystal or ceramic vases, terra cotta pots (lined), novelty containers shaped like bunnies or crosses. For whimsical designs, accessories include plush animals such as bunnies, chicks, lambs; Easter bonnets; silk carrots, radishes, or cabbages; or eggs, birds, and nests. **Plush animals** are

8–18. Easter themes can be nostalgic, such as an Easter bonnet design, or religious with lilies and a cross. In the Easter bonnet design, the flowers were designed in a floral cage attached to the hat. In the lilies and cross design, the cross was fashioned from rustic fence posts and secured within a container with quick-setting concrete.

stuffed figures, animals, or other items that can be added as accessories (use small ones) to floral arrangements. For religious themes, the cross, a stone (the stone was rolled away), a crown of thorns, an open bible, and symbolic flowers, such as white lilies and calla lilies are all meaningful and appropriate accessories.

A *novelty design* is a unique whimsical imaginative arrangement of flowers that resemble kittens, bunnies, clowns, birthday cakes, or ice cream sodas, just to name a few. A novelty design is appropriate for children, holidays, special occasions or anniversaries, birthdays, and hospital designs. Special construction techniques are needed to design these cute arrangements.

Designing an Easter Novelty—an Easter Bunny

1. Select a white 9-inch bud vase and fill it with floral preservative solution.

2. Wire a white standard chrysanthemum (football mum) with #22-gauge wire and bend the flower head slightly forward.

3. Cut out Styrofoam™ hands and feet. The feet have three toes and the hands resemble mittens. Be sure to make both a left and a right hand (refer to Figure 8–17). Spray the cutouts hot pink and let dry.

4. And now, the ears. Take two white chenille stems and bend in half, shaping each one to resemble a slightly curving bunny ear. Trace each ear's shape on pink springy fabric or #9 or #40 ribbon. Fold the front sides of the fabric inward and cut out two for each ear. For the ribbon, place two lengths of ribbon together with the front sides touching and cut out two for each ear. Glue the fabric or ribbon to the front and back of the chenille stem ears. (Optional: just the front side can be covered.) Lay aside until ready to assemble.

5. Position the hot pink feet in front of the bud vase. Cut out slightly to match the rounded shape of the bud vase. Use hot glue or floral adhesive to attach the feet to the bud vase. Be sure that the feet are firmly attached before proceeding.

6. To make the tail, use quilt filling, called polyester cotton, to form a round ball. Spray it hot pink, let it dry, and glue to the back of the bud vase.

7. Place the white mum in the vase with the slightly angled stem facing forward. Wedge a small piece of Styrofoam on each side of the stem to support it. (The Styrofoam should be hidden by the bow.)

8. Using either a white or pink chenille stem, wrap it around the stem two times to form the arms. Cut the "arms" to the same length and insert each end into a hand.

9. Slide the ears in between the petals of the mum to determine the best location. Hot glue the ears to the mum, placing the ears deeply within the petals to give support. The ears should stand upright.

10. Next, create the face. Use eyes purchased from a craft shop or wholesale florist or cover two corsage pins with pink floral tape. For the nose, spray a small white pompon mum a hot pink color; remove the stem when dry. For the mouth, fashion a 3-inch piece of pink chenille stem (spray it hot pink). Lay each part on the face of the mum. Adjust as needed and hot glue in place.

8–19. A cute bunny is a great novelty design for Easter.

11. Add a bow with streamers to make a festive bow tie.

Designing an Easter Basket with a Plush Bunny

1. Select a pastel basket with a handle and a liner. Position moistened floral foam securely into the basket and tape it to the liner.

2. Green up the design to form a one-sided equilateral triangle suitable for an Easter buffet table.

3. Add the yellow foxtail lily (snapdragons or other line materials can be substituted) to form the height (1½ times the width of the basket).

4. Insert the width placements, both carnations and alstroemerias.

5. Place mini carnations to form the outermost contour in front of the handle.

6. Cover the back (or lower part) of the Easter bunny (plush animal) with a corsage bag (to keep the toy dry). Wrap the plush animal two or three times with paddle wire, twist the wires and cut them shorter to form a stem, and insert into the design on the right side.

8–20. A plush bunny can be added to an Easter basket or other special arrangement.

7. Add four or five roses to form the top part of the triangle. Add two more line materials to form the shape on the left side.

8. Fill out the right side of the triangle with alstroemeria and the left side with statice. Add some deeper statice placements. Add carnations to complete the triangle.

9. Add more foliage, as needed, to cover the foam.

10. Cover the back of the design and fill the container with floral preservative solution.

MOTHER'S DAY

Mother's Day was first celebrated on the second Sunday in May in Lincoln, Nebraska, in 1908 and quickly caught on as a widespread holiday in other states. What better way to honor Mother than with a beautiful bouquet of flowers? Spring colors as well as monochromatic schemes are good choices. Corsages and many types of designs are excellent gifts for Mother on her day. Suitable containers include teapots, teacups, mugs, ceramic and pottery containers, watering cans, pots, or other containers with a gardening theme, and baskets. Birds and nests, soaps and sachets, picture frames, garden tools or novelty items, and jewelry are accessories to add to Mother's Day designs.

Designing a Spring Basket with Plants

Potted plants and cut flowers are a welcome springtime combination for a Mother's Day design. Designs of all sizes can incorporate plants. The pot is covered with a corsage bag or larger plastic bag to keep the floral preservative solution in the floral arrangement from mixing with the soil that may drain from the potted plant. The plastic bag also keeps the plant from becoming over-watered.

1. Select a low basket with a liner. Add saturated floral foam to the basket, leaving adequate space for adding two pansy plants.

2. Cover the containers of the two pansy plants with corsage bags and place both plants in the basket. Place one in the front on the left side and one in the center of the right side.

3. Green up the basket with huckleberry, salal, and leatherleaf in an informal rounded shape.

4. Add pussy willow to give height on the upper left side. Add a stem or two on the lower right side.

5. Add heather in a radiating manner to define the rounded shape.

6. Position white daisy chrysanthemums and yellow freesias to fill the round shape.

7. Insert some purple statice to add color and depth. Tuck a few sprigs deeper into the design.

8–21. Add plants to a floral design to increase the enjoyment. Cover the container of the potted plant with plastic.

8. Cover the foam with foliage and moss. Green up the back of the design.

9. Fill the container with floral preservative solution. **Do not water the plants with this solution.** Check the plants' soil for dryness before watering.

A Spring Contemporary Design

A new and creative design style, called contemporary design or free style, may be a pleasing change for a Mother's Day arrangement. ***Contemporary design*** is a term that describes an arrangement that is designed using the latest trends in floral design. Contemporary design is imaginative and bends some of the principles of design. It may be one-sided or all-around. Some of the techniques used in contemporary design are grouping, binding, pillowing, pavé, and terracing. Grouping plant materials together is also used in naturalistic designs. ***Binding*** is a technique of physically tying stems together for physical support and beauty. ***Pillowing*** describes the technique of placing flowers very low and close together within a design. These clusters form peaks and valleys like a landscape. ***Pavé*** is a technique of positioning plant materials very close together to cover floral foam in organized lines or areas. Pavé is a jeweler's term that refers to jewelry with stones placed so close together that no metal shows. ***Terracing*** means to place plant materials in a series of different levels, one above another. For example, galax leaves can be placed horizontally on the side of a design with five or six leaves placed in a stair-step fashion.

8–22. A spring contemporary design is creative, imaginative, and may bend some of the principles of design. Grouping, binding, and pillowing are techniques used in this design.

1. Select a low bowl and place saturated floral foam with 1 inch extending above the container rim.

2. Insert a calla lily on the upper left side, using a 3:1 proportion to the container width. Place a second calla low and on the right side. Use the binding technique to tie the removed stem of the second calla in a diagonal way between the two calla lilies. Use natural raffia. ***Raffia*** is the fiber of a palm tree (*Raphia ruffia*) used like string or ribbon to tie things together. It is available in many colors.

3. Insert three pussy willow stems for an interesting line.

4. Use the pillowing technique to place four roses in the center and close to the floral foam.

5. Group sweet peas on the left side and low in the back. Use groupings of seeded eucalyptus on both sides of the roses and in the back.

6. Add salal leaves on the lower right side and to the back left side to cover foam and continue the line of the calla stem.

7. Cover any foam that shows with moss.

Autumn Holidays and Themes

Autumn is a time of rich, beautiful colors, combined with the grains and fruits of the harvest. Halloween, Thanksgiving, and many harvest themes are all inspiring for the floral designer. Warm colors predominate, as well as rustic or pottery containers and baskets. Containers fashioned from pumpkins and cornucopias are quite common for this time of year. Accessories center around trick or treating (Halloween) or the harvest season (Thanksgiving).

Designing a Halloween Centerpiece in a Pumpkin

1. Select a small- to medium-size pumpkin. Cut a large opening and clean out the inside. Save the pumpkin "cap" with stem to add as an accessory later. Carve a jack-o'-lantern face, if desired.

8–23. A lined pumpkin is a fun and appropriate container at Halloween.

2. To absorb excess moisture, add a small amount of silica sand inside the pumpkin. Line the pumpkin with a plastic bag, overlapping the rim slightly with the plastic. Cut the moistened foam to fit snugly, leaving 1 inch above the rim and an area to water the arrangement.

3. Green up the design to create a round centerpiece.

4. Using fall mums in bronze and gold colors and orange safflower, fill in the round centerpiece shape. The outline may be triangular or round.

5. Add fall leaves, acorns (hot glued to a #22-gauge wire), and a branch (optional).

6. Add foliage to cover the foam. Fill the plastic liner with floral preservative solution without watering the pumpkin.

7. Check the pumpkin frequently for signs of softness or decay. The pumpkin should last a week and should then be discarded. Transfer the centerpiece to a clay pot or basket with a liner.

Thanksgiving Centerpiece

A cornucopia is the traditional Thanksgiving centerpiece container. A **cornucopia** is a cone or horn-shaped container; it is also called a horn of plenty. The finished arrangement should look as if an abundance of the harvest is flowing out of the container. The cornucopia arrangement shape resembles one half of an oval centerpiece. Add accessories to enhance the harvest theme, such as grains, leaves, gourds, pumpkins, and decorative corn.

8–24. A cornucopia centerpiece is traditional for Thanksgiving. The centerpiece is one half of an oval shape with the container forming the other half.

1. To design in a wicker cornucopia or horn of plenty, place a low saucer with a moistened piece of floral foam on the lip of the horn. Hot glue and/or wire the saucer securely to the cornucopia.

2. Green up the oval shape.

3. Add wheat to elongate the oval. Add colorful fall mums and golden alstroemeria to fill out the oval shape.

4. Insert wheat throughout the centerpiece to unify the design.

5. Add floral preservative solution by placing the arrangement near a sink and carefully watering it. Allow time to drain or dry any spills with a towel.

CHRISTMAS

The Christmas season is a glorious time of lights, tinsel, and pine. Red and green are the traditional colors, but color schemes may vary depending on the decor of the person's home. Burgundy and gold, silver and red, green and white, and even maroon and pink can be Christmas color schemes. The poinsettia makes its debut as a centerpiece flower. Be sure to condition the cut stem with very warm water. Holly and evergreens are beautiful seasonal additions to any Christmas arrangement.

8–25. Count the days until Christmas while enjoying a seasonal arrangement, complete with accessories.

Centerpieces, wreaths, garlands, vase arrangements, and geometric shapes all have their place for this festive season. Containers include all types of vases, metallic and ceramic containers, baskets, or containers may be fashioned from toys. Suitable accessories include ornaments, a nutcracker, a nativity scene, toys, stockings, Santa Claus, elves, reindeer, angels, snowflakes, and even cookie cutters. Candles are especially popular at Christmas, including votive candles. **Votive candles** are short, stocky candles that are placed in holders (votive candleholders). Ribbon loops are another festive way to add ribbon to a Christmas centerpiece without adding a bow. Make one ribbon loop and a streamer; place a hairpin over the ribbon ends, wrapping one wire around the other. The wire becomes the stem to insert into the centerpiece.

8–26. An oval Christmas centerpiece features pine cones, ribbon loops, variegated holly, and evergreens with votive candles as accessories.

Christmas Wreath

A Christmas wreath adds a festive touch to any Christmas decor. Wreaths are also quite charming as a centerpiece placed on a table with candles or other accessories. Typical wreath decorations are a bow, ribbon flourishes, cones, and seasonal accessories. Wreaths may be designed for any season or time of the year with a variety of plant materials, including evergreens, silver king artemisia, or a variety of herbs or everlasting flowers.

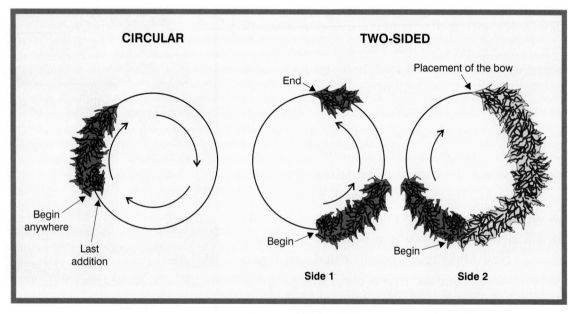

8–27. Wreaths may be designed in two different ways—circular or two-sided.

Wired wreaths are designed in the same basic way with overlapping placements of plant materials that are attached to a wire frame. Mixed evergreens or other materials are bunched into small groups (3 to 5 inches in length) and wired onto the frame. The next bunch should be approximately the same length and thickness and wired with the tip ends covering the cut ends of the previous bunch. Each bunch should slightly overlap with a smooth transition in shape among all of the bunches on the ring.

Round metal wreath frames may be purchased in various diameters. A small wreath may also be fashioned from a metal hanger that is bent into a round shape. Do not untie the hanger; just bend it into a round shape. For a single ring frame, the frame should be wrapped with paddle wire at ½-inch intervals to provide friction for holding each bunch in place. **Paddle wire** is wire wound on a piece of wood; it is available in most gauge sizes. Using paddle wire makes wrapping the plant material onto the frame very efficient and fast. The paddle allows the designer to pull the wire tight to ensure a snug attachment.

Christmas wreaths may be designed as circular or two-sided.

Circular wreaths are designed in a continuous overlapping fashion until the wreath is completed. The last grouping of evergreens needs to fit under the very first group and then be wired onto the frame. The advantage of the circular wreath is the wreath may be decorated as either a symmetrical or asymmetrical design. The bow may be placed anywhere according to the chosen style. The disadvantage of the circular wreath is that although the needles lay flat on one side, they may project forward on the other side. To compensate for this, attach accessories or pine cones to hold the evergreens flat.

Two-sided wreaths are designed in two parts, starting at the base of the wreath. When one side is completed, the next side is also designed from the bottom up. A bow is positioned where the two sides meet. The two-sided wreath has a design style limitation because the bow always needs to be placed at the top to cover where the two sides meet. The advantage is that the needles on both sides lay nicely due to gravity.

OTHER THEMES

Designs celebrating life's happy occasions may be designed around a myriad of themes and ideas. The possibilities are endless, limited only by the planner's and floral designer's creativity. The most common themes and parties revolve around birthdays and anniversaries. The birth of a baby is a popular floral theme.

8–28. A baby's birth is often celebrated with flowers (and toys).

8–29. Bon voyage themes may emphasize tropical flowers, coconuts, and colorful and appropriate accessories.

Parties and social events should reflect the personality of the honored guest(s). For children, the party may center on themes like the circus, cowboys, race cars, being a princess, magic, farm or zoo animals, or favorite hobbies.

Themes based on movies, songs, or plays could be the basis for an event. Other social events may focus on travel, adventure, or a particular country or region. Bon voyage or going-away parties may use these themes.

Summer themes could be Garden Party, Backyard Fun, Baseball Days, Wet and Wild, or The Good 'ole Summer Time. A nostalgic theme can be challenging and unique. Near the Fourth of July or election-time, patriotic themes can be quite popular. The color scheme is obvious—red, white, and blue, yet accessories and draping add uniqueness to a design.

Use your imagination to dream up ideas for parties and social events. The colors schemes, flowers chosen, design styles, and accessories help create the expression necessary to carry out the particular theme. Be creative!

8–30. A patriotic theme is a great one for the fourth of July or election-time.

REVIEWING

MAIN IDEAS

Centerpieces were developed by the English in the eighteenth century and have become a traditional favorite when entertaining guests. It is important that guests be able to see over the centerpiece. Typical centerpieces include bud vases, small vase arrangements, and round or oval centerpieces designed with floral foam.

A round centerpiece is round when viewed from above, but can be rounded or triangular in outline when viewed from the side. An elongated centerpiece can be oval or diamond-shaped when viewed from above, but can be rounded or triangular in outline when viewed from the side (like the round centerpiece).

The steps of making a centerpiece include securely positioning the floral foam, greening up the width of the design in a radiating fashion, and then positioning additional foliage to form the outline. Flowers are added to establish the height and then the width. The width flowers are placed in an equidistant way from the center of the design. Additional flowers are added to fill out the shape. Flower facings should be varied, showing radiating angles with no two flowers alike. Fillers and foliage are then added as needed to add color and cover the foam.

A conical centerpiece is cone-shaped or is a three-dimensional isosceles triangle. It can be a terrific tabletop Christmas tree or a striking design with fruit or vegetables combined with flowers and foliage. A conical centerpiece needs either a floral foam base or a chicken wire base.

Accessories can add to the expression of the centerpiece, holiday design, or theme. Be sure that the accessories are in harmony with the theme or style, necessary, properly placed, and not overdone in kinds or amounts. Suitable accessories may include candles, wired seasonal items, natural cones, fruit, balloons, or plush animals.

Before agreeing to design flowers for an event, be sure to carefully consider the responsibility and find out as much information as possible. Ask many questions about the location, theme, colors, and designs needed.

Flowers can play a pleasing integral part of every season and many major holidays. Some of the major holidays are Valentine's Day, Easter, Mother's Day, Halloween, Thanksgiving, and Christmas. Novelty arrangements can be a fun design to create at the holidays. Novelty designs are whimsical, creative arrangements of flowers, designed to resemble an animal, a birthday cake, a clown, a person, or any other imaginative theme.

Contemporary designs may be an option for a holiday arrangement. Contemporary design is a style that incorporates the latest floral design techniques. Some techniques include binding, pillowing, pavé, and terracing.

Wreaths may be designed at Christmas and many other times of the year. Although many types of plant materials may be used, the technique for designing a wreath is basically the same. Plant materials are bunched into small groups on 3 to 5-inch lengths and wired onto the frame. The bunches should slightly overlap with a smooth transition in shape among all of the bunches on the ring. Wreaths may be circular or two-sided in design.

Other centerpiece or design themes for parties or social events are limited only by the designer's creativity. Themes may be child-oriented, bon voyage, summer themes, or nostalgic ones. Be creative!

QUESTIONS

Answer the following questions using complete sentences and correct spelling.

1. What purpose does the centerpiece serve? What are some general guidelines for centerpiece design?

2. How is the top view shape of a centerpiece determined? What shapes may the outline (side view) of a centerpiece be?

3. What are the steps in designing a centerpiece?

4. What are conical centerpieces? What are some locations or ways that they may be displayed or used?

5. How do you determine if accessories should be used?

6. When designing the flowers for an event, what questions should you ask? List five.

7. How do you make a liner for a basket or container that does not hold water?

8. What is a novelty design? How do you make one?

9. What are three techniques used to create a contemporary design?

10. What are two techniques to make a wired wreath?

EVALUATING

Match the term with the correct definition. Write the letter of the term on the line provided.

a. raffia
b. pavé
c. novelty design
d. candle holders

e. cornucopia
f. contemporary design
g. binding
h. votive candles

i. conical centerpiece
j. pillowing

_____1. A plastic design mechanic for securing candles in arrangements.

_____2. Placing flowers low and close together in a design to form undulating heights.

_____3. A traditional container resembling a horn.

_____4. Physically tying stems together for artistic beauty and support.

_____5. Short and stocky candles that provide small pinpoints of lighting near a centerpiece.

_____6. An arrangement style designed using the latest trends in floral design.

_____7. A three-dimensional isosceles triangle.

_____8. Placing plant materials very close and low in a design forming patterns or lines.

_____9. A unique whimsical arrangement that uses flowers to create other objects, animals, or ideas.

_____10. The fiber of a palm used like string or ribbon for tying things together.

EXPLORING

1. Choose a theme that is not listed in the chapter. Gather the plant materials, container and mechanics, and accessories to create that theme. Choose the appropriate design style and color scheme. Give the display a title.

2. Create a centerpiece for a family holiday. Add candles and two other types of accessories (ribbon loops, fruit, cones, unique figurine, etc.).

3. Make a novelty design of your own creation. Gather the container, flowers, and supplies. Use your imagination to create the details of the face, body, clothing, and/or shape. Gauge the reaction of a wide range of people and ages.

CHAPTER 9

Designing Wedding Work

OBJECTIVES

This chapter is about floral designs for weddings. It has the following objectives:

1. Describe typical wedding floral needs.
2. Explain the process of floral design for a wedding.
3. Identify and describe types of wedding bouquets.
4. Explain how to service a wedding.

TERMS

aisle runner
aisle runner tape
altar arrangements
arm bouquet
candelabra designs
cascade bouquet
chuppah
colonial bouquet
crescent bouquet
floral foam holder
hand-tied bouquet
joining point
kneeling bench
pew decorations
toss bouquet
unity candle arrangement

9–1. Flowers add to the beauty of a wedding.

A WEDDING is a big day in the life of a bride and groom. A floral designer needs to be knowledgeable about planning and designing a wedding. A wedding consultation appointment should be a time to learn about the bride and groom and their ideas for their wedding, but it is also a time to help them with wedding hints and suggestions.

There are many kinds of designs that are unique to a wedding, such as bouquets, pew decorations, and other specialized floral pieces. Designing the specific flowers needed for the ceremony and the reception will make a floral designer more knowledgeable and experienced.

FLORAL NEEDS FOR A WEDDING

The wedding planning process is an important time for the prospective bride and groom. Many decisions need to be made about the wedding ceremony and reception. An experienced floral designer can help guide the couple through the planning process of selecting the wedding flowers.

*T*HE CONSULTATION

Once the date of the wedding is set, the bride-to-be will call for an appointment with the florist. The site of the wedding consultation should be in an area where the conversation will be undisturbed by telephones or other people. Provide a table and enough chairs to accommodate three or four people. The bride-to-be may bring the groom, a friend, or her mother.

At the first meeting, the floral wedding consultant will ask about relevant dates and times and information about the dresses and colors. It is helpful to have a wire service selection guide or book on wedding flowers to allow the bride-to-be to see specific bouquet styles or flowers. Some florists provide a portfolio of other outstanding weddings or examples of wedding bouquets designed in silk. The consultant should have a wedding order form and extra paper for sketching.

The Wedding Order Form

The wedding order form (see Figure 9–3) is the most helpful tool for the floral designer in planning weddings. A complete order form (purchased or composed by the designer) reminds the consultant of all possible wedding flower needs. The bride-to-be can decide which floral pieces fit her wedding and budget. It is noted on the order sheets the person who traditionally pays for each floral part of the wedding. However, each couple

9–2. The wedding consultation area of a floral shop should have all the necessary wedding planning tools—order forms, bouquet examples, candelabra or unity candle design ideas, selection guides, and other wedding books.

WEDDING ORDER FORM

THE BRIDE

Bride's Name _____

Email _____

Address _____

City, State, Zip _____

Phone (W)_____ (H) _____

Fax_____ Pager _____

THE GROOM

Groom's Name _____

Email _____

Address _____

City, State, Zip _____

Phone (W)_____ (H) _____

Fax_____ Pager _____

WEDDING CEREMONY

DATE _____

LOCATION _____

ADDRESS _____

City, State, Zip _____

Directions to Church _____

Person Who Will Unlock the Church _____

TIME _____

SET-UP TIME _____

Phone _____

Phone _____

WEDDING RECEPTION

DATE _____

LOCATION _____

ADDRESS _____

City, State, Zip _____

Manager's Name _____

Directions to Site _____

MAIL BILL TO: _____

Address _____

TIME _____

SET-UP TIME _____

Phone _____

Caterer _____

Phone _____

City State, Zip _____

9–3. A wedding order form is an invaluable wedding planning tool.

WEDDING FLOWER NEEDS

	EXPENSES	
	BRIDE	GROOM

THE BRIDE (Sketch the bouquet on the back of form)

Bridal Gown, Style, and Color _____

BOUQUET STYLE_____ _____

COLORS, FLOWERS _____

_____

Floral Headpiece/Veil _____ _____

Toss bouquet _____ _____

Going Away Flowers _____ _____

Presentation Bouquets — Mothers _____ _____

Virgin Mary _____ _____

MAID OR MATRON OF HONOR (Sketch on back) **Number** _____

Dress Style and Color _____

BOUQUET STYLE_____ _____

COLORS, FLOWERS _____

_____

Floral Headpiece _____ _____

BRIDESMAIDS (Sketch on back) **Number**_____

Dress Style and Color _____

BOUQUET STYLE_____ _____

COLORS, FLOWERS _____

_____

Floral Headpiece _____ _____

FLOWER GIRL

Dress Style and Color _____

BOUQUET STYLE_____ _____

COLORS, FLOWERS _____

Totals _____ _____

CORSAGES

Corsage Style #1 _____

Number _____   **Price Each** _____   **Total** _____

Brides Mother   **Groom's Mother**

Name _____   Name _____

Dress Color/Style _____   Dress Color/Style _____

Bride's Stepmother   **Groom's Stepmother**

Name _____   Name _____

Dress Color/Style _____   Dress Color/Style _____

Corsage Style #2 _____

Number _____   **Price Each** _____   **Total** _____

Bride's Grandmothers   **Groom's Grandmothers**

Name _____   Name _____

Name _____   Name _____

Corsage Style #3 _____

Number _____   **Price Each** _____   **Total** _____

_____ Soloists   _____ Gift Table Attendants

_____ Musicians   _____ Cake Servers

_____ Minister   _____ Punch Servers

_____ Candle Lighters   _____ Rice Bag Attendants

_____ Guest Book Attendant   _____ Favors Attendants

_____ Special Relatives   _____ Hostesses

_____ Special Friends   _____ Service Personnel

Bride's Total Expense for Corsages _____

BOUTONNIERES

Tuxedo Style _____   **Color** _____

	EXPENSES	
	BRIDE	GROOM

Groom _____   _____

Best Man _____   _____

____ Groomsmen _____ $ ____ each   _____

____ Ushers _____ $ ____ each   _____

____ Fathers _____ $ ____ each   _____

____ Grandfathers _____ $ ____ each   _____

____ Stepfathers _____ $ ____ each   _____

Ring Bearer _____   _____

____ Ministers _____ $ ____ each   _____

____ Candle Lighters _____ $ ____ each   _____

____ Musicians _____ $ ____ each   _____

____ Soloists _____ $ ____ each   _____

____ Others _____ $ ____ each   _____

Bride's Expense for Groom's Boutonniere _____

Groom's Expense for the Boutonnieres _____

9–3 (Continued)

WEDDING CEREMONY FLOWERS

(Bride's Expense)

Set-up Time _____

____ Altar Arrangements_____

Price each _____ Total _____

____ Candelabra _____

Price each _____ Total _____

Unity Candle Flowers _____ _____

Kneeling Bench _____ _____

Arch_____ _____

Chuppah _____ _____

____ Pew Decorations_____

Price each _____ Total _____

____ Aisle Decorations _____

Price each _____ Total _____

Aisle Runner _____ feet long _____ _____

Plant Rental _____ _____

Guest Book Table _____ _____

Other_____ _____

Bride's Total Expense for Ceremony Flowers _____

Sketch:

RECEPTION FLOWERS

(Bride's Expense)

Set-up Time _____

HEAD TABLE

Centerpieces _____   _____

Decorations (Garlands, etc.) _____   _____

Other   _____   _____

CENTERPIECES

Style   _____

Flowers   _____

Number of Tables _____   Size, Shape of Tables_____

Accessories (Mirrors, votives, etc.)_____

Price each _____   Total _____

CAKE TABLE

Cake Description_____

Cake Top_____

Other Floral Pieces _____

Base of Cake _____

Other Decorations — Toasting Glasses _____   Knife _____

Cake Table Total _____

Bride's Total Expense for the Reception Flowers _____

REHEARSAL DINNER FLOWERS

Location   _____

Date _____   Time _____   Centerpieces _____

Corsages _____   Boutonnieres _____

Groom's Total Rehearsal Dinner Expense _____

Bride's Total Expense _____   **Groom's Total Expense** _____

9–3 (Continued)

may decide for themselves the payment arrangements and convey them to the floral designer.

TYPICAL FLORAL NEEDS

The order form outlines typical floral needs for a wedding ceremony and reception. Flower needs for the wedding ceremony are church decorations, the bouquets for the bride, maid or matron of honor, bridesmaids, and flower girl, and boutonnieres for the groom and groomsmen, ring bearer, and ushers. The parents and grandparents of the bride and groom receive flowers to wear; the parents may also receive a presentation bouquet from the bride and groom during the ceremony. Many other special people who are involved in the ceremony, such as a minister, musicians or soloist, attendants at the guest book or gift table, and special friends or relatives, may also be given a corsage (or boutonniere) to wear. For the reception, typical floral needs include the centerpieces, the head table decorations, cake table decorations, and other decorations as needed. Other flower needs would be the rehearsal dinner decorations.

ORDERING THE FLOWERS

Be aware of the bunch sizes when taking a wedding order. If the bride-to-be orders roses only in the parents' presentation bouquets, then just six of a bunch of 25 will be sold. Take orders so almost all of the roses in a bunch will be used. A few extra flowers may be necessary to allow for unforeseen needs, such as an extra boutonniere or a flower damaged in shipping.

For each type of design, make a list of the flowers needed. Some floral designers make a sketch of each bouquet or major design to help visualize the design and flower amounts needed. Tabulate the totals needed for each type of flower. Then, the bunch amounts can be calculated. Call the wholesaler well in advance to ensure that the flowers will be available. Depending on flower needs and availability, two or three sources (wholesale florists) may be necessary to completely fill the flower order.

DESIGNING THE WEDDING FLOWERS

Once the planning and ordering has been successfully completed, the designing process begins. A few aspects of the wedding can be started well ahead of the wedding week. Pew bows can be created and supplies can be ordered and gathered. Most of the design work will, however, be done during the last day or two before the wedding.

WHOLESALE FLOWER LIST

Wedding of _____   Date _____

Flowers/Foliages	Color/Cultivar	# Needed	Bunch #	Source	Cost/Bu	Total

Total Wholesale Flower Cost: $_____

9–4. A list of flowers needed for each wedding helps the floral designer to be organized and efficient when ordering from the wholesale florist.

BOUQUET TYPES

The bouquet that the bride-to-be carries should reflect the personality of the bride and the style of the gown and wedding. Bridal bouquet choices are the colonial, the cascade, variations of the cascade, an arm bouquet, a hand-tied bouquet, and other special bouquet designs. The flower selections will also help to define the formality and style of the event. Classic styles may feature roses and calla lilies; contemporary, high-style designs may incorporate tropical flowers or alstroemeria; traditional styles may feature carnations or daisies; elegant styles may combine rubrum lilies and lisianthus.

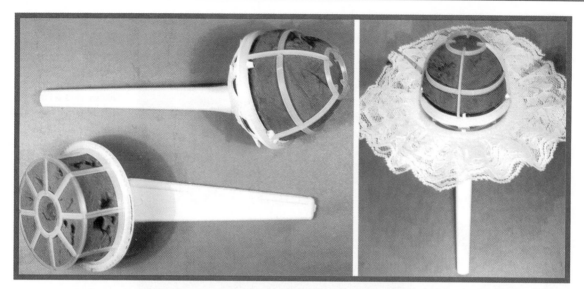

9–5. A saturated floral foam holder allows flowers to last longer in bridal bouquets.

Bouquets may be designed in a floral foam holder or wired and taped. A ***floral foam holder*** has floral foam encased in a plastic cage with a handle. The holder allows a designer to position flowers and foliage into a saturated piece of floral foam, which helps the flowers to last longer. Another advantage is that the bouquets may be designed a day or two before the wedding. One word of caution is that a bouquet designed in a floral foam holder should not be thrown because of the weight and the wet mess that it will make when caught.

Finishing sprays and dips may be used on the finished bouquets. These products minimize water loss and reduce transpiration for bouquets in floral foam holders or for ones that are wired and taped. Stems can be secured into the floral foam with a product that forms a tacky or sticky glue-like bond between the foam and the stems. An example is Flora-Lock™. Completed bouquets should be allowed to dry for a short time after application of any sprays or dips and then placed in a sealed plastic delivery bag in the cooler. Bouquets can be placed upright in a bud vase or bouquet stand or placed on cushions of colorful waxed tissue before being sealed in plastic bags. Add a mist of water to the flowers, avoiding the ribbons or bows.

Colonial Bouquets

The ***colonial bouquet*** is a round bouquet that is based on the English nosegay of the Georgian and Victorian eras. This style is popular for both brides and bridesmaids.

1. Place the entire floral foam holder into a floral preservative solution to saturate it. Allow it to drain for a few minutes before using it. Use a stand or a bud vase filled with water to support the holder upright to design in.

9–6. The colonial bouquet is a round bouquet that is popular for both brides and bridesmaids. Colonial bouquets can be designed with a variety of flower sizes as well as ribbons.

9–7. The steps in making a colonial bouquet include greening up the floral foam holder (1 & 2), adding centered showy flowers (3), filling in the round shape with flowers (4), and adding filler flowers (5) and any foliage to cover the floral foam.

2. Add a collar of foliage around the back outside edges. Mix two or three types of foliage for variety.

3. Green up the center of the bouquet with foliage.

4. Add a few showy or bright flowers (or the most expensive flowers—roses) in the center of the round shape.

5. Position the flowers along the outside edge to form the round shape.

6. Fill in the center with additional flowers and filler flowers.

7. Check to see if any floral foam shows and add foliage as needed. Add foliage in the back of the holder to cover the foam. A bow or lace collar can also be added in the back to cover the foam.

8. Mist, seal in plastic, and store in a cooler or cool place.

Cascade Bouquets

A *cascade bouquet* has a full, rounded central area with an eye-catching trailing line(s) of flowers and foliage. The cascade bouquet shape has many variations, including the

9–8. The cascade bouquet is a trailing bouquet style that can be designed with many variations.

9–9. The longer stems of the trailing section of the cascade bouquet are wired together and inserted into the floral foam holder. The wire is hooked around the plastic cage in the back of the holder to ensure that the stems do not fall out of the bouquet.

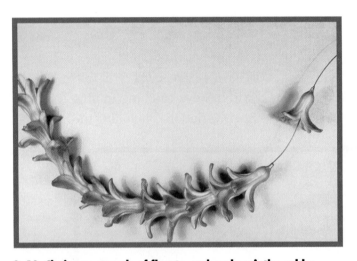

9–10. Chains or strands of florets, such as hyacinths, add a lovely touch to a cascade bouquet.

crescent. The **crescent bouquet** is one variation of the cascade bouquet that is designed in a C shape. The cascade style is a beautiful design for elegant or formal weddings.

The cascade bouquet is basically designed the same way as the colonial bouquet with the exception of the beginning placement of the trailing foliage and flowers. The foliage and flowers are placed in a pleasing trailing manner and then wired together. The wire and the stem ends are inserted into the floral foam holder; the wire is brought out the back of the holder and fashioned around one of the supports of the plastic cage. This wiring technique ensures that the heavy, longer stems will not fall out of the bouquet.

Chains or strands of florets, such as hyacinths or stephanotis, may be added to cascade bouquets.

Arm Bouquets

An arm bouquet is a classic and time-honored style of bouquet. An **arm bouquet** is a grouping of flowers that is tied together and cradled in the bride's left arm as she walks down the aisle with her father.

The arm bouquet is a versatile design because it may be carried during the wedding ceremony and then placed in a vase to adorn the head table during the reception. Presentation

9–11. The arm bouquet is a classic bouquet style. These two brides carried arm bouquets in ceremonies that were 70 years apart.

bouquets (to the parents), or the Virgin Mary bouquet, are designed using the same technique as the arm bouquet.

1. Gather three calla lilies, three blue irises, Italian ruscus, salal leaves, corkscrew willow, a roll of floral tape, and a long, taped #24-gauge wire. Remove the lower leaves on the foliage.

2. With the left arm bent, lay two stems each of Italian ruscus and salal along the forearm, holding the grouping where the bow will eventually tie it together.

3. Position the three calla lilies in a vertical arrangement. Nestle the corkscrew willow in and around the callas.

4. Place the three irises in a triangular manner around the callas. One in the upper right, one in the center left, and one below the calla lilies near the bow.

5. Add greens to form a framework around the flowers as needed.

9–12. An arm bouquet requires very few flowers to make a distinctive bridal bouquet.

6. Using green floral tape, tape several times around the stems where the bow will be tied on. The floral tape will protect the calla lily stem from being cut by the wire. Adding leaves around the calla lily stems will also give protection.

7. Wire the stems securely together. The loose wire ends can be wrapped around the stems additional times or trimmed off.

8. Make a #9 bow with streamers and wire it on. Use a foot of matching ribbon to wrap around the wires once and then tie it in a knot. Trim off excess ribbon.

9. Trim the cut ends of the flowers and foliage shorter, if necessary, and at varying lengths.

10. The arm bouquet may be placed in a vase with floral preservative solution until carried. Before handing to the bride, dry the stems thoroughly with a towel.

Hand-Tied Bouquets

A **_hand-tied bouquet_** is a natural-looking gathering of flowers and foliage with the stems tied together. Hand-tied bouquets may be adorned with ribbon, cording, or tulle. Any combination of flowers and foliage may be incorporated into a hand-tied bouquet. Once considered informal, this style may be designed for any type of wedding with the flower selection determining the informality or formality.

9–13. A hand-tied bouquet is a lovely style of bouquet for any type of wedding—formal or informal.

1. Gather the desired flowers and foliage. Have a taped #24-gauge wire or chenille stem ready to use. Remove any leaves on the lower part of the stems.

2. The floral designer may start with a foliage base of a few greens grouped together, such as plumosa fern, leatherleaf, or sprengeri fern. Group the stems in a radiating fashion. (Or, the designer may start with the flower groupings.)

3. Starting in the center, begin adding flowers through the foliage framework. Vary flower sizes and look for pleasing color combinations.

4. Add flowers in a slightly angled placement as the shape is filled out.

5. Add foliage and filler as desired.

6. When the rounded shape is completed, wire the stems with a taped #24-gauge wire or chenille stem. Add ribbon to cover the wires or chenille stem. Add a bow, streamers, or tulle as the design dictates.

7. Trim the stems at even or slightly varied lengths and place into a vase with floral preservative solution. Dry the stems before handing to the bride-to-be or bridesmaid.

Other Bouquet Styles

Wedding bouquets can be designed on a fan, a muff (winter weddings), or parasols. These styles can be designed like a corsage and wired or pinned to the accessory. Brides may choose to carry a bible of their mother's or grandmother's. Bridesmaids may carry bouquets designed in a basket. A flower girl typically carries a basket of flowers with loose petals easily accessible for her to drop along the bridal aisle.

Toss Bouquet

A ***toss bouquet*** is a small, wired and taped bouquet that is tossed by the bride to one of her unmarried female friends or relatives during a traditional part of the wedding reception activities. The bride turns around and throws this small bouquet over her shoulder. The lady who catches the bouquet is then thought to be the next one to get married. A bouquet designed in a floral foam holder should **never** be used as a toss bouquet. A floral foam bouquet is too heavy and would make a wet mess when caught. The experienced floral designer will recommend a small bouquet to prevent the bride from throwing her own bouquet. The bride often wants to keep her bouquet to have it preserved (by pressing or silica sand covering), whether it is designed in a floral foam bouquet holder or wired and taped.

9–14. A toss bouquet is a small wired and taped bouquet used during a traditional part of the wedding reception. The bride with her back turned tosses this small bouquet over her shoulder to an unmarried female friend or relative. That lady will be the next to wed, as the saying goes.

1. Gather small to medium flowers in suitable colors, foliage, floral tape, long #24- or #22-gauge wires, and ribbon.

2. Wire by the appropriate method 10 to 12 flowers, 8 to 10 foliage pieces, and 7 to 8 filler flowers placements.

3. Starting in the bouquet center, position wired flowers and foliage pieces together. **Do not wrap the wires around each other,** just press them together. A #28-gauge wire can be wrapped occasionally around the *joining point* (place where the stems converge) to keep the stems together, if needed.

4. Continue adding flowers and foliage to form the rounded shape. The toss bouquet should have a rounded shape and contour. Add some small flowers or buds deeper within the bouquet.

5. Finish the toss bouquet by adding a collar of lace or foliage (salal wired with the stitch method).

6. Store the toss bouquet in a sealed plastic bag in the cooler.

FLOWERS FOR THE HAIR

The bride may choose to wear flowers on her veil. Flowers that are designed like a corsage can be attached on or near the veil. A small chaplet may be attached to the back of certain

9–15. At weddings, flowers are often worn in the hair or attached to the veil.

types of veils. The flowers are designed using a wreath or garland technique. The bride may also choose to have the bridesmaids and flower girl to wear flowers in their hair. These flowers may be just a simple sprig or two of baby's breath placed in the hair, flowers hot-glued to a floral comb, or a chaplet or halo of flowers. The flower girl might also wear a halo or chaplet of flowers. These flowers are designed as a garland or wreath onto a wire that is formed into a circle and pinned on with bobby pins.

FLOWERS FOR THE CEREMONY

The flowers for the wedding ceremony may be as simple or elaborate as the bride wishes. Typical floral pieces include altar arrangements, candelabra designs, unity candle flowers, and pew bows or decorations. Other floral decorations might include floral designs for an arch, a chuppah, or a kneeling bench, aisle decorations, and blooming or foliage plants. A *chuppah* is a canopy under which the Jewish bride and groom stand to be married. A *kneeling bench* is requested for some weddings for the bride and groom to kneel for prayer during the ceremony. Both the chuppah and the kneeling bench may be adorned with flowers in foam cages that are attached to them.

The floral designer usually positions the aisle runner, a traditional part of the ceremony. An *aisle runner* is a fabric or cloth-like paper covering for the center aisle during the wedding ceremony; the aisle runner is pulled down the aisle by the ushers after the guests are seated to create a clean surface for the bridal party to walk upon. The floral designer typically purchases it and pins or tapes it at the front of the church before the ceremony. *Aisle runner tape* is double-sided tape that can secure the aisle runner to the tile without the

9–16. A single altar arrangement can be centered between two candelabras for a lovely setting for the wedding ceremony.

tape showing. If the aisle runner is placed on stairs, it should be pinned or taped to each step to avoid tripping someone.

Altar Arrangements and Candelabras

Altar arrangements are floral designs placed near the altar of the church to provide a lovely floral framework for the bride and groom during the wedding ceremony. Altar arrangements should be highly visible, large designs, including vase arrangements or designs arranged in floral foam. The colors should harmonize and blend with the overall color scheme of the wedding as well as the colors of the church. Two altar arrangements are usually symmetrically placed at the front of the church. For some church settings, a single altar arrangement may be more appropriate; a single altar piece is very appropriate when placed between two candelabra designs.

Some churches practice the lighting of candles at weddings as a traditional part of the ceremony. An evening wedding is also enhanced by the presence of candlelight. Candelabra designs may supplement or substitute for the altar arrangements as a framing and focal area for the bride and groom. *Candelabra designs* are formal, dignified arrangements of flowers attached to candelabras, which hold seven or more candles. The flowers are

9–17. The floral mechanic for a candelabra design is a spray bar wired to the candelabra frame.

9–18. A unity candle arrangement is a low, horizontal centerpiece with a centered candle that the bride and groom light during the wedding ceremony to symbolize their union in marriage. This unique arrangement also has the bride and groom's candles within the design.

designed in floral foam cages or floral foam spray bars that are attached to the candelabra. The design is similar to a sympathy easel design.

Another traditional arrangement placed on or near the altar is the unity candle arrangement. A *unity candle arrangement* is usually a low, horizontal centerpiece with a centered candle that the couple light during the wedding ceremony to symbolize their union in marriage. Several types of special pillar candles are available to purchase for placing in unity candle arrangements.

Pew Decorations

Another unique feature of a wedding is the decoration of pews. *Pew decorations* are bows, flowers, or floral designs that are attached to the end of the pews in the aisle where the bridal party walks. Some pew decorations are more elaborate to denote the family pews. Bows do not have to be placed on every pew. In fact, adding decorations on every other or every third pew can be just as decorative and effective. Some brides may wish to decorate only the family pews.

Bows may be designed with #9 or #40 ribbon or a combination of widths and colors to match the wedding colors. The bows should have long streamers. Tulle adds a soft romantic look. The bows should look uniform and should be designed by

9–19. Typical pew decorations are bows with long streamers. Floral pew decorations can be designed in a floral foam holder specifically for pews.

the same person or two persons with the same style. Attach the bows carefully to the pews with tape or a rubber band. The rubber band (subtle, blending color to the pew) is placed horizontally around the pew end with the bow attached to the rubber band. Flowers may be attached to the bow for a more floral effect. For a larger floral effect, use a floral foam mechanic designed to create pew decorations. Floral pew decorations are usually one-sided with an upright or rounded shape, as well as some trailing or cascading foliage, such as ivy or ferns.

9–20. A colorful basket of flowers can adorn a guest book table.

Guest Book

The guest book is a standard feature at every wedding. Sometimes the table on which the guest book is placed is too small for any flowers so a bow is the only decoration. If the table is large enough, a basket of flowers or other suitable centerpiece design can be placed on it to attract the guests' attention. The attendant can then ask each guest to sign the register.

RECEPTION FLOWERS

The floral decorations for the reception can be as varied as each bride's personality. The location also dictates many of the floral features. Common reception decorations are centerpieces at the guests' tables, the head table decorations, the cake table decorations, and possibly an entryway feature, such as an arch.

Head Table Decorations

The head table is a place of honor for the bridal party. Head table decorations enhance the setting for the bride and groom. Typical head table decorations are centerpieces often featuring the bride's and bridesmaids' bouquets and floral garlands. Garlands of similax or sprengeri fern can be purchased from the wholesale florist, which is a time-saver for the floral designer. The garlands are draped across the front of the head table. Flowers and ribbons may be hot-glued into the garland for touches of matching wedding colors. Small bouquets or clusters of flowers are attractive adorning the table and garland. The garlands are securely

9–21. A head table or cake table can be adorned with garland and flowers.

pinned to the table skirting. Manufactured table clips can be purchased to attach the garland.

Cake Table Decorations

The wedding cake is a focal point at the reception. The cake table decorations should all revolve around the wedding cake to emphasize it, not distract from it. The wedding cake can be enhanced with flowers placed on top and with foliage and loose flowers at the base. Cakes with tiers might have flowers on each tier. The flowers can be designed like corsages or in a floral foam base. Do not place the flowers directly on the cake; place the flowers on a doily or a plastic separator, which can be provided by the baker.

Depending on the style of the wedding, garland is also appropriate to decorate the cake table. Small flowers can be hot-glued into the garland. Sometimes the toasting glasses and

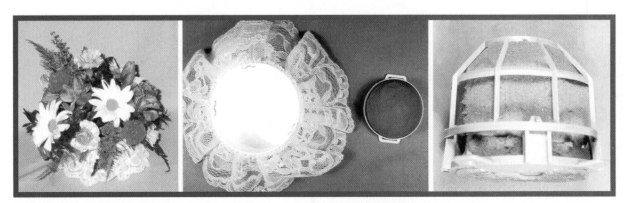

9–22. The flowers for the cake top can be designed in a special container designed for that purpose or in a small floral foam foundation.

the cake knife are decorated with a small bow or small floral accent. If a punch bowl is placed on the cake table, the base of the bowl can be decorated with flowers that coordinate with the cake base flowers.

Other Reception Decorations

An entryway arch into the reception might be included in the reception area decorations. Flowers for an arch can be designed as presentation bouquets (like the arm bouquet) and attached by tying with ribbon. Hidden water tubes will extend the lasting qualities of the flowers. Flowers may also be added to an arch by inserting them into a moistened floral foam cage or spray bar that is securely attached to the top or sides of the arch.

Potted plants are a nice feature when grouped around a small stage area, near an arch, or an entryway. The containers should be foil or fabric wrapped with bows in appropriate colors.

SERVICING A WEDDING

Items to Include in a Wedding Servicing Kit

Extra pins (corsage, boutonniere, straight, and safety)
Bobby pins, floral combs, comb, hair spray
Florist knife, shears
Scissors, extra ribbon
Floral tape, wires, chenille stems
Small glue gun and extra glue sticks
Matches or lighter
Needle and thread, extra buttons
Anti-static spray
Tissues, moist toilettes, anti-stain toilettes
Aspirin, antacid tables, chewing gum, breath mints
Small first aid kit
Fingernail polish or extra pair of nylons

Other Items to Bring When Servicing a Wedding

Small rechargeable hand vacuum
Dust pan and hand broom
Drop cloth (for easy clean-up when designing on-site)
A small vase for extra flowers

9–23. Items to include in a Wedding Servicing Kit.

The florist is responsible for delivering the wedding flowers to the ceremony and to the reception site. The reception site requires more set-up time because of the cake flowers and garlands. Many florists and wedding consultants offer additional services for a fee, that is, servicing a wedding. Servicing a wedding includes helping with the details of distributing the flowers, pinning on corsages and boutonnieres, lighting the candles as needed, positioning the aisle runner, working with the bridal party on the proper holding of the bouquets, and possibly transporting wedding ceremony flowers to the reception.

The floral wedding consultant should direct the bridal party to hold the bouquets in a relaxed manner with the arms slightly bent at the elbows and near the waistline. The flowers should face outward, not downward. If the bouquet is designed in a foam bouquet holder, the holder should be held angling downward (never to the side).

A servicing kit is a recommended item for the wedding consultant who services weddings. The kit allows a floral designer to have extra items that might be needed by the bridal party before the wedding. Items can be carried in an unobtrusive carry-all, tackle box, or other type of box or basket with a handle.

REVIEWING

MAIN IDEAS

A wedding is an important day for the bride and groom. Planning is vital to the success of a beautiful wedding. The floral designer becomes a wedding consultant to help the couple choose the flowers for the big day. The wedding consultation site should be in an area where conversation will be undisturbed by telephones. Selection guide and books of wedding flowers are helpful to guide the bride-to-be's decisions.

The wedding order form is the most helpful tool for the floral designer in planning weddings. Typical floral needs for the wedding ceremony are church decorations, the bouquets for the bride and her bridal party, boutonnieres for the groom and his party, and corsages and boutonnieres for family and special people or attendants during the ceremony. For the reception, typical floral needs include the centerpieces, the head table decorations, cake table decorations, and other decorations as needed. The rehearsal dinner will also warrant some floral decorations.

The efficient floral designer will make a detailed list of flowers needed for each design, tabulate the totals, calculate the number of bunches, and call the wholesale florists in advance.

The bouquets that the bride-to-be may choose for her and her bridal party are a colonial bouquet, a cascade bouquet with many variations, including a crescent bouquet, an arm bouquet, and a hand-tied bouquet. Bouquets may be wired and taped or designed in a floral foam holder.

The colonial bouquet is a round bouquet, suitable for both the bride and her bridesmaids. The cascade bouquet has a full, rounded central area with a trailing line(s) of flowers and foliage. The cascade bouquet can be designed with many variations, including the crescent bouquet. An arm bouquet is a classic style with a grouping of flowers that are tied together; the bouquet is cradled in the bride's left arm. A hand-tied bouquet is a natural-looking gathering of flowers and foliage with the stems tied together. Other bouquet styles include bouquets designed on a fan, a muff, a parasol, a bible, or in a basket.

A flower girl may carry a basket or small bouquet with loose petals easily accessible to her to drop along the bridal aisle. A toss bouquet is a small wired and taped bouquet that is tossed by the bride to one of her unmarried female friends or relatives during a traditional part of the wedding reception activities.

The bride or bridesmaids may wear flowers in the hair. A chaplet, a small floral comb, or just a few sprigs of baby's breath in the hair add to the beauty of the bridal party.

The flowers for the ceremony include altar arrangements, candelabra designs, unity candle flowers, and pew bows or decorations. Other floral decorations might include adorning an arch or a chuppah, a traditional canopy under which a Jewish bride and groom stand to be married. An aisle runner is also a traditional part of many wedding ceremonies.

The reception flowers include decorating the head table with centerpieces (often, the bride's and bridesmaids' bouquets) and garlands. Garlands are gracefully draped along the front of the table. Flowers and ribbons can be added by hot-gluing them.

The cake table decorations are another part of the reception flowers. A cake top of flowers and a base of greens and loose flowers add color and beauty to the reception. Other reception decorations may include placing flowers on an entryway arch and positioning green and blooming plants.

Servicing a wedding means to help with the details of distributing and pinning on personal flowers, positioning the aisle runner, lighting candles, and helping the bridal party with the proper way of holding the bouquets. Bouquets should be held with the arms slightly bent and near the waist; the bouquet should be held with the flowers facing outward (not downward). A servicing kit is a recommended item for the floral designer who services weddings.

QUESTIONS

Answer the following questions using complete sentences and correct spelling.

1. What takes place during a wedding consultation? What supplies or items are helpful when consulting on weddings?

2. Why is a complete wedding order form indispensable?

3. Before calling the wholesale florist, what is the process of determining wedding flower needs?

4. Why are finishing sprays and dips used?

5. What is a cascade bouquet? What are some variations of this style? Use sketches when needed.

6. How is an arm bouquet different from a hand-tied bouquet?

7. What are two advantages and two disadvantages of designing a bouquet in a foam bouquet holder?

8. What are some typical wedding ceremony flowers? Be thorough.

9. What are some typical reception flowers?

10. Why is servicing a wedding necessary?

EVALUATING

Match the term with the correct definition. Write the letter of the term on the line provided.

a. cascade bouquet

b. toss bouquet

c. joining point

d. pew decorations

e. arm bouquet

f. hand-tied bouquet

g. candelabra designs

h. aisle runner

i. foam bouquet holder

j. colonial bouquet

_____1. A plastic cage filled with floral foam with a handle.

_____2. A trailing bouquet from a full, rounded center.

_____3. A round bouquet.

_____4. A floral arrangement attached to a candle-holding framework, used to enhance the wedding ceremony and feature the bride and groom.

_____5. A small wired and taped bouquet designed for use at the reception during a traditional activity with the bride and her single female friends and relatives.

_____6. The place where the stems converge.

_____7. A natural-looking gathering of flowers and foliage tied together with ribbon or string.

_____8. Bows, flowers, or floral designs placed along the aisle where the bride and groom walk into the ceremony.

_____9. Fabric or covering for the center aisle during the wedding ceremony.

_____10. A vertical placement of flowers and foliage tied together physically and visually with a bow.

EXPLORING

1. Go to your church and sketch the floor plan of the sanctuary. Sketch the location of two candelabra designs, an altar arrangement, a unity candle design, and pew decorations.

2. Purchase two foam bouquet holders. Gather flowers and foliage to design a colonial and a cascade bouquet. Moisten the bouquet holder and create both styles of bouquets. Note the amount of flowers and foliage used. Which design do you prefer?

3. Sketch a three-tier wedding cake centered on a round table with skirting. Design a cake table. List the colors, chosen flowers, and supplies needed. Sketch your idea.

4. Create a timeline of activities that the floral designer must complete from the time the bride-to-be has her initial wedding consultation with you until the wedding flowers are delivered and set up. Refer to other chapters if necessary.

CHAPTER 10

Designing Sympathy Flowers

OBJECTIVES

This chapter is about the design of sympathy flowers. It has the following objectives:

1 Explain the importance of sympathy flowers.

2 Identify and describe typical sympathy pieces.

3 Explain the delivery process.

TERMS

casket saddle	fireside basket	half-couch casket spray
casket inset piece	flat spray	papier-mâché
casket spray	full couch	set piece
dish garden	full-couch casket spray	standing spray
easel	full-couch lid spray	sympathy flowers
easel spray	half couch	

FLOWERS play an important part in the grieving process. Their beauty and colors can symbolize love, respect, and thoughts of sympathy and concern. Sympathy flowers give a comforting presence to the bereaved person's family at the visitation and funeral services. Typical sympathy pieces come in many styles and types, such as casket sprays, baskets of flowers, sprays, set pieces, and wreaths. A floral designer should be knowledgeable about design types and construction when designing flowers for funerals.

10–1. Sympathy flowers are important to honor the deceased and comfort the living.

IMPORTANCE OF SYMPATHY FLOWERS

Sympathy flowers are flowers that are sent to a funeral home or a funeral service to honor the deceased or to comfort the bereaved. Flowers add warmth, vitality, and a softening garden-like presence to the uncomfortable atmosphere before and during the funeral service. Research by the American Floral Endowment and the Society of American Florists Information Committee concluded that flowers at the funeral home and funeral service serve the important roles of honoring the life of the deceased and giving comfort and some relief or softening of sorrow for the living.

TYPICAL SYMPATHY FLOWER DESIGNS

Typical sympathy flowers include the family flowers, which are ordered by the family to honor their loved one. The family flowers typically include the casket spray, a casket inset piece (usually from younger family members), and sometimes a matching arrangement. A particularly attractive setting occurs when the family orders two matching arrangements for either side of the casket.

When the family comes to the floral shop to order family flowers, the tactful florist will find a quiet or private area for the family to make their decisions. Treat the family in a tactful, compassionate, business-like fashion to guide them through their decisions. Provide books and selection guides to make the process an easier one.

Other sympathy flowers include arrangements, basket designs, easel and flat sprays, and set pieces, such as wreaths, organization symbols, hearts, or crosses. Blooming and foliage plants as well as dish gardens are also typical sympathy expressions. A *dish garden* is a grouping of different types of plants potted in the same container. Flowers in water tubes, accessories, and bows are often added to decorate plants. The most popular expressions of sympathy vary from region to region. When sending sympathy flowers as a wire order to another area, check the selection guide to choose the most appropriate type.

CASKET SPRAYS

A ***casket spray*** is a floral arrangement that is placed on the top of a casket during a funeral service. A casket spray is ordered and sent by the immediate family members. The

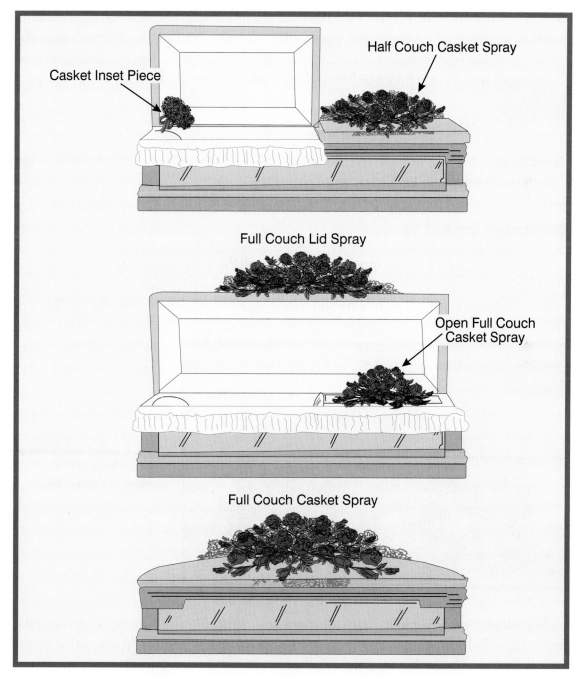

Casket Inset Piece

Half Couch Casket Spray

Full Couch Lid Spray

Open Full Couch Casket Spray

Full Couch Casket Spray

10–2. The types of casket sprays . . . A half-couch casket spray has the most widespread usage throughout the country. The full-couch casket spray has two variations for flower placements.

type of casket determines the size of the casket spray. Caskets are available as half couch and full couch.

A **full couch** is a casket with a one-piece lid, which may be closed or open. An open full couch has an inner lid on the right side. A **full-couch casket spray** is a large casket piece that is placed in the center of a closed full couch. A **full-couch lid spray** is a large casket piece placed in the center of the open lid of a full couch. The full-couch lid design is placed in a stand (hidden by the lid) that displays the spray sideways or is attached to the wall by a bracket on the wall. A smaller casket spray may be placed on the inner lid. Full-couch casket sprays range from 4 to 5 feet wide or wider. (The typical casket is slightly longer than 6 feet.)

A **half couch** is a casket with a two-piece lid; the head (left side) of the half couch is open during the visitation services. A **half-couch casket spray** is a floral piece that is placed on the right side of a half couch. A half-couch casket spray should be at least a yard wide (3 to 3.5 feet).

Half-Couch Casket Spray

The foundation for a casket spray is a **casket saddle**, a container with a rounded base, that fits the curving contours of a casket lid. Casket saddles are molded plastic and available in many sizes and shapes. The flowers and foliage should completely cover the saddle.

10–3. A casket saddle has a rounded base to fit the contour of a casket lid.

The shapes of a half-couch casket spray may be an oval (or fan), crescent, or triangular (or T-shaped). These designs should be low (12 to 14 inches) to allow transporting by the funeral director. Script denoting the relationship of the deceased (such as, Loving Wife, Dear Husband) is often attached to the long streamer on the bow.

1. Position the brick(s) of floral foam to fit the casket saddle, moisten, and securely attach to saddle (by accompanying supports or by taping).

2. Green up the outline of the design—oval (or fan), crescent, or triangular (or T-shaped). Use a combination of greens, such as salal, leatherleaf, flat fern, or huckleberry, to form the basic framework. Finer textured foliage, such as sprengeri fern, tree fern, and ming fern, can add softness and interest.

3. Add flowers to form the width and contour placements. Some flowers should angle toward the back of the design. Some casket sprays will be viewed from the back.

4. Add the center of interest flowers, such as fully open or unique ones.

5. Place the bow in a central or slightly off-center position. Some designers make a bow from individual loops and streamers wired to wood picks that are placed in a composite way to form the look of a bow.

10–4. Half-couch casket sprays may be designed as oval (or fan) (top left), crescent (top right), or triangular (T) (bottom) shapes.

6. Place additional mass or form flowers in a radiating pattern to fill in the desired outline.

7. Add filler flowers and additional foliage as needed to complete the shape, add softness, and cover the floral foam.

Casket inset piece

The family often orders a casket inset piece to coordinate with the colors and styles of the other family floral pieces. A **casket inset piece** is a small design displayed inside the casket lid. This design is traditionally sent from the younger family members—children or grandchildren. The casket inset piece may be designed like a corsage and placed on a satin pillow, heart, or cross. Some satin forms come with a floral foam mechanic attached to it. Other options are covering Styrofoam™ shapes (a cross or heart) with flowers by gluing or pinning. Another casket inset piece is a floral rosary, which may be used for the service of a devout Catholic. Rosary forms are available at the wholesale florist. The form has cone-shaped clamps to place around rose buds (or carnations). The floral rosary is draped and secured to the fabric in the lid of the casket by the funeral director.

10–5. The casket inset piece is a small design sent by the younger family members and is pinned to the lid of the casket.

Arrangements

Many sympathy tributes are arrangements designed in floral foam. The designs are typically oval, fan-shaped, or triangular. Symmetrical styles are the most common, but asymmetrical designs can also be tastefully created as a sympathy tribute.

10–6. Sympathy tributes may be designed in a variety of containers and design styles. A triangular design in a rustic basket (top left). An oval shape in a basket with a handle (top right). A fan-shaped design in a ceramic container (bottom).

The containers may be ceramic, plastic, papier-mâché, or baskets. Plastic containers with a handle are available and quite versatile. *Papier-mâché* containers come in various shapes and sizes and are made of a sturdy, molded, water-holding, paper-like material.

Many types of baskets are available and can be designed with a variety of design styles. A *fireside basket* is a curved, open basket with a handle. A sympathy arrangement may be

10–7. Papier-mâché containers come in various shapes and sizes.

designed in this type of basket by wiring a small utility container (and foam) to the basket (like the cornucopia technique). The fireside basket may be designed in two ways, either as a centerpiece or as a one-sided design. A centerpiece can be designed by placing the foam and container in the center of the basket. For a one-sided design, tip the basket forward and wire the utility container and foam to the front side of the basket near the handle (see Figure 4–30). Fireside baskets are often placed on the floor under or near the casket.

A floral designer must take care to design a sympathy tribute with sturdy mechanics. Floral foam should be securely taped to the container. For papier-mâché containers, the tape should be stapled to the paper-like rim to secure it. Avoid filling containers with excess water or sending arrangements or easel sprays that are leaking water.

EASEL DESIGNS

An easel design is any design that is displayed on an **easel**, which is a tripod-like stand for holding floral designs. Easel designs are unique to sympathy tributes. Sprays, wreaths, and set pieces are examples of easel designs.

Easel Sprays

An **easel spray**, also called a **standing spray**, is a one-sided flower arrangement placed on an easel. Easel sprays are designed as either symmetrical or asymmetrical styles in a variety of shapes, including a radiating oval (called a double-end spray), vertical, triangular, or diamond-shaped. The easel spray for a funeral service and the candelabra design for a wedding service are designed with similar mechanics.

10–8. Easel sprays may be symmetrical or asymmetrical.

The mechanics for an easel spray include various types of spray bars or a plastic cage (to insert a brick of floral foam). The mechanic is securely wired to the easel with #10- or #24-gauge wire or a chenille stem. Easels may be wooden, heavy wire, or crafted from bamboo or branches. The wire easels may be covered with moss, ribbon, branches, or horsetail (*Equisaetum*)—split vertically and slid over the wire frame).

1. Attach the spray bar or cage with saturated floral foam to the easel.

2. Green up the design to form a framework in the desired shape.

3. Add line flowers (and linear filler) to the outline.

4. Place striking or fully opened flowers near the center of interest. If a bow is to be added, make one and position it near the center of interest.

5. Add additional mass flowers to fill in the shape. Repeat the center of interest flowers elsewhere in the design (being sure to balance them).

6. Cover any exposed floral foam with foliage and filler.

10–9. A set piece is a special shape, such as a cross, which is displayed on an easel.

10–10. This wreath was designed in a floral foam wreath ring. Allow ample time to drain before delivery.

A **flat spray** is a triangular, one-sided spray that is regionally popular as a sympathy tribute. The flat spray may be hand-tied, that is, designed somewhat like a wedding arm bouquet, or arranged in Styrofoam™.

Set Pieces

Easel designs that are designed as special shapes, such as wreaths, crosses, hearts, pillows, or organizational emblems, are called **set pieces**. The set pieces may be fully covered with flowers or have just one or two areas of flowers.

Instead of covering the form entirely with flowers, any set piece frame may be partially wrapped with ribbon or bold leaves, such as ti, aspidistra, or dracaena leaves. The ribbon or leaves are secured on the underneath side with corsage pins or greening pins, respectively, to begin the wrapping. The ribbon is wrapped entirely around the wreath or heart frame with overlapping placements, except for the area where the floral cage will be attached. Leaves must be wrapped one at a time with overlapping placements, pinning each one securely with greening pins.

Set pieces can be designed on floral foam frames, Styrofoam™ (also called hard foam) shapes, or vine or twig forms. Some mechanics are a combination of hard foam frame with a wettable floral foam area to add the fresh flowers. When using any floral foam base, the foliage and flowers are inserted directly into the foam to create the desired shape. Needless to say, sympathy flowers last longer in floral foam mechanics.

Clusters of flowers may be added to hard foam or twig bases by attaching a foam cage. Cages are easily attached to twig forms by wiring them on with chenille stems or enameled wire. To wire a cage onto a hard foam base, attach the wires to the cage and then insert the wires through the foam. Position wood picks or toothpicks on the underneath side of the hard foam and wire around them. The wood picks or toothpicks

10–11. A wreath may be fully covered with flowers or have one (or two) area of floral emphasis.

will keep the wire from cutting through the hard foam. This technique works for any set piece that needs a floral accent. Floral accents can also be added by attaching a foam cage (with a chenille stem) to one leg of the easel.

A heart may be designed as an open heart, a solid heart with or without floral accents, or a broken heart. An open heart is heart-shaped with the center removed; floral accents may be added to one side or centered at the bottom of the heart. A solid heart is the full heart shape that is completely covered with flowers, usually with a floral accent. A broken heart has a solid covering of white flowers with a zigzag line of red flowers.

Organizational symbols or emblems are designed on hard foam bases and match the organization's insignia. These bases are available at the wholesale florist. The floral design should match the colors and placements as closely as possible for each organization. Flowers are designed to solidly cover the form, often with a foliage or ribbon outline.

Creating the Outline for Set Pieces

Sturdy leaves, such as salal, magnolia, or galax leaves, or pleated #40 ribbon are pinned to the underneath side of the base with greening pins or corsage pins, respectively, to create

10–12. A heart set piece may be designed as an open heart, a solid heart, or a broken heart.

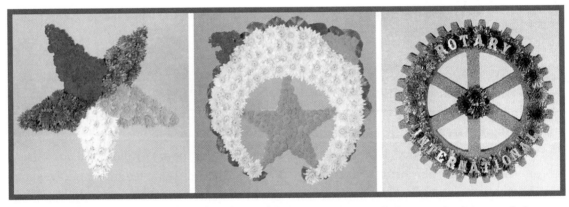

10–13. Organizational sympathy designs are unique set pieces that match the organization's symbol or emblem. (Left to right—Eastern Star, Shriner, and Rotary) (Courtesy, Teleflora)

an outline for set pieces. The leaves should overlap each other. The leaves and the ribbon pleating should extend out from the base an inch or two.

Attaching Flowers to Hard Foam Bases

Mass flowers, such as carnations or decorative or pompon chrysanthemums (pomps), are the most successful for completely filling in color for an area of a set piece. Flowers may be

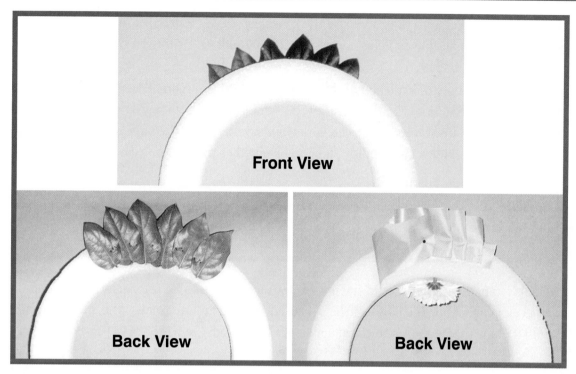

Front View

Back View

Back View

10–14. To outline a set piece form, pin leaves or ribbon in overlapping patterns to the underneath side of the base.

attached to hard foam bases by pinning, gluing, or attaching with toothpicks. The stem is removed from each flower. A corsage pin can be placed through the center of the flower into the hard foam; a generous amount of pan melt glue can be applied to the back of each flower before positioning on the form. Using toothpicks is the oldest method; attach one pointed

10–15. Flowers may be pinned, glued, or picked in a solid manner to completely cover areas of a set piece form.

end of the toothpick into the calyx and the other end of the toothpick into the hard foam. Sometimes for small flowers, it is easier to use only half of a toothpick with the cut end inserted into the foam.

The flowers should be attached to the frame in a consistent manner with all of the flowers facing the same direction. On the edges of the form, the flower facings are gently curved to cover the frame. The flowers are placed very close together as in the pavé technique. Foliage can be used to provide a green color and can be glued or pinned on with greening pins.

DELIVERY

Each sympathy design should have a card attached to it. The information included on the envelope would be the name of the deceased and the funeral home. The enclosure card should include the sender's name and a message, if desired. On the back of the card, the flo-

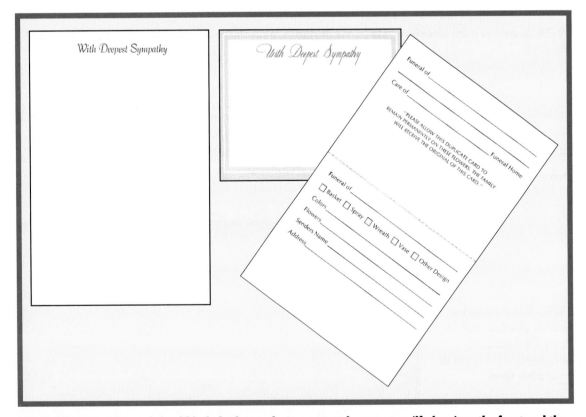

10–16. The sympathy card should include the sender's name and a message (if given) on the front and the sender's name, complete address, and a description of the sympathy tribute on the back. The envelope should include the name of the deceased and the funeral home.

rist should print the sender's name and full address and a short description of the floral piece that was sent. Providing this information to the bereaved family is an essential service.

Once the sympathy tributes are completed, the designs are delivered to the appropriate location. Most florists will keep the obituary section of the newspaper handy to ensure the delivery to the proper site at the proper time. Timely delivery and proper mechanics will help to ensure a good working relationship with the funeral director.

REVIEWING

MAIN IDEAS

Sympathy flowers honor the deceased and give a comforting presence to the family of the deceased. Typical sympathy flowers include the family flowers, which are ordered by the immediate family. The family flowers include the casket spray, the casket inset piece, and a matching floral tribute. Other sympathy tributes include arrangements, basket designs, easel and flat sprays, set pieces, and plants.

A casket spray is a floral arrangement that is placed on the top of a casket during the visitation and funeral service. A full-couch casket spray is a large casket piece (4 or 5 feet) that is placed in the center of a closed full couch. A full-couch lid spray is a large casket piece that is placed in the center of the open lid of a full couch. A half-couch casket spray is a floral piece that is placed on the right side of a half couch and is 3 to 3.5 feet wide.

Casket sprays are designed using a casket saddle with floral foam. A casket saddle has a rounded base to fit the contour of a casket lid. Casket sprays may be oval (or fan), crescent, or triangular (or T).

A casket inset piece is a small design displayed inside the casket lid. This design is traditionally sent from the younger members of the family.

Typical sympathy arrangements are symmetrical and oval, triangular, or fan-shaped. Asymmetrical designs are also a suitable style. Appropriate and common containers for sympathy arrangements are ceramic, plastic (with a handle), papier-mâché, or baskets. Fireside baskets are open and curving baskets with a handle. These baskets can be designed as centerpieces or one-sided arrangements.

An easel spray or standing spray is a one-sided flower arrangement placed on an easel. Easel sprays may be symmetrical or asymmetrical and a variety of shapes, such as oval, vertical, triangular, or diamond-shaped. The mechanics for an easel spray include various types of spray bars or plastic floral foam cages.

A flat spray is a triangular, one-sided, hand-tied spray (or arranged in hard foam) that is regionally popular as a sympathy tribute.

Easel designs that are designed as special shapes, such as wreaths, pillows, hearts, crosses, and organizational emblems, are called set pieces. The set pieces may be solidly covered with flowers or have just one or two areas of flower. The rest of the frame may be covered with ribbon or leaves.

Each sympathy design should have a card attached to it, except for the family flowers. The enclosure card should include the sender's name and a message (if given); on the back of the card, the sender's complete address and a short description of the floral piece should be given. The envelope should include the name of the deceased and the funeral home.

Prompt and efficient delivery of sympathy flowers is very important. Proper mechanics are also very important.

QUESTIONS

Answer the following questions using complete sentences and correct spelling.

1. Why are sympathy flowers important?

2. What are typical family flowers? What is the proper way to treat bereaved customers who are ordering the family flowers?

3. How is the size of a casket spray determined?

4. How is a casket spray different from a centerpiece?

5. What are some typical casket inset designs? Who sends these flowers?

6. What are set pieces? How are solid set pieces designed?

7. If a customer wants a set piece but cannot afford to have it fully covered with flowers, what can you suggest as an alternative? Give two suggestions and the design mechanics for creating these suggestions.

8. What is written on the enclosure card and envelope?

EVALUATING

Match the term with the correct definition. Write the letter of the term on the line provided.

a. easel spray   e. dish garden   i. flat spray
b. casket inset piece   f. fireside basket   j. full couch
c. half-couch casket spray g. casket saddle
d. set piece   h. standing spray

_____1. A triangular one-sided, hand-tied design.

_____2. A special shape, placed on an easel, that is fully covered with flowers or has one or two floral accent areas.

_____3. A casket with a one-piece lid.

_____4. A small design displayed inside the casket lid.

_____5. A selection of a variety of plants potted in the same container.

_____6. A container with a rounded base.

_____7. An open container with curved sides and a handle.

_____8. A one-sided flower arrangement placed on an easel.

_____9. A floral tribute that is placed on the right side of the casket.

_____10. A spray that stands in an easel.

EXPLORING

1. Purchase a hard foam and wettable foam wreath ring. Gather flowers and foliage to complete both wreaths. Choose two different design styles. Design each type using the proper mechanics and note the difference in lasting qualities of the flowers depending on the design mechanic used.

2. Interview a funeral director in person or on the phone. Ask about both the good and bad points when working with sympathy flowers and florists. Make a list and use it as a reminder when designing sympathy flowers.

3. Create a fireside basket design, first as a centerpiece. Adapt the basket to design a one-sided arrangement.

11

Designing with Everlasting Flowers

OBJECTIVES

This chapter is about the use of everlasting flowers in floral design. It has the following objectives:

1 Describe when and how to harvest everlasting flowers,

2 Explain the methods of preserving plant materials.

3 Describe designing with everlasting plant materials (dried and silk).

TERMS

covering method
desiccant
drying agent
everlasting plant materials
fixative

freeze-drying method
using glycerin
hanging method
pick machine
potpourri

pressing
shattering
silica gel
silica sand
wooden pick

11–1. Everlasting materials are long lasting and attractive, even in storage. These materials are hung from a grapevine at the back of the classroom.

Plant materials that can be successfully dried or preserved are called dried flowers or *everlasting plant materials*. Silk or other manufactured flowers are also everlasting materials. Everlasting flowers or "everlastings" are very long lasting but do not really last forever. However, the term everlasting emphasizes the fact that these preserved or manufactured materials will continue to add color and texture to a setting for an extended time.

Dried or everlasting flowers bring the outdoors in with memories of the summer garden and its beauty and color. These plant materials have many of the same attractive qualities as their fresh counterparts and can be designed in many of the same ways. Everlastings have the added benefit of looking attractive while storing them in plain view.

WHEN AND HOW TO HARVEST EVERLASTING FLOWERS

Few people take full advantage of the wealth of materials from the garden and nature that can brighten and enliven an interior. Many beautiful flowers, pods, leaves, and grasses may be gathered from spring, summer, and fall gardens and roadsides to dry or preserve for enjoyment as wreaths or arrangements indoors. The methods of preserving plant materials range from very simple to more involved and are chosen according to the type of plant material.

Flowers, pods, and grasses may be harvested in any season. For the best results and longest lasting qualities, flowers and other materials should be picked at the peak of color and shape. Look for the brightest colors for each type because some fading will occur.

The consequences of gathering plant materials after their peak is the condition known as **shattering**, which is a breaking apart or falling out of petals, seeds, or other plant parts. Grasses and cattails have very noticeable consequences if harvested too late. Ornamental grasses, including pampas grass and maiden grass, should be harvested just before peak or just before the grass plumes "fluff out." If picked when the grass plumes are already fuzzy looking, the grasses will totally "fuzz" a room when brought into a warm interior. Cattails should be harvested in summer when they have turned dark brown. The "old" cattail will shatter if harvested in fall.

The time of day for harvesting is also important. Plant materials should be picked when it is dry. Do not harvest when there is dew or any moisture on the plant. The middle of the day is an optimum time to avoid dew from the morning and any collecting moisture at nightfall. Do not harvest when the plant is wilted.

Spring	Summer	Fall
Daffodils	Black-eyed Susans	Bittersweet
Pansies	Blue Salvia	Chrysanthemums
Peonies	Cattails	Grasses (early fall)
Pussy willow	Gomphrena	Hydrangea
	Pods — honesty, poppy	Pods — iris, okra
	Wheat	
	Yarrow	

11–2. Flowers, pods, and grasses should be collected at their peak in any season for drying or preserving.

Most plant materials can be harvested by cutting them with a knife, scissors, or florist shears. Cones can be picked from the tree or the ground.

Harvest flowers and leaves at different stages and sizes. Flowers can be chosen as buds, partially open flowers, and fully open flowers.

PRESERVING METHODS

Different methods of drying and preserving can be used depending on the type of plant materials. Experience and trial and error testing will help determine promising drying methods for new materials. A floral designer should always dry or preserve more materials than actually needed to account for some losses.

Some plant materials require no extra care in drying, other than harvesting them at the proper time to avoid shattering. Examples include many types of pods (honesty or silver dollar plant, iris, poppy, okra, honey locust, milkweed), cones (spruce, pine, fir), seed heads (purple coneflower, teasel), and other materials, such as corn tassels and brown dock (a linear dark-brown roadside plant). A weed to one person may be a great dried flower to the next person.

11–3. One person's weed is another creative person's bride. The materials used to create this bride were simply harvested from nature and dried by the hanging method. The bride is fashioned on a chicken wire frame with gray Spanish moss, yellow goldenrod, white asters and 'The Pearl' yarrow, brown dock, corn husk bows and face, and various pods and open flowers for the bouquet.

HANGING METHOD

The **hanging method**, also called the hang dry method, is a method of collecting plant materials having a low moisture content and bunching them to hang upside down to dry. Some flowers and leaves dry with very little change in appearance; others will appear slightly wrinkled or puckered. Flowers with a higher moisture content can also be dried but may have a more puckered or wrinkled appearance.

Annuals	Perennials
Accroclinium *(Helipterum)*	Artemisia, Silver King, Silver Queen
Baby's breath (annual type)	Baby's breath ('Perfecta', 'Bristol Fairy')
Bells of Ireland	Drumstick *(Craspedia)* — Zone 6
Blue salvia	German Statice
Celosia (feather wheat, plume, cockscomb)	Globe centaurea, globe thistle
Dusty Miller	Goldenrod
Globe amaranth (gomphrena)	Grasses
Larkspur	Lady's mantle *(Alchemilla)*
Love-in-a-mist pods	Lamb's ear
Marigolds	Lavender
Statice	Roses
Strawflowers	Sea holly *(Eryngium)*
Wheat	Sea lavender *(Limonium latifolium)*
Winged everlasting *(Ammobium)*	Yarrow (yellow and white — 'The Pearl')

11–4. Many annuals and perennials that are easily dried with the hanging method can be grown in the garden.

11–5. Flowers that have low moisture content can be gathered, bunched, and hung upside down to dry. This method is called the hanging method or hand dry method (from left to right—carnations, roses, statice, globe amaranth).

This method works well for both annuals and perennials, such as baby's breath, blue salvia, plume or cockscomb celosia, goldenrod, clover-like globe amaranth or gomphrena, grasses, larkspur, lavender, love-in-a-mist pods, and strawflowers.

The hanging method is easy to do and requires only a few supplies, such as rubber bands, hooks or clothes hangers, and twist-ties to tie the bunches onto the hanger (if used). An airy, warm, dry area away from direct sunlight is an ideal place to help the drying process.

The steps for the hanging method are as follows:

1. Gather plant materials—Depending on the nature of the leaves and the desired finished look, the foliage may be left on the stems. Optional: Remove all the unnecessary foliage to hasten the drying process.

2. Bunch the stems into small amounts (8 to 12 stems) and fasten with a rubber band. Large flowers can each be hung separately.

3. Hang the bunches upside down in an airy, warm, dry area away from direct sunlight. The bunches may be placed on a hook or tied to a clothes hanger. A clothes hanger is also a flexible and mobile way to store the dried flowers.

4. When dry, store the bunched plant materials in dry place away from rodents. These bunches can be a decoration until used for an arrangement or wreath.

Hanging Method Variation

A variation of the hanging method is needed for plants with a daisy-like or larger flower heads. Placing the stems upside down causes the petals to droop down rather than remain open and flat. For these types of flowers, hang the flowers through a chicken wire frame or a crate with the flower heads up. The flower head rests on the wire and dries with natural-looking petals.

11–6. Flowers with daisy-like or large flower heads should not be hung upside down because the petals dry with an unnatural appearance. Place the stems through chicken wire with the flower heads up.

Examples of flowers to dry this way are blanket flower or gaillardia, carnations, coreopsis or tickseed, peonies, purple coneflower, sunflowers, sunflower heliopsis, and zinnias.

Another variation of the flower heads up hanging method is to place the ends of the stem in a little water in vases below the chicken wire. When the water evaporates, do not replace it and allow the material to dry in the vase. Some flowers will even dry nicely in an arrangement designed in floral foam that has dried out.

A third variation is to place these flowers in their chicken wire frames in a cooler to dry slowly and retain color. A small amount of water for the stems can again be incorporated. Some flowers will dry better with a gradual process.

COVERING METHOD

The **covering method** is a method that uses a drying agent to maintain the shape of the flower as it is drying. **Drying agents** or **desiccants**, such as silica sand, silica gel, fine-grain kitty litter, and borax and cornmeal, draw the moisture out of the flower or leaf. The desiccant holds the flower shape while the drying process takes place.

Silica sand is an inexpensive white builder's sand that can be purchased at home builder supply stores. When the sand becomes too moist to be effective, the granules of sand will stay on your fingers. By heating the sand at a low-temperature for several hours, the moisture can be removed. **Silica gel** is available as white crystals or color-indicator crystals that change colors when the gel is too moist to use. Silica sand is lighter in weight than silica gel and generally dries flowers faster. Both silica sand and silica gel can be reused many times. Borax can be used alone or in combination with cornmeal. Fine-grain kitty litter, borax, and cornmeal are available at grocery stores. These desiccants have a one-time use.

The covering method is effective for flowers that wilt too drastically for the hanging method. These flowers may have fragile petals or high moisture content. The covering

2-Dimensional Flowers
FACE DOWN

3-Dimensional Flowers
FACE UP

11–7. For the covering method, two-dimensional flowers can be dried face down in the drying agent; three-dimensional flowers should be dried face up in the drying agent.

method works for these flowers because the sand or drying agent holds the petals in place as the moisture is removed. Examples of flowers that can be effectively dried with the covering method are black-eyed Susans, daffodils, dahlias, delphiniums, carnations, chrysanthemums, cymbidium orchids, dendrobium orchids, freesias, roses (both methods work for roses), and snapdragons. Experimentation is the best way to learn if this method will work for a particular flower. The results could be positive and surprising; it seems like uncovering buried treasure.

The supplies needed for this drying method are pans or boxes, a drying agent, a microwave (optional, but faster), a strainer (to remove flower petals or leaves after each use), a paint brush (to brush off small amounts of drying agent), and containers to store the dried flowers.

Flowers may be placed in the drying agent in two ways depending on the flower shape. Two-dimensional flowers (such as daisies, daisy mums, and sunflowers) can be positioned face down onto the sand. Three-dimensional flowers (carnations, dahlias, orchids, and roses) would be smashed if positioned in the same way so these flowers must be positioned face up with the stem portion placed into the sand first. The sand is then poured carefully around (and within it, in some cases) the flower, maintaining its shape as much as possible.

An option for the covering method is the choice of air drying at room temperature or microwave drying. Air drying may take a week (longer for thicker flowers) and any type of pan or box can be used for drying the flowers. The length of time to air dry flowers will depend on the thickness of the petals, the flower shape, and the humidity in the room. Microwave drying should be done only in microwave-safe dishes. The flowers are dried on high for 2 to 4 minutes and then left in the drying agent overnight to cool. All plant parts must be covered before microwave drying or the area will smell like a burnt jungle.

A tip for the covering method is to completely fill each pan or container with the same type of flower to ensure uniform drying of the entire pan. Different flowers will dry at different rates of time and should be kept separate. Once a flower has been removed from the drying agent, it is nearly impossible to cover it back up if it has not dried thoroughly.

The covering method steps are:

1. Place an inch of drying agent in the bottom of the container. It should be microwave-safe if microwave drying.

2. Position the flowers (face down for 2-D, face up for 3-D) on the sand. Fill the entire container with like flowers.

3. Carefully cover the flowers with drying agent, work around the edges of each flower and build up the agent until the flower is completely covered. For air drying, the stems can be left uncovered; for microwave drying, the stems should be

	Air Drying	Microwave Drying
Containers	Any type	Only microwave safe
Length of Time — Thin petals	5–7 days	2 minutes on high/overnight
Medium	7–9 days	3 minutes on high/overnight
Thick	9–12 days	4 minutes on high/overnight
Stem Coverage	Optional	Completely covered
Stem Wiring	May be wired	Absolutely no wired stems

11–8. Comparison of air drying and microwave drying.

completely covered. Cover the flowers with approximately an inch of drying agent at the top of the container.

4. Dry the flowers with the 1) air drying technique or 2) microwave drying technique.

5. Uncover the flowers by carefully pouring off some of the drying agent on the top into another box or container. Brush away the drying agent in and around the petals and gently remove the flower. Use a brush to remove any excess desiccant from the petals.

6. Store the dried flowers carefully in containers in a dry area until used.

GLYCERINIZING

A glycerin solution can be used to preserve foliage, such as fall-color leaves and eucalyptus, and some filler flowers, such as goldenrod, hydrangea, and sea lavender. **Glycerinizing** preserves foliage and fillers through the process of a glycerin solution being transported up the stem (xylem), which preserves the plant material and causes it to remain pliable and flexible.

Glycerinized plant materials are flexible and can be curved or shaped; plant materials dried by hanging or covering can be quite fragile and easily broken. The comparison of dried and glycerinized eucalyptus is very striking because the glycerinized eucalyptus bends and is very pliable; the dried eucalyptus cannot be curved without breaking into many pieces.

Some glycerinized plant materials have also been dyed in the same process. It is quite common to have a choice of glycerinized eucalyptus in green, brown, or other colors. Glycerin and glycerin dyes may be purchased at craft or hobby shops or chemical supply stores.

Keep plant materials in water until ready to be treated. For the best results, choose foliage such as beech, holly, forsythia, plum, and any with bronze or reddish leaves. Most foliage and fillers will darken in color after glycerinizing. The treated materials will have a smooth satiny finish and will last indefinitely. Treated materials may be used in fresh arrangements as well as dried ones. Water does not affect glycerin-treated foliage.

To preserve foliage and fillers using glycerin, follow these steps:

1. Harvest foliage branches or fillers to be treated. Remove any damaged leaves. Wipe off any dust or debris with a damp cloth.

2. Mix 1 part glycerin with 2 parts warm water. Warm water is taken up the stem (xylem) more efficiently.

3. Place 4 to 5 inches of the glycerin solution in a narrow container. Maintain this level throughout the process.

4. Place the cut ends of the branches in the solution. Make a fresh cut before putting the stems in the solution. The top of the branches may be brushed with the glycerin solution to hasten the process.

11–9. Beech leaves darken to a bronze color and are pliable and long lasting when treated with a glycerin solution.

5. Watch the plant materials for the desired color. Check the materials after one week. The foliage or filler is ready to be removed from the solution when oiliness is felt on the leaf surface.

6. Remove the plant materials from the solution. Hang them upside down in bunches until dry. Store away from direct sunlight.

Some foliage, such as English ivy, galax leaves, and leatherleaf, is more successfully preserved by completely immersing the stems in a 50:50 solution of glycerin and warm water.

Pressing

Pressing plant materials is a very old technique of carefully placing flowers and foliage between absorbent paper to flatten and preserve them in a two-dimensional form. Many kinds of plant materials can be pressed for use in pictures, stationary, bookmarks, greeting and gift cards, business cards, jewelry, ornaments, pillows, and to cover vases. Nearly every

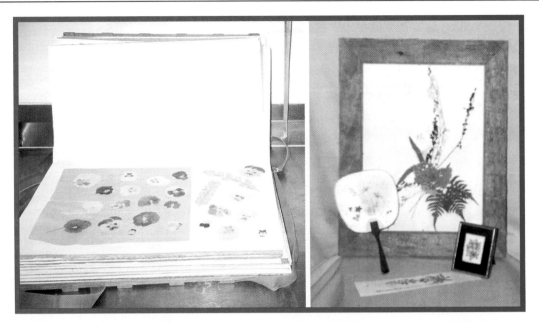

11–10. A plant press is an effective way to press many types of flowers and foliage, including pansies. Pressed flowers can be designed on pictures, fans, and bookmarks.

type of flower or foliage can be pressed, including pansy, Queen Anne's lace, ferns, scented geranium leaves, larkspur, and pinks (*Dianthus*).

Flowers and leaves can be successfully pressed with a plant press, phone books, or a homemade plant press, made by gathering newspapers or phone books, and blotting paper or paper towels. Follow these simple steps:

1. Start the homemade plant press with a flat piece of plywood. Alternate layers of newspapers or corrugated cardboard, one piece of blotting paper, two paper towels, one piece of blotting paper, and more newspapers or cardboard. Or use a phone book with paper towels between the pages. Or use a plant press.

2. Collect fresh plant material at different stages of development. Do not allow the materials to wilt; begin pressing them at once.

3. Starting with the lowest layer, place the flowers and foliage between two paper towels. Carefully position each flower or leaf to lay flat and not touch another one.

4. Continue adding layers of paper and towels and pressing flowers and foliage between the two paper towels.

5. When the stack is 12 inches high, place a thin plywood board over the top and add weight, such as bricks, concrete blocks, or heavy books, distributing the weight evenly.

6. Dry the plant materials in a dry, warm, well-ventilated area.

7. Check the top layer after a week. Fresh towels may be substituted to prevent mold. Allow one to three weeks to dry. When the plant materials have completely dried, transfer them to boxes, folders, or an old phone book.

Potpourri

Potpourri is a scented mixture of dried petals, flowers, buds, leaves, spices, fragrance oils, and a fixative. A *fixative* is necessary to hold or to "fix" the scent for an extended period (up to a year or more). Fixatives, such as powdered orris root (the root of the Florentine iris) or fragrance crystals (a specially formulated form of salt with fragrance added), can be purchased at craft, herb, and health food stores.

Potpourri is a unique way to cover (by gluing) a topiary form, a round Styrofoam or sweet-gum ball ornament, or a clay pot or other vase. Another idea is to place a thin bud vase inside a wider clear vase and add potpourri between the two vases to give a lovely garden look with interesting texture and color (see Figure 11–11). For the vase technique, the dried plant materials do not need the fragrance added. Skip steps #3 and #4. A fresh or dried design can be created in the smaller vase.

11–11. Potpourri is a fragrant mixture of dried flowers, buds, petals, leaves, oils, and a fixative. Potpourri can add color and texture to vases.

The steps in making potpourri are very simple and easy to follow.

1. Dry the plant materials by placing them in a single layer on paper towels, newspaper, or fine mesh screens.

2. Once the materials are thoroughly dried, store different colors separately. Mixtures can be made based on color and texture. Choose red and green for a Christmas holiday theme or bright yellows and lime greens for a citrus fragrance.

3. Whole and powdered spices (no more than a teaspoon at a time) and a few drops of fragrance oil are added to provide a pleasant scent. Mix thoroughly.

4. Add a fixative. Use a teaspoon for each quart of plant materials. Mix thoroughly.

5. Cover tightly and place away from direct sunlight. Stir and mix the mixture every week or 10 days. Check at the end of a month for the desired fragrance. Add drops of fragrance oil or spices if necessary.

FREEZE-DRYING METHOD

Freeze drying is a commercial method of freezing the flowers first before drying them. Flowers are placed in large refrigerated vacuum chambers that remove the moisture from the plant tissues. The flowers look very natural and hold their color. The cost of the chamber is prohibitive for most people.

DESIGNING WITH EVERLASTINGS (DRIED AND SILK)

Designers of dried or silk arrangements must employ the same principles and elements of design that are used with fresh flowers; however, some of the mechanics and specific techniques are slightly different. Designing with dried and silk flowers gives much flexibility to the designer. Stems can be lengthened or manipulated into various shapes. Materials may be glued, wired, and taped in a wide variety of ways that are not possible with fresh materials. A diverse range of containers can be used, including those that do not hold water. In many

11–12. Designing with everlasting flowers gives the designer much flexibility. Many styles and containers (including those that do not hold water) are possible with dried flowers.

ways, designing with dried or silk flowers is much easier than with fresh flowers because wilting is not a concern. Also, designs will not need water; wilted petals or leaves do not need to be removed. Care should be taken to avoid sunny or humid areas.

STEM TECHNIQUES

Many flowers or leaves are dried without any stems at all. Both dried and silk flowers may need stems to be lengthened or strengthened. The methods used will depend on the flower type and stem thickness. New or added stems should be taped with floral tape in the appropriate matching color before using them in a design.

To create a new stem, a heavy wire can be glued (with pan melt glue or glue from a glue gun) and secured to the flower. Another method is to use the daisy hook wiring method.

To lengthen or strengthen stems, several methods are available. 1) A *pick machine* attaches a metal pick or stem to single or clustered silk or dried flowers to add length and strength. 2) A *wooden pick*, a narrow, pointed piece of wood (available in several lengths) with a wire attached at the top, can add stem length. Stems can be lengthened or strengthened by wrapping the wire on the pick around both the stem and the wooden pick. 3) Stem length can be added for a short flower by placing it into a hollow stem removed from another flower. Tape the flower to secure it. 4) A designer can tightly tape a short flower or leaf to a longer stem without wire or glue or hollow stem. This method is quick, but the taping must be very secure to keep the material from falling out. 5) Hot glue can attach a longer stem to a short flower or leaf.

To operate a pick machine, begin by loading the metal picks into the slot at the top of the machine. Next, the handle is pulled forward to feed the pick into the front of the machine. The stems of the dried materials are placed over the top part of the pick. The stems should be thick enough to allow the pick to grasp them; if too thin, the stems will slip out of the pick. Then the handle is pushed downward with a firm steady grip. The prongs on the pick close over the stems of the dried materials, clamping the stems tightly. The dried material is ready to use in a design.

11–13. Both dried and silk flowers can be lengthened and strengthened by using metal picks from a pick machine, wooden picks, and hollow stems.

11–14. Add several flowers or fillers to a design with one placement to increase quickness in designing.

To shorten designing time, several flowers, fillers, or leaves may be attached to one stem and placed into a design. Adding several small filler flowers on the same metal or wooden pick or hollow stem shortens the design time and gives a full look to the design. Larger flowers can be wired (at slightly differing heights) and taped to quickly add color, depth, and fullness to a design.

To secure silk flowers and leaves, some silks may need to be removed from their stem, hot glued, and reattached to the stem. Before designing with silks, determine if this step is necessary with a gentle tug on a silk flower or leaf. If the parts come off easily, gluing is essential to secure them.

To shape silk flowers, use the wired petals, leaves, and stems and position these parts in a natural way. Unfurl the petals and stage the flowers to look partially to fully open; position the leaves to appear growing and not wilted; the stems may be slightly curved to look "real."

Designing Tips

Floral foam created specifically for silk and dried flower arranging is available. The foam should be securely attached to the container or wreath frame by gluing or wiring. To keep the wire from cutting through the floral foam, moss can be added before wiring. Moss is also used to conceal the floral foam and other mechanics (wiring and gluing). Wooden picks can also be placed at the foam edges to keep the wire from cutting through the floral foam.

11–15. Floral foam can be attached to containers by gluing or wiring. Moss will prevent the wire from cutting through the foam as well as camouflage the foam and other mechanics (wiring and gluing).

When designing, each stem may be glued (use pan melt glue and a quick dip) before placing it into the arrangement. Experienced designers (who will not change their mind about placement) can use this technique as they design; novices may want to glue the stems of the finished arrangement.

Designs with everlastings should not appear flat. Layering, the technique of placing some flowers deeper than others within an arrangement, will add fullness and avoid a flat look. Some flowers and fillers will appear quite "leggy" and layering avoids the see-through appearance.

Display finished designs away from direct sunlight and high humidity. Sunlight will fade the colors and humidity will "wilt" dried flowers.

Dried and silk materials are long lasting and low maintenance. These types of designs will need occasional cleaning by dusting with a lightweight feather duster, spraying with a commercial spray designed for cleaning dried and silk flowers, or a quick dusting with a hair blow dryer on a low setting.

11–16. Layering is a technique of placing flowers or fillers deeper in an arrangement to add depth and create fullness, avoiding a see-through, "leggy" appearance. Add layering materials near the beginning of the designing process.

REVIEWING

MAIN IDEAS

Everlasting plant materials may be dried, preserved, or manufactured (silk, paper) and are very long lasting. Flowers and plant materials may be harvested in any season when at (or just before) their peak color and shape. Gathering materials too late may cause shattering, the falling or breaking apart of petals, leaves, seeds, or other plant parts. Harvest materials at different stages and sizes during the middle of the day.

Methods to dry or preserve plant materials are the hanging method, covering method, treating with glycerin, pressing, making potpourri, and commercial freeze drying. The hanging method is ideal for plant materials with low moisture content. Flowers are bunched, fastened with a rubber band, and hung upside down to air dry. For daisy-type flowers, hang the flower heads through chicken wire for drying with a natural appearance. The covering method is a method that uses a drying agent to maintain the flower shape as it dries. Examples of drying agents include silica sand, silica gel, kitty litter, borax, and cornmeal. Flowers with high moisture content or fragile petals can be successfully dried with the covering method. Flower shape determines the manner in which flowers are placed in the drying agent, either face up for three-dimensional ones or face down for two-dimensional daisy-like ones. Another option is air drying at room temperature or microwave drying.

Stems of fillers or foliage can be treated with glycerin, called glycerinizing. The glycerin solution is transported up the stem through the xylem, preserving the plant material and making it pliable and long lasting.

Pressing plant materials preserves them in a two-dimensional form. A plant press, phone books, or homemade press can be used to press flowers. Potpourri is a scented mixture of dried petals and other plant parts, spices, fragrance oils, and a fixative. A fixative is an additive, such as orris root or fragrance crystals, for holding or "fixing" the fragrance. Pressed flowers and potpourri can be attached to pictures or vases for interesting textures and colors. Freeze drying is a commercial method of freezing the plant materials before drying them in vacuum chambers.

Designing with everlasting plant materials, both dried and silk, gives the floral designer much flexibility. Stems can be added, lengthened, and strengthened with wire, metal or wooden picks, hollow stems, taped stems, or hot glue. Several stems can be added as a cluster to the arrangement to shorten designing time. Silk flowers can be shaped to look as if they are alive.

Floral foam created specifically for silk and dried flower arranging is available. Use moss to conceal it and wire or glue it to the chosen container. Layering is a technique of placing some flowers deeper within an arrangement to add depth and fullness.

Display finished designs of everlasting plant materials away from direct sunlight and high humidity. These designs may need occasional cleaning with a feather duster, commercial spray for cleaning silk or dried materials, or a dusting with a hair blow dryer.

QUESTIONS

Answer the following questions using complete sentences and correct spelling.

1. What are four advantages of designing with everlasting plant materials compared to fresh materials?

2. Why do dried plant materials shatter? How is shattering avoided in ornamental grasses?

3. What is the best time of day and the best stage of development to harvest plant materials for drying?

4. What is the hanging method? What types of flowers are dried with the hanging method? What is a variation of that method? What flowers work well with that method?

5. Why are some flowers dried by the covering method instead of the simpler hanging method? How are flowers placed in the drying agent?

6. How is a glycerin solution used to preserve plant materials? What are examples of plant materials that are successfully treated with this method?

7. What are ways that pressed flowers can be used?

8. How can dried flowers with short stems be used in designing?

9. What are two tips when designing with silk materials?

10. What is the maintenance of everlasting floral designs?

EVALUATING

Match the term with the correct definition. Write the letter of the term on the line provided.

a. potpourri
b. shattering
c. silica gel
d. fixative

e. desiccant
f. layering
g. covering method
h. pick machine

i. pressing
j. using glycerin

_____1. A drying agent that draws moisture from a flower.

_____2. The method of preserving plant materials in a two-dimensional form between paper or towels.

_____3. A drying agent with color-indicator crystals.

_____4. A device to attach a metal stem to a single flower or cluster of flowers.

_____5. A powdered or crystal-like substance that holds the fragrance in potpourri.

_____6. A method in which a liquid substance replaces the water in the stem or xylem and preserves the plant material in a pliable manner.

_____7. A fragrant dried mixture made of petals, buds, leaves, spices, oils, and a fixative.

_____8. A technique of placing flowers or fillers deeper within a floral design.

_____9. The breaking apart of the plant parts or seeds.

_____10. A method of surrounding the flower with a drying agent to hold its shape and dry the flower in a natural-looking way.

EXPLORING

1. Choose three types of plant materials from the garden—a flower, a foliage, and a smaller flower or filler. Dry or preserve each one by the hanging, covering, using glycerinizing, and pressing methods. Compare the results for each type and choose the preferred method(s) for each one.

2. Visit a garden center or florist that stocks a variety of silk flowers and foliage. Evaluate the flowers for a natural appearance and for wired petals, leaves, and stems. Buy three to five realistic-looking types, including both flowers and foliage, and create a design.

3. Select five kinds of flowers and leaves and press them with a homemade plant press. When the plant materials are completely dry, cover a clay pot or other vase with the pressed materials. The container can be completely covered or enhanced by a few carefully placed materials. Make a dried design for the new container.

CHAPTER 12

Pricing Design Work

OBJECTIVES

This chapter is about pricing floral designs. It has the following objectives:

1 Explain the importance of effective buying.

2 Explain how to determine the costs for floral arrangements.

3 Describe typical pricing strategies.

TERMS

broker	multiple unit pricing	retail price
combined pricing	nested basket	tie-in pricing
cost of goods	net profit	unit cost of goods
gross sales	odd end pricing	variable ratio mark-up
hardgoods	operating expenses	wholesale cost of goods or
labor	percentage mark-up	wholesale price
leader pricing	pricing strategies	wholesale florist
multiple price points	ratio mark-up	

12–1. Retail flower shops sell to the public. (Courtesy, Jasper S. Lee)

PRICING, along with proper buying practices, is a very important responsibility of the owner or manager of a retail florist shop. Beautiful and well-constructed designs must be appropriately priced to motivate customers to buy. The combination of effective buying and pricing will determine if a shop will be profitable or not.

Pricing and buying well does not have to be a mystery. A well-informed and conscientious person can unlock the mystery by following a few guidelines and determining which pricing method and other strategies fit their needs.

IMPORTANCE OF BUYING

Buying can be a challenging part of the floral business. Finding the right plant materials at the right price at the right time is somewhat like fitting the pieces of a puzzle together. Knowledge, organization, and planning are a big part of being a good buyer. Flexibility and adaptability are also important because plant materials may not be available when ordered.

SOURCES OF GOODS

A retail florist may purchase flowers and foliage from wholesale florists, growers, a flower market, or a broker. A florist may use a combination of these sources.

Wholesale Florists

A **wholesale florist** is a purchasing link between the grower or broker and the retail florist. Some wholesale florists (also called wholesalers) may sell only fresh plant material. The wholesale florist that sells both fresh and nonperishable materials (vases, supplies) can provide one-stop shopping for the retail florist. An advantage of ordering from a wholesaler instead of a grower is the flexibility in ordering the desired number of bunches, instead of an entire box. In general, retail florists may have two or three favorite wholesalers due to varied delivery times and added availability of inventory from which to choose.

Growers

Growers, both foreign and domestic, will supply to a florist directly if the quantities ordered are large enough. Florists may order large quantities of roses at Valentine's Day and carnations and chrysanthemums during the rest of the year directly from the grower. Mixed boxes of specialty flowers and greens are also popular items to order directly from growers.

Flower Market

Some large cities have their own flower market. At the flower market, all of the local wholesalers are represented. The retail florist can compare and buy a wide variety of plant materials.

Brokers

A **broker** is an agent who purchases flowers, contacts customers (both wholesalers and retailers), and sells his or her inventory. A broker may purchase flowers directly from growers or from an auction. Often, a broker may never see or physically handle the plant materials, but will sell from inventory lists.

BE A SUCCESSFUL BUYER

A successful buyer is informed about flower quality and price, effective in building a good working relationship with the suppliers, and knowledgeable about the manner and quantities in which flowers are sold.

12–2. A broker purchases flowers, contacts customers, and sells inventory. (Courtesy, Kuhn Flowers, Jacksonville, FL)

Flower Quality and Price

An effective buyer is an informed buyer. Try to learn who sells the finest quality flowers, both at the grower and wholesale level. Keep notes about the quality of flowers received and request by name the growers with good quality. Learn about the handling practices of the wholesale florists. Ask questions, such as "Is floral preservative used?" "How fresh are these flowers?" "When were these flowers shipped?"

Expect quality from a supplier and always inspect each shipment for the desired quality and freshness. Remember, there will be a small amount of loss or damage in the normal handling and shipping of fresh flowers. Do not call the supplier for small claims of loss, but do inform them when an entire or part of a bunch is damaged, wilted, or very poor quality. Work to build an honest and cooperative relationship with your suppliers.

An effective buyer will be interested in both the price and the quality of plant materials. Sometimes high-quality flowers and foliage deserve a higher price. Also, prices will often go higher for flowers that are in high demand during a specific holiday or season. Expect to pay more for roses and red flowers at Valentine's Day.

Building a Good Relationship with Suppliers

A successful buyer can build a good relationship with suppliers by being honest, trustworthy, and loyal. A florist should be honest about the quality expected and the amounts of flowers needed. Let wholesalers know immediately if quantities change to avoid over-buying. Pay the bills on time to build trust. Although using only one wholesaler is not a wise idea, be a loyal and dependable buyer when purchasing from the two or more chosen suppliers.

Flower and Foliage Buying Tips

A buyer needs to know bunch sizes for typical flowers and foliage. Flowers may be bunched in 10s or 25s, or sold by the single stem. Review this material in Chapter 3 (Care and Handling of Fresh Flowers and Foliage). If the amount per bunch is in question, do not hesitate to ask the supplier.

In general, a better price will be given for materials that are purchased in greater quantities. For example, buying one to four cases of foam may cost $20.00; buying five to nine cases would cost $19.50. By planning ahead, an effective buyer will anticipate needs and purchase in larger amounts to save money in the long run.

Determining Unit Cost of Goods

Since supplies and plant materials are sold in bunches, rolls, or cases, the price for a single unit or item should be calculated. The **unit cost of goods** is the price of a single item determined by dividing the overall bunch or case price by the number of items in the bunch or case. For fresh flowers, a physical count of the stems when the shipment arrives may be the best idea to ensure the correct unit cost of goods.

This unit cost is also an important figure to add to the arrangement costs. The cost of each addition to a floral design should be recorded and included in the price. A designer should not give away supplies, but should charge a fair amount for each added item. For example, a poinsettia decorated with foil and a bow would be more expensive than one just chosen from the greenhouse with no decoration. To charge the same amount for both is to give away profit.

The unit cost of goods should be calculated for everything. Keep a separate list for supplies (or **hardgoods**) and for fresh flowers and foliage. Update these prices as needed. The prices of supplies will not change as quickly as fresh flower prices. The unit costs of flowers should be recalculated after each delivery.

Small design vase:	$18.00 per case ÷ 36 (vases per case)	= $0.50
Tulips:	$7.50 per bunch ÷ 10 (tulips per bunch)	= $0.75

12–3. To determine the unit cost of goods, divide the cost by the overall number of items in the case or bunch.

The unit cost of goods is a wholesale cost, not a retail price. The total of all unit costs of goods is the **wholesale cost of goods or wholesale price**. A **retail price** is the florist's selling price determined from the wholesale cost of goods (wholesale price) or other method as described in the next section.

Combined Pricing for Supplies

Combined pricing is a method of adding the total costs for typical supplies used for an arrangement. Combined pricing can be calculated for designs arranged in commonly used vases or containers. As a time-saver, each regularly used vase can have a combined price for the supplies posted near it. The typical supplies for that vase would be the costs of the vase,

COMBINED PRICES Supplies Needed and Costs			
6" PLANT	**Costs**	**9" BUD VASE**	**Costs**
Foil		Bud vase	
#9 ribbon		Floral preservative	
Card, envelop, cardette		Card, envelop, cardette	
Care tag		Care tag	
Wrapping supplies		Wrapping supplies	
Wax tissue		Wax tissue	
Cellophane		Cellophane	
Ribbon		Ribbon	
TOTALS	_____		_____

12–4. Combined pricing for typical supplies used to decorate a plant or design an arrangement in a specific vase can make pricing quick and more efficient.

floral foam and tape (if appropriate), floral preservative, wire, card, envelope, cardette, wrapping materials (typical for the shop), and care tag. The combined price of the supplies can be quickly added to the costs of the fresh flowers and foliage.

METHODS OF PRICING DESIGN WORK

Pricing design work may vary with each floral shop depending upon the type of shop and profit strategies. However, there are some general guidelines for determining price. The ratio mark-up and the percentage mark-up are two types of pricing methods.

RATIO MARK-UP

The **ratio mark-up** method of pricing relies on a predetermined increase (or mark-up) from the wholesale cost of goods. The selling price is called the retail price. Hardgoods (or supplies) typically have a 2:1 mark-up; perishables (flowers and foliage) typically have a 3:1 mark-up. In other words, to determine the retail cost or the selling price, multiply the wholesale cost for supplies by 2 and the wholesale cost of flowers and foliage by 3.

Typical Ratio Mark-up		
Perishables	Carnations	10@$.30 = $3.00 × 3 = $9.00
	Leatherleaf	10@$.10 = $1.00 × 3 = $3.00
Hardgoods	Vase	1@$.90 = $0.90 × 2 = $1.80
	Floral Preservative	1@$.05 = $0.05 × 2 = $0.10
		TOTAL $13.90
Across-the-Board 3:1 Pricing Ratio		
Perishables	Carnations	10@$.30 = $3.00 × 3 = $9.00
	Leatherleaf	10@$.10 = $1.00 × 3 = $3.00
Hardgoods	Vase	1@$.90 = $0.90 × 3 = $2.70
	Floral Preservative	1@$.05 = $0.05 × 3 = $0.15
		TOTAL $14.85

12–5. An example of pricing the same vase arrangement with two different methods. A typical ratio mark-up would be 2:1 for hardgoods or non-perishables and 3:1 for perishables (flowers and foliage). Another florist might use an across-the-board 3:1 pricing ratio. (Note the price difference.)

These ratios may vary from florist to florist; some ratios may be a consistent 3:1 for both perishables and non-perishables. Others charge a 5:1 mark-up or more for labor-intensive design work, such as wedding work (see variable ratio mark-up).

The weakness in this system is the failure to plan for net profit and to consider overhead costs and operating expenses. The ratio mark-up can make pricing guesswork because the time to design and complete the arrangement is not considered.

Adding Labor Charges

To account for the design time (or labor), a labor charge can be added to the ratio mark-up total. This charge may be based on the hourly wage although the astute owner may want to add fringe benefits and other employee costs to the hourly wage. For example, let's pretend that a floral designer makes $7.00 per hour. By including health care or other costs to this hourly rate, the true hourly employee wage (or cost to the employer) may be $13.00 per hour.

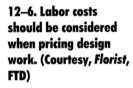

12–6. Labor costs should be considered when pricing design work. (Courtesy, *Florist*, FTD)

Let's figure some design labor charges. First, think of the minutes spent in completing an arrangement as a fraction of an hour. For example, 45 minutes is ¾ of an hour or .75, 30 minutes is ½ hour or .5, 20 minutes is 1/3 of an hour or .33, and 15 minutes is ¼ of an hour or .25.

For a vase arrangement that requires 15 minutes of design time, multiply $7.00 (the hourly wage) times .25. $7.00 × .25 = $1.75. The labor charge for the design would be $1.75 using the hourly wage. The labor charge for the $13.00 per hour rate (employer's actual costs) is $3.25. $13.00 × .25 = $3.25. An employer would be paying for the extra $1.50 from profits if it is not included in these labor charges. A florist may want to post a chart for standard labor charges for the design time.

Vase arrangement in Figure 12–5	Total	$13.90

15 minutes to complete

$13.00 (employer's actual hourly labor costs) × .25 (1/4 hour) = $ 3.25

New total with labor = $17.15

12–7. Labor charges may be added with the ratio mark-up method.

Another method to calculate labor would be to add a 10 to 20 percent labor charge to the final price. A design costing $13.90 would have a $2.00 labor charge (15 percent) or a $2.75 labor charge (20 percent). Notice that these labor charges are less than the previous example based on the employer's actual hourly labor costs.

Variable Ratio Mark-Up

Variable ratio mark-up has different mark-ups depending on two factors—the type of design or the type of flower and the labor required to design with it. Labor-intensive designs or flowers would have a higher mark-up. Hardgoods would still have a 2:1 or 2.5:1 mark-up.

Type of Design	Mark-up
Basic arrangements, bud vases, boxed flowers, decorated plants	3:1
Creative designs, corsages	4:1
Wedding flowers, party flowers, special designs requiring time and attention	5:1 (or more)

12–8. Different mark-ups for different types of designs are called creative ratio mark-ups.

The strength of the variable ratio mark-up is that the labor aspect of designing is included in the design. However, the planning for net profit is still a matter of guesswork. Another weakness may be the confusion of so many mark-ups. The owner can periodically post a

Type of Flower	Labor Required	Mark-up
Form flowers (orchids, lilies, tropicals, standard or Fuji mums)	low	2½:1
Average flowers (carnations, gladiolus, roses — need de-thorning)	medium	3½:1
Filler flowers (spray mums, daisies, statice, baby's breath, heather, foliage)	high	4:1

12–9. Some florists may use variable ratio mark-up for the different labor-requiring types of flowers.

		Ratio Mark-up	Variable Ratio Mark-up
Standard carnation	$0.24/stem	$0.72	$0.84
Orchid	$1.20/flower	$3.60	$3.00
Pompon spray mums	$0.60/stem	$1.80	$2.40 (5–7 placements)

12–10. Comparison of flower prices calculated with both ratio mark-up and variable ratio mark-up.

retail price list with the varying mark-ups included (but not shown) without causing confusion to the employee.

PERCENTAGE MARK-UP

The **percentage mark-up** is a pricing method that plans for profit. The percentage mark-up method is the wholesale cost of goods divided by the cost of goods percentage as determined by the shop's financial statement. This pricing method requires the florist to analyze the business' financial records to determine the percentages of the four major aspects of gross sales (the total amount of sales for the year). At first, this analysis may be time-consuming, but once completed, the percentage mark-up is easy to calculate.

First, let's look at the four major parts of gross sales and some typical percentages based on averaged figures.

Gross sales	=	Operating Expenses	+	Labor	+	Cost of Goods	+	Net Profit
100%	=	35%	+	20%	+	30% (30–33%)	+	15% (12–15%)

The four areas will vary somewhat from shop to shop. *Gross sales* are the total dollar amounts that the florist sells. *Operating expenses* include the costs of running the business, such as rent or costs of owning the building, salaries, selling costs (for wire services fees, advertising), delivery costs, and administrative costs. The operating expenses may be lower if the florist owns the building, requiring no mortgage payment or rent. *Labor* is an operating expense that is calculated separately. Labor is the cost for the required time to design the specialized products that florists sell. *Cost of goods* is the cost of purchasing merchandise and materials that comprises the designs, plants, and giftware sold by a florist. *Net profit* is the return on the florist's investment, which can be reinvested or considered as the owner's income. The florist can plan for profit in a range of 10 to 15 percent. In the sample shown, if a 15 percent profit is planned, the cost of goods should be 30 percent; if 12 percent profit is projected, the cost of goods can be 33 percent.

Now, how do these figures relate to pricing? The cost of goods used in a design is calculated as 30 percent of the design price. For each arrangement, 30 percent of the price will be the actual wholesale cost of the flowers, foliage, and supplies.

Let's use the vase arrangement in Figure 12–5. The wholesale cost of goods is $4.95. To find the price, the cost of goods is divided by the cost of goods percentage. This method is also called the divisional percentage mark-up. Remember, the cost of goods is divided by the cost of goods percentage.

$$\$4.95 \div 30\% \text{ or } \$4.95 \div .3 = \$16.50$$

12–11. Rent or the costs of owning the building are part of the operating expenses. (Courtesy, Kuhn Flowers, Jacksonville, FL)

Pricing Method	Price
Ratio mark-up (2:1 and 3:1)	$13.90
Ratio mark-up (3:1 for everything)	$14.85
Ratio mark-up plus labor	$17.15
Variable mark-up by flower type (carnations 3½:1)	$14.95
Variable mark-up by type of design (basic—3:1)	$13.90
Percentage mark-up (30% cost of goods)	$16.50

12–12. A comparison of the different pricing methods for the same carnation vase arrangement is an interesting exercise.

The strength of the percentage mark-up is the planning for profit and knowing the specific percentages for each category, including cost of goods, for the individual floral shop. Although the preparation of this information may take some time, the effort will pay off with an efficient pricing system. A disadvantage is that the employee may not know wholesale prices of goods to make the calculations. However, the manager or owner could determine prices using this method for specials and for numerous commonly purchased designs, plants, and corsages. Planning for profit is profitable!

If the customer requests an arrangement for a specific amount, the price is multiplied by 30 percent to determine the cost of goods that can be used to make the arrangement. For example, a $20.00 arrangement should have $6.00 of wholesale costs in flowers, foliage, and supplies, including the vase.

$$\$20.00 \times 30\% = \$6.00 \text{ or } \$20.00 \times .3 = \$6.00$$

A florist must decide which pricing method fits the management style and the type of operation. The method chosen should provide the owner with enough profit without charging exorbitant prices.

PRICING STRATEGIES

Pricing strategies are well-planned methods and practices of pricing to attract customers to the floral shop and to motivate them to buy the products, perhaps more than originally planned. Using pricing strategies can help to increase sales volume and gross sales.

12–13. Signs on in-store displays is one way to inform customers about individual prices. (Courtesy, FTD)

PRICING STRATEGIES TO ATTRACT CUSTOMERS

A good retailer is always thinking of ways to attract new customers to the floral shop. Advertising through window displays or print media can lure new buyers into the shop. Leader pricing, tie-in pricing, and advertised specials offering a good buy or a free item can also bring new customers.

Leader Pricing

Leader pricing is a method of offering commonly purchased and recognizable items, such as carnations, daisies, roses, or special giftware, at a significantly reduced price compared to the competition. This strategy will attract new buyers and price-conscious customers and give the impression that all of the prices are more reasonable than the competition. The leader pricing method can be effectively used when good buys have been negotiated with trusted suppliers.

Multiple Unit Pricing

Multiple unit pricing is a strategy to encourage the customer to come to the shop and then buy more by offering price breaks for purchasing additional items. For example, one iris costs $1.75 and three irises cost $4.50 (a $.75 savings). The customer will feel that they are getting a lot for their money.

Advertised "end of the week" bouquet specials can encourage customers to stop by and pick up some flowers. Make (or purchase) cheerful mixes of flowers, give the bouquets a catchy title, and place the display in a prominent place to encourage the buyer. The single stems, priced individually, cost more than the mixture, which encourages the customer to buy the whole bunch.

A "buy one, get one free" special is another multiple unit pricing strategy. This method attracts customers to the shop because of the great bargains being advertised. Plan ahead for this method and work with the suppliers to find some good flower buys. Use this strategy carefully so the shop will not develop a "discount store" image.

STRATEGIES TO MOTIVATE MORE BUYING

Price Everything

Everything in the store should be priced to motivate a customer to buy. If a customer cannot figure out a price for something, she may just walk away and not buy it. Individual price tags can be tied on or pressed on like stickers. Signs or color-coded tags or stickers are another way to inform a customer about individual prices without placing a price tag on each one. The signs should be highly visible and informative to grab attention and encourage the buyer. For example, signs could be placed in each flower container informing the customer that these flowers are $1 each or 3 for $2.50. Every container would have its own pricing sign. Other decorative signs could price candles, ribbon, or vases. One-of-a-kind items should have an individual price tag to avoid confusion.

Rounding Prices

A common pricing strategy is to round up a price that comes out an odd number, such as $22.37 or $22.53. The price would be rounded up to the nearest 50 cents or dollar. The $22.37 price would be rounded up to $22.50 and $22.53 to $23.00. Do not round $22.53 to $22.50 because the loss of 3 cents will mean lost profits. For larger items, the price may be rounded from $122.53 to $125.00. All employees should be consistent and price by rounding in the same way.

Odd End Pricing

Some florists and other retailers prefer to price items with another rounding technique. **Odd end pricing** is rounding a product's price to $12.95 or $12.99, instead of a $13.00 price. The psychology is that the $12.95 price seems less expensive than $13.00 and will entice a customer to purchase something. If the odd end pricing method is adopted, the florist should choose the number to use—$.95 or $.99 and then consistently use it for all of the products and designs.

Multiple Price Points Strategy

Multiple price points is a method of pricing and displaying several related designs or products in varying sizes and varying prices to provide customer choice. The multiple price points will let the customer choose among various designs, such as a vase arrangement with 6, 9, or 12 flowers. Another offering to provide multiple price points would be to design in "nested" baskets. *Nested baskets* are baskets in three different sizes with one placed inside another. These three baskets could each have a unique style and mixture of flowers, each with a different price. The different price points or levels give the customer more choice and satisfaction when purchasing flowers.

Tie-In Pricing

Tie-in pricing is a method to encourage customers to buy related items by offering special discounted prices when the products are purchased at the same time. The florist can offer tie-in pricing for items that are a natural fit, such as a potted plant and watering can or a beautiful centerpiece and candles. Effective display of these items and eye-catching signs can motivate the shopper to purchase both products for a good price.

REVIEWING

MAIN IDEAS

A florist may purchase flowers, foliage, and other supplies from wholesale florists, growers, flower markets, and brokers. To be a successful buyer, the florist should be knowledgeable about flower quality, price, and helpful buying practices and should try to build a good relationship with suppliers.

The unit cost of goods is the price of a single item, calculated by dividing the overall bunch or case price by the number of items in the bunch or case. The unit cost of goods should be calculated for every item in an arrangement or item sold. Lists of up-to-date unit cost of goods should be calculated on a regular basis. Combined pricing is a method of determining the total costs of typical supplies used in an arrangement.

The methods of pricing design work are the ratio mark-up and its variations and the percentage mark-up.

The ratio mark-up method of pricing relies on a predetermined mark-up from the wholesale cost of goods. Hardgoods or supplies typically have a 2:1 mark-up; perishables (flowers and foliage) typically have a 3:1 mark-up.

The ratio mark-up has several variations. One variation is to add a labor charge. This labor fee can be calculated on the employee's hourly wage or the employer's actual cost of labor, which is the hourly wage plus fringe benefits and other employee costs. Another method to calculate labor would be to add a 10 to 20 percent labor charge to the final price.

The variable ratio mark-up is yet another type of ratio mark-up. Different mark-ups are figured depending on either 1) the type of design, or 2) the type of flower and the labor required to design with it. Basis designs and bud vases have the common 3:1 mark-up and the pricing would not change from the ratio mark-up method. Creative designs and corsages would have a 4:1 mark-up; wedding and party flowers would warrant a 5:1 mark-up because of the labor involved.

The weakness of the various ratio mark-up methods is the failure to provide for profit in a definitive way. Profit planning is a guessing game. Labor is also accounted for in some variations but not others.

The percentage mark-up is a pricing method that plans for profit. Net profit is one of four areas comprising gross sales. Net profit, the florist's return on the investment, should fall within a 10 to 15 percent range. A typical florist may have a 30 to 33 percent cost of goods percentage. If the florist chooses a 30 percent cost of goods percentage, 30 percent of a design's selling price should be the wholesale cost of goods. For a $20.00 arrangement, $6.00 is the wholesale cost of goods used to design the arrangement. $20.00 is multiplied by 30 percent to compute the wholesale cost of goods. To determine a price after designing, a design with $5.00 cost of supplies used will cost $16.66 or $16.70. The $5.00 is divided by 30 percent. This method is also called the divisional percentage mark-up because the wholesale cost is divided by the percentage.

Pricing strategies are well-planned methods and practices of pricing to attract customers to the floral shop and to motivate them to buy products. Strategies to attract new customers include leader pricing and multiple unit pricing. Leader pricing is a method of offering commonly purchased and recognizable items, such as carnations and roses, at a significantly reduced price compared to the competition. Multiple unit pricing is a strategy to encourage a new customer to come to the store and then buy more by offering price breaks for purchasing additional items. Advertised specials can also encourage buying multiple items as well as a "buy one, get one free" campaign.

Strategies to motivate increased buying include pricing everything, rounding up prices to even or odd end amounts, having multiple price points, and using tie-in pricing. Pricing everything in the store makes it quick and convenient for the customer to know the price of an item and then buy it. Rounding prices up to easy numbers such as 50 cents or the dollar or rounding up to odd end amounts, such as $14.99, plays on the psychology of the numbers chosen in the minds of the customer. Even pricing is clear-cut and easy to remember; odd end pricing makes the product seem less expensive. Having multiple price points—differing sizes and prices of items—gives the customer choice and more satisfaction in flower selection. Tie-in pricing encourages an additional purchase of a related product with the purchase of certain item. For example, with each centerpiece purchase, candles may be purchased for 50 cents off the purchase price.

A florist must decide which pricing strategies to adopt and then use them in a consistent way.

QUESTIONS

Answer the following questions using complete sentences and correct spelling.

1. Where can a florist purchase flowers and supplies needed to conduct a retail business?

2. Why is buying an important responsibility for the florist?

3. What is a unit cost of goods? How is it calculated?

4. What is combined pricing? How can this method save time when pricing?

5. How are retail prices determined using the ratio mark-up method?

6. What are weaknesses of the ratio mark-up method of pricing?

7. What are two ways to charge for labor using the ratio mark-up method?

8. What are the four major parts of gross sales? What are some typical percentages for each part, as well as gross sales?

9. How is the percentage mark-up method calculated?

10. What are four effective pricing strategies for attracting and motivating customers to buy?

EVALUATING

Match the term with the correct definition. Write the letter of the term on the line provided.

a. retail price
b. leader pricing
c. wholesale cost of goods
d. odd end pricing
e. multiple price points
f. broker
g. hardgoods
h. wholesale florist
i. pricing strategies
j. unit cost of goods
k. ratio mark-up
l. percentage mark-up

_____1. Rounding up to $9.99 or $9.95 so the design seems less expensive.

_____2. An agent who purchases and sells flower inventory.

_____3. The selling price.

_____4. The price of a single item in a case or bunch.

_____5. The pricing methods and practices to attract and motivate customers to buy.

_____6. Selling common items at significantly reduced prices.

_____7. A source of fresh and perishable materials linking the retail florist and the grower or broker.

_____8. Offering items of varying sizes and prices as a customer choice.

_____9. The total of all unit costs of goods, both perishable and non-perishable, in an arrangement.

_____10. Supplies or non-perishable items.

_____11. A pricing method that plans for profit.

_____12. A pricing method that relies on a predetermined increase from the cost of goods.

EXPLORING

1. Price a vase arrangement of 15 mixed flowers and 10 stems of foliage. Use the following wholesale prices: $.50 for 5 flowers, $.75 for 5 flowers, and $1.00 for the last 5 flowers, foliage at $.25 per stem, vase at $1.00, floral preservative at $.05. The design time was 15 minutes. Price this arrangement using 1) ratio mark-up, 2) ratio mark-up plus labor, 3) percentage mark-up. Choose a rounding up strategy and list the three prices. Compare the three prices; rank them from most expensive to least expensive. Which method would you use and why?

2. Use the variable ratio mark-up to figure the price of another design using the 15 flowers in a $3.00 vase with $1.00 foam. All costs listed are wholesale. For this method, the five $.50 flowers are filler flowers (high labor), the five $.75 flowers are average labor-requiring ones, and the five $1.00 flowers are form flowers with low labor requirements. Compare this price to the first three.

3. Visit a florist and list how many pricing strategies are being featured. Note your own reaction to the strategies. Which type or types do you think are the most tempting for a buyer? Why?

CHAPTER 13

The Retail Flower Shop

OBJECTIVES

This chapter is about the retail flower shop. It has the following objectives:

1 Describe the qualifications to be a florist

2 Know the types of flower shops

3 Learn the basics about good location and starting a floral shop

4 Describe the importance of marketing and promotion

5 Explain the importance of effective sales skills

6 Learn about effective packaging and delivery

7 Explain key aspects of an effective flower shop floor plan

TERMS

bucket shop
business plan
carriage trade shop
clearinghouse
demographic study
display
empty nest couples

fictitious name statement
filling florist
franchise
gray market
marketing
marketing mix
promotion

resale permit
satellite shop
sending florist
stem shop
tax number
up-selling
visual merchandising

13–1. A successful florist has a strong base of knowledge about both designing and selling flowers.

THE retail flower shop business is so much more than designing with flowers. A good floral designer should ask, "What other qualifications should I have to become a successful florist?" The astute florist should be aware and knowledgeable about the niche that their business fills in their location. Marketing, advertising, and effective selling, packaging, and delivery are each important facets of the florist business.

QUALIFICATIONS TO BE A FLORIST

What does it take to be a successful florist? A successful florist needs floral knowledge, business understanding and know-how, and highly developed personal qualities.

FLORAL KNOWLEDGE

Most people enter the florist trade because of their love of flowers and plants. A floral designer wanting to open his or her own shop should also have training and knowledge of cut flower and foliage care and handling, elementary and advanced floral design training, and knowledge of effective display techniques. Creative flair and the ability to spot or keep up with trends can give any florist an edge.

Beginning designers can learn floral skills by working at a flower shop and by taking courses at the high school, community college, and university levels. Floral design schools at various locations throughout the country and the world also offer intensive training of three- or four-week duration. Gaining experience by working at several types of shops is great training to someday own and operate a floral shop.

BUSINESS KNOWLEDGE

The business side of being a florist is very important. For example, a knowledgeable florist will want to develop business skills in advertising and marketing, buying and inventory con-

Floral Knowledge	Business Skills	Personal Attributes
Flowers	Advertising	Honest
Care/handling	Marketing	Trustworthy
Design	Personnel management	Consistent
Display techniques	Buying and inventory management	Self starter
Creativity	Pricing knowledge	Motivated
Trend watcher	Computer skills	Energetic
	Bookeeping/accountancy skills	Patient
	Salesmanship skills	Tactful, compassionate
	Good communicator	Ethical
	Delegator	Friendly, polite
		Goal oriented

13–2. Qualifications of a successful florist.

trol, effective pricing strategies, computer skills, bookkeeping and accounting, and training a sales force.

Since it is difficult to be proficient in every area, be sure to hire competent, trustworthy people in the areas in which you are weak. Some florist businesses are partnerships to allow the combining of strengths. For example, one partner may be a great businessperson while the other partner is a creative and artistic floral designer who does not care about the daily ins and outs of the business.

Involvement in the Chamber of Commerce and other community activities can be a smart business practice. Community involvement helps the florist to be knowledgeable about local business issues and builds name recognition and possibly a greater customer base.

PERSONAL ATTRIBUTES

Personal skills are equally important for a successful florist. Personal qualities, such as honesty, trustworthiness, drive and energy, patience, tact, compassion, consistency, and integrity, are valuable attributes for the ethical businessperson. A florist who is a "people person" and a good communicator is a win-win combination for employees and customers alike. A florist who is dependable and pays creditors on time is a valuable member of the community.

TYPES OF FLOWER SHOPS

Retail flower shops are as varied as the people operating them. However, florist shops do fit into some broad categories. Florist shops can be full-service shops, large-volume shops, carriage trade businesses, specialty shops, or stem shops. Flower shops can be satellite operations or franchises.

FULL-SERVICE

A full-service neighborhood flower shop is the traditional type of retail florist. This type of shop offers a wide range of services and products. A full-service neighborhood shop is a member of a wire service, does wedding and sympathy work, and all types of design work.

The person who owns and operates a full-service neighborhood shop should have good business and design knowledge and be versatile in many areas, such as waiting on customers, ordering and picking up flowers, doing some book work, setting up window displays, and arranging flowers. This florist is good at many duties and enjoys both flowers and a variety of activities, rather than organizing and motivating others.

LARGE-VOLUME FLORIST

A large-volume florist sells a large quantity of design work because of an excellent, well-executed marketing plan. This type of shop has identified the floral needs of its market area. Eye catching, profitable, often mass-produced designs, and effective marketing and advertising are the key aspects of a large-volume shop. A large-volume shop can be mostly full service but with restricted, but profitable, product lines and design services. Much time is spent on planning, budgeting, financing, and training.

The person who runs a large-volume florist is a businessperson who understands what customers want and is effective in creating marketing ideas and strategies to excite the customer to buy the product. This florist is an organizer, a planner, and a motivator of employees.

PARTY/WEDDING FLORIST

The party/wedding florist shop is a specialty shop that has restricted its design services to event planning, that is, party work and wedding work. The specialty shop should be located in a market area that can support this type of design specialization. Sometimes, the party/wedding flower shop will work cooperatively with other related businesses, such as bridal gown shops, caterers, wedding rental places, and printing places, specializing in wedding and party invitations.

The person who is a party and wedding florist should be extremely creative and resourceful in carrying out ideas. It is important to be creative and dramatic as well as a good communicator who can sell these ideas to the client. A party/wedding florist likes the challenge of making a striking statement with each new event and likes to work on a flexible, varied schedule.

CARRIAGE TRADE SHOP

A **carriage trade shop** provides extensive personal service to a limited, elite clientele. This type of shop may offer the same services as a full-service shop but in a lavish, upscale manner to a limited customer base. Corporate accounts and wealthy clientele make up the customer base.

13–3. A carriage trade florist provides lavish, personal, full service to a limited elite customer base.

A person who operates a carriage trade shop must first develop name and reputation recognition with the desired customers. A designer should be very creative to consistently design new and striking floral designs. It is also essential to understand and to effectively communicate with these types of customers.

STEM SHOP OR BUCKET SHOP

A **stem shop** is a cash and carry operation that offers a wide variety of flowers and foliage by the single stem or as bunches. Another name for a stem shop is a **bucket shop** because the flowers are sold out of containers or buckets directly to the public. A stem shop does not offer arrangements or delivery. The product line is fresh flowers and possibly a few vases. A high-traffic area is essential for the success of a stem shop.

13–4. A stem shop sells flowers, rather than arrangements and services.

An operator of a bucket shop should enjoy fresh flowers and foliage but not be interested in the artistic design aspect of the florist business. This type of owner should be conscious of customers' preferences and be an effective buyer of the needed product. A stem shop fits a person with a low-key management style and good mathematical skills. Generally, just a few employees are needed to run this type of shop.

SATELLITE SHOP

A **satellite shop** is a second business location operated by a large full-service flower shop. Some full-service shops open a second location in a shopping mall or strip mall. The mall location is primarily for merchandising and selling, not for designing because of the expense of the space. Other satellite locations may be in a hospital gift shop or office building.

The owner who decides to add a satellite shop should be well versed in the business aspects of a multi-shop operation. Planning, organization, and training of sales personnel for the second location are valuable skills needed to make the satellite shop financially viable.

FRANCHISES

A **franchise** is a flower shop that is purchased from and operated according to the parent company's operating specifications. The owner pays a percentage of the gross sales to the parent company. There are not many franchise retail flower businesses, but the advantage of a franchise business is name recognition and proven business techniques and products. The initial cost of purchasing the franchise can be quite high.

A person interested in purchasing a franchise should have strong business skills. Since the franchise determines the designs and product line, a strong floral design background is not a requirement. A proven business and advertising track record appeals to some florists who are not interested in building a business but running one.

In summary, a prospective florist should match his or her interests and skills to the requirements of a particular type of flower shop. The type of floral shop should also fit the location, geographical area, and desired target market.

LOCATION, LOCATION, LOCATION

A floral expert was once asked what were the three most important components of a successful flower shop. He replied, "Location, location, location!" Location must be important!

A prospective florist should research the state, the city, and then the neighborhood before selecting an established business or a new site. Look at the number of competing businesses in the city or neighborhood. As a general rule, 15,000 people can support one flower shop. Determine the size and then the population of the prospective area to be served. Divide the population by the current number of flower shops to see if the market is already saturated with florists in that area. Also, look at traffic flow, parking accessibility, site visibility, and availability of wholesale florists. Look at the population trends. A site in a growing area has much potential.

Besides the geographical research, both economic and demographic information should be gathered before making a decision about location. This information can be obtained from the county regional planning commission, the chamber of commerce, or the library. Look at the economic factors of a location, such as employment and income of the customer base, the per capita retail sales, and the health of the local business economy.

Geographic Factors	Economic Factors	Demographic Factors
State, city, neighborhood	Employment	Population age
Population	Income	Education
Population trends	Per capita retail sales	
Number of competing businesses	Health of the local businesses	
Traffic flow		
Parking		
Site visibility		
Availability of wholesale florists		

13–5. Is this location a good one? Factors to consider.

A **demographic study** is the reporting of the size and distribution of population in a specific area. Demographics can reveal the population age and education level. The age of the population can be important to the florist because of age-specific buying habits. For example, singles and couples from ages 25 to 45 usually have higher discretionary income and have great potential as good flower buyers because of their entertaining habits and spontaneous purchases. Couples or single parents with children at home (any age) are more children-oriented and spend less on flowers except for holidays, such as Mother's Day or Christmas. The **empty nest couples** (younger than 65, still employed, children no longer at home) have great potential as good flower buyers because of higher discretionary income and entertaining needs. The **gray market** (over 65, generally retired) spends money on traditional flower needs, such as holidays or birthdays, and usually have more controlled spending due to a fixed income.

A BUSINESS PLAN

A **business plan** is an organizational business tool to state the business' purpose and goals and estimate the financing needed to fund the new florist. A description of the proposed business is an integral part of the business plan. The business plan is an essential document to present to a banker when seeking financing.

A business plan may include (but is not limited to) the following sections:

Introductory Material

Title Page — Logo
Company name and address
Owners' names and telephone numbers

Table of Contents

Statement of Purpose — 1) Business goals
2) Purpose of this document
• Application for financing
• Give summary of specific capital needs

Business Data

Market and Competition Analysis

Description of the Business — Type of flower shop
Business niche
Products and services

Business Operation — A description of operation from product procurement to manufacturing, sales, and delivery

Location — Give a description of the site
Give building specifications (floor plan)
List traffic-flow count
For a new location, identify at least two location options

Marketing Plan — The marketing plan will describe the initial promotion and advertising strategies as well as the long range plans for advertising and promotion

Future Change Strategies — List the long-range plans for growth and expansion

Management Team

Operating Personnel

Venture Development Schedule — For a new business, show a 12-month time frame of the business from its conception to its opening

Proposed Use of Requested Capital

Critical Risks and Problems — List the difficulties and problems that may occur after the business is open and the plans to overcome them

Summary

Financial Data

(The prospective owner will need to submit a personal financial statement.)

Capital Needs and Sources — List the source of all capital, including the owner's funding and other loans and investments.

Capital Equipment List — List all equipment needs, including a cooler, computer system, delivery vehicle, display tables, wrapping tables, design tables, office furniture, and non-inventory items.

Balance Sheet at the Start of the Business

Break-Even Analysis

Income Forecast

Cash-Flow Analysis

Balance Sheet — Three year summary and three yearly forecasts

Loan Proposal

A prospective owner should consult with a certified public accountant to prepare portions of the business plan. Other information can be included in the appendix, such as the floor plan and shop front illustration, biographical information about the owner(s), and an equipment list for a similar operation.

Business Licenses and Requirements

Business licenses are a required part of operating legally as a florist. The required permits and licenses are regulated at the federal, state, county, and local levels. Since state, county, and local regulations vary widely, a florist should thoroughly check with state, county, and local officials to determine proper compliance.

Five important licenses or requirements are new business, employer, resale, professional, and special use. The first three areas are the most critical for the business aspects of starting a new flower shop.

NEW BUSINESS LICENSES

New business licenses include a fictitious name statement, any operating licenses required by the state, county, or local governments, and any local building permits. A *fictitious name statement* is a document that must be filed with the county to register the business name and prevent another business from using that name in the county. The florist is required to pay a filing fee and publish the fictitious name statement in two publications in the county. For information on zoning laws, occupancy permits, and fire code compliance, check with the county clerk's office and the local city hall.

13–6. A florist must have a resale license to sell flowers, collect tax, and buy goods from a wholesaler.

EMPLOYER REQUIREMENTS

Any florist who has employees must have a Federal Employer Identification Number (FEIN). Some states also require a State Employer Identification Number. Both the Internal Revenue Service and the Social Security Administration use the FEIN to identify the florist's business. If a florist is a sole proprietorship with no employees, the florist's social security number is used instead of a FEIN to identify the business. Contact the Internal Revenue Service to apply for a FEIN and to request federal tax forms required of a new business. A floral business must complete quarterly and year-end payroll tax returns.

A florist with one or more employees must comply with the Occupational Safety and Health Administration (OSHA) requirements. The latest regulations are available from the Department of Labor in Washington, D.C.

RESALE LICENSES

Every business must have a **resale permit** or license (also called a **tax number** or seller's permit) to register the business as a seller, to collect sales tax, and to buy goods for resale from a wholesaler without paying tax. (This license does not apply to states that do not collect tax.) A tax number or resale license is applied for with the state's Department of Revenue. Once the permit or number is received and used, the florist must remit sales tax to the state on a monthly, quarterly, or yearly basis, depending on the state. Check with the local county clerk's office or city hall to determine if municipal or county resale licenses are required.

PROFESSIONAL LICENSES

Professional licensing for florists is not mandatory in most states. The regulations should, however, be researched with the state Department of Agriculture before proceeding with financing and a new business. Many wire services and state florists' associations are providing certification programs to increase the educational and professional level of the florist industry.

SPECIAL USE LICENSES

Special use licenses include a liquor license and a pesticide applicator's license. Check with local and state agencies for the details. The pesticide applicator's license is administered through the state Department of Agriculture. The use of helium is regulated with required helium tank inspections and possible additional regulation in the future.

IMPORTANT AFFILIATIONS AND SUBSCRIPTIONS

Affiliation with a wire service is an integral part of providing good service for customers. The wire services (in the order of their establishment) include Florists' Transworld Delivery Association (FTD) and Teleflora. A florist who sells a wire service order is called a **sending florist**. The sending florist sends the order by phone, computer, or fax to a florist in the city and zip code of the person who will receive the flowers. The florist who fills or designs the order and delivers it is called the **filling florist**. Each month, the **clearinghouse**, the wire service's main office, settles the accounts for each florist and sends a bill or a check to the florist. The sending florist receives a small percentage of each order sent.

Membership in state florists' associations, allied (regional) florists' associations, and other professional floral design organizations can help the florist by providing continuing

American Academy of Floriculture
c/o Society of American Florists
1601 Duke Street
Alexandria, VA 22314
(800) 336-4743

American Institute of Floral Designers
720 Light Street
Baltimore, MD 21230
(301) 752-3320

American Floral Marketing Council
c/o Society of American Florists
1601 Duke Street
Alexandria, VA 22314
(800) 336-4743 or (703) 836-8700

Professional Floral Commentators—International
c/o Society of American Florists
1601 Duke Street
Alexandria, VA 22314
(800) 336-4743

Society of American Florists
1601 Duke Street
Alexandria, VA 22314
(800) 336-4743

13–7. Trade organizations.

Floral & Nursery Times (biomonthly)
P.O. Box 8470
Northfield, IL 60093
(847) 784-9797

Floral Finance (monthly by Teleflora)
11444 W. Olympic Blvd.
Los Angeles, CA 90064
(800) 456-7890

Floral Management (monthly by SAF)
Society of American Florists
1601 Duke Street
Alexandria, VA 22314-3406
(800) 336-4743
(703) 836-8700

Floral Mass Marketing (bimonthly)
Cenflo, Inc.
549 W. Randolph Street
Chicago, IL 60606
(312) 236-8648

Florists' Review (13 times a year)
Florists' Review Enterprises, Inc.
P.O. Box 4368
Topeka, KS 66611
(913) 266-0888

Flower News (weekly)
549 W. Randolph Street
Chicago, IL 60606
(800) 732-4581

Flowers & (monthly by Teleflora)
11444 W. Olympic Blvd.
Los Angeles, CA 90064
(800) 321-2654

Flowers & Profit (monthly by Teleflora)
P.O. Box 51390
Tulsa, OK 74152
(800) 555-9185

Holland Flower (quarterly by the Flower Council
  of Holland)
Flower Council of Holland
250 West 57th Street
New York, NY 10019
(212) 307-1818

The Retail Florist (monthly by Teleflora)
11444 W. Olympic Blvd.
Los Angeles, CA 90064
(800) 456-7890

Supermarket Floral (monthly)
Vance Publishing
7950 College Blvd.
Overland Park, KS 66210
(913) 451-2200

SAF: Business News for the Floral Industry
Society of American Florists
1601 Duke Street
Alexandria, VA 22314
(800) 336-4743

13–8. Floral industry publications.

education and networking opportunities. The Society of American Florists (SAF) is a national trade association, which lobbies for and represents the needs of all facets of the industry. Any qualified floriculture-related business or individual may apply.

Several organizations are joined by invitation only or by meeting specific requirements. These organizations include AIFD (American Institute of Floral Designers), AAF (American Academy of Floriculture), and PFCI (Professional Floral Commentators). For continuing wire service membership, florists pay 1 percent of outgoing wire orders as their dues.

Subscription to floral industry publications is also an important education source. A complete list is given.

MARKETING AND PROMOTION

EFFECTIVE MARKETING

Effective marketing is an essential aspect of the successful florist. **Marketing** is the process of selling products and providing services that the customer wants or needs. The goal of marketing is to determine the most effective marketing mix and marketing strategies for the targeted customers.

A **marketing mix** is a combination of activities and shop characteristics, such as advertising, shop layout, window display, writing educational articles for the newspaper, pricing strategy, and selling techniques that a florist implements to attract and retain his or her targeted customers. A shop's marketing mix will vary depending on the target market (targeted customers).

Every florist should follow these five guidelines or steps for effective marketing:

1. Define the specialties or strengths of this floral business.

2. Define the targeted customers or target market.

3. Determine the products the customers want to buy.

4. Determine how to communicate the message.

5. Decide the specific products and services to offer the target market.

This case study will follow the five steps of effective marketing:

◆ Step 1—A florist who defines his shop's specialties or strengths realizes that creating and selling flowers for non-holidays is an important emphasis and strength.

◆ Step 2—The targeted market would traditionally be the gray market and empty nesters; however, this florist wants to bring in more customers in the singles and couples groups.

◆ Step 3—The gray and empty nest groups want traditional, high-quality arrangements. The singles and couples want more contemporary styles and more casual, loose arrangements.

◆ Step 4—To reach the new targeted group, the florist tries three activities. He runs a radio spot on a station with a large group of 25- to 45-year-old listeners, gives an arranging demonstration for the local young women's group in town, and changes the shop layout and window display to emphasize both types of design styles.

◆ Step 5—The florist determines that he will offer the following products based on the targeted customers.

For the **gray market** and **empty nest couples,** he will continue to offer traditional centerpieces and one-sided designs.

To attract new singles and couples customers, two upscale designs, a vase arrangement of unique flowers for $20 and a high-style design for $30, will be promoted.

PROMOTION AND ADVERTISING

Promotion encompasses a variety of activities that lead to public name recognition. These activities—the tools of promotion—are advertising, community involvement, contests, coupons, demonstrations, direct mail, educational articles or a newspaper column, logo and image development including the packaging and delivery vehicle, effective selling techniques, public relations, publicity, signage, and window display.

As a part of the marketing mix, advertising can effectively communicate products and services that the floral shop can provide. The most common type of advertising for a flower shop is yellow pages advertising. It is a necessary (and expensive) type of advertising because so many floral customers conduct their business over the telephone. Other types of advertising for the florist include web sites, radio spots, newspaper ads, direct mail pieces, and school or community publications. Coupons or punch cards have been used successfully by many florists to not only promote flower use but also to advertise floral services.

IMPORTANCE OF EFFECTIVE SALES SKILLS

Hiring and training excellent sales staff is a highly effective means of promotion. An effective salesperson is invaluable to the retail florist. What makes someone a good salesperson?

QUALITIES OF A GOOD SALESPERSON

A good salesperson is a positive, motivated person who likes to work with people and is knowledgeable about flowers. Hiring someone with a friendly, personable, positive manner is important to the image of the flower shop. The person can then be trained in shop procedures and in flower care and information. Other qualities to look for in a good salesperson are good communication skills and the ability to think quickly and work under pressure. Enthusiasm about flowers and a high energy level are very helpful attributes of a top-notch salesperson.

A good salesperson should be a good listener and a thorough note-taker. When making telephone sales, the phone should be answered promptly with a greeting, the shop's name, and the person's name. Smile while talking on the phone because the positive attitude will come across to the listener.

Whether taking telephone orders or in-store orders, the effective salesperson asks appropriate questions and learns all the vital information, such as occasion, desired design style and colors, price range, message on the card, complete delivery information and phone number

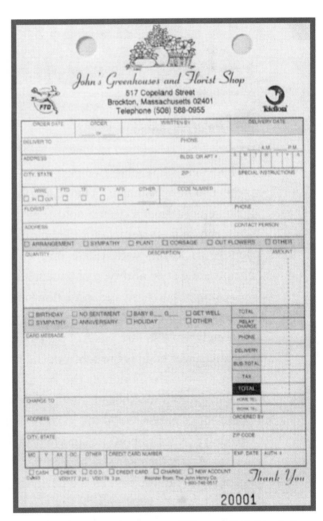

13–9. An effective salesperson will learn all of the vital information needed to make the sale.

(street address, not a box number), and the payment method. The successful salesperson directs the conversation without being pushy. When describing flowers, use descriptive terms, such as velvety red or soft and fine-textured, to help the customer to visualize the product. In the store, a good sales staff uses the selection guides to help the customer decide the appropriate arrangement to purchase.

Other techniques of good personal selling are to match the customer's mood, voice rate, and volume and to practice up-selling. *Up-selling* is the sales practice of persuading a customer to make a larger purchase than originally planned by suggesting several ranges of price, not just the least expensive, and offering related products.

EFFECTIVE PACKAGING AND DELIVERY

PACKAGING

Packaging can serve two purposes—to protect the design from the weather and to promote the shop's image. The effective packaging of flowers is necessary to protect the arrangement from extreme cold (below the freezing point) and high winds. For very cold days, the delivery vehicle should be running and warmed up and the arrangement should be double packaged with tissue and cellophane, plastic or paper. An attractive, image-announcing style and type of packaging should be planned and consistently carried out.

A simple bud vase and loose flowers can be covered with sleeves. Larger bunches can be packaged with cellophane, tissue, paper, or a combination of the two. The bunch is centered diagonally on a square piece of packaging material. One side is loosely folded over the flowers; the lower edge is brought up; the other side is folded over the flowers. Neatly fold the edges. Staple the bunch at the bottom and the side or attach with the shop's packaging sticker. In cold weather, bring the top portion down to cover the flowers and staple again. Some shops prefer to roll the loose flowers in the paper and staple, seal with a sticker, or tie with a length of ribbon. Be sure to attach the card.

Arrangements or bridal bouquets can be protected with plastic delivery bags. Place the arrangement in the bag, blow a cushion of air into the bag, and tie with a matching or signature color of ribbon.

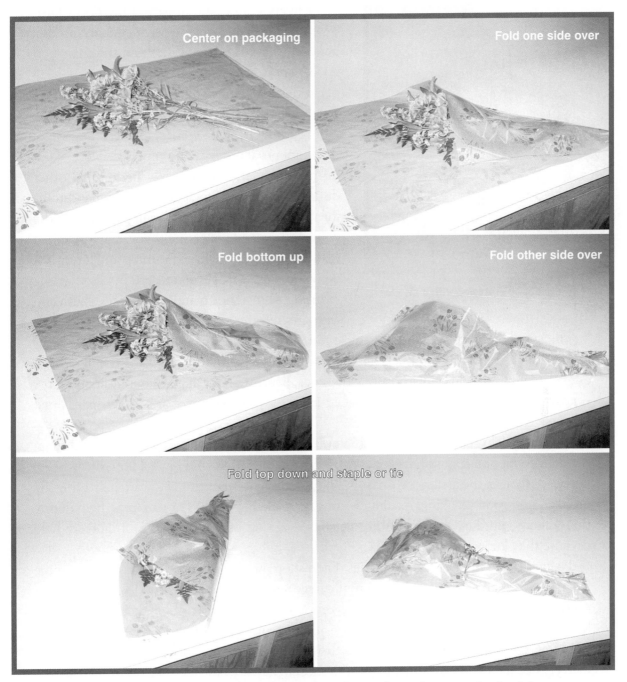

13–10. Attractive packaging can protect flowers from the weather and promote the shop's image.

13–11. A centerpiece can be protected with a plastic delivery bag.

DELIVERY

Delivery is an essential part of the florist business. The delivery person is an important link between the designing process and the customer. A delivery person is responsible for general upkeep of the delivery vehicle (cleaning exterior and interior, checking gas and oil), efficient scheduling and routing of the deliveries, efficient loading of the floral products, safe and timely delivery of floral products, and occasionally performing other duties as assigned. Efficient scheduling and routing means to group orders by their proximity in the delivery area and delivering them in an organized manner. Some shops have morning and afternoon deliveries, others deliver to certain areas in the morning, such as north and east and the south and west areas in the afternoon.

Efficient loading of the delivery vehicle starts with placing the last-to-be-delivered items in the vehicle first with the closest and easiest-to-reach products comprising the first deliveries. Tall items should be placed along the sides. Every item should be securely anchored or supported with sandbags, bricks, or placed in boxes of newspapers or compartmentalized carriers.

Since the delivery person may be the only contact a customer has with the floral shop, the delivery person should have a neat appearance, be polite, and have a friendly manner, knowledgeable of the area, good driving ability, conscientious attitude toward delivering the product, and good speaking, reading, writing, and spelling skills. For part-time help during the holidays, off-duty police and fire personnel are an excellent source of delivery help because they know the area so well.

Deliveries fall into several categories. Each shop owner or manager needs to determine what distances and locations the different categories cover and also the delivery charges for each category. The most common category is the normal or regular delivery, which is located within the predetermined everyday delivery area for the shop. The next category would be the out-of-area deliveries, which would have a larger delivery charge. A timed delivery occurs when a customer requests a special delivery time for a special anniversary or birthday. Special or last minute deliveries occur when the customer has forgotten or did not know about a floral need until the last minute. Holiday deliveries comprise the last category.

THE FLOOR PLAN

The components of a flower shop floor plan are the sales area, the design area, the wedding consultation area, and an office. Depending on the size of the florist shop, other areas may include a separate packaging and delivery area as well as a conditioning area for the newly received cut flowers and foliage.

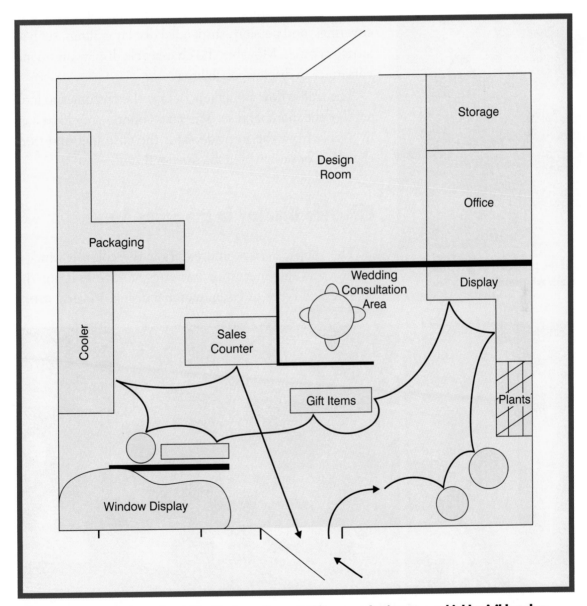

13–12. This floor plan has moveable display units, a wedding consultation area, a highly visible sales counter and cooler, and an open traffic flow that allows easy and comfortable movement through the entire sales area.

13–13. One of the purposes of effective display is to attract attention.

SALES AREA

The sales area starts at the outside window display and the front door. The sales area should be an inviting area with display units, tables, and shelves, the cooler, the sales counter and computer and cash register, window display, and a plant area (optional). This area should have adequate lighting, durable and attractive flooring and wall coverings, and possibly, suspended display ceilings, such as lattice or vines. Movable and changeable display units lend versatility in display possibilities.

The traffic flow should encourage the customer to look at all of the merchandise. The sales counter should be easily visible from the front door for the customer and from the office or design area for the floral staff.

Effective Display in the Sales Area

The shop's signage and exterior, the colorful window display, and the interesting vignettes or settings inside the shop are all types of visual merchandising. *Visual mer-*

13–14. Vignettes or display settings that are carried throughout the floral shop in various ways can unify the sales area.

13–15. Educating the customer is one of the purposes of attractive displays.

chandising is a coordinated effort and plan to attract customers to the flower shop and to motivate those customers to buy flowers and related products. **Display**, the pleasing visual arrangement of flowers and products, is one component of visual merchandising. Planning, coordinated buying, inventory control, advertising, and the coordination of the displays with the shop's image are other components of effective visual merchandising.

The primary purposes of any display are to attract attention, creating surprises and interest, motivating the customer to want to buy, and generating sales. Other secondary purposes of a display are to educate the customer, to create and reinforce the shop's image, to showcase flowers and products, to unify the sales area, and to emphasize and reinforce the current advertising campaign.

DESIGN AREA

The design room or work room should include design benches, easily accessible storage for containers and supplies, a receiving and delivery area for incoming wholesale orders, as well as outgoing finished arrangements, an office, a storage cooler, a supply and props storage area, and a potting area (if needed). The design area needs good lighting, easily accessible water source (faucets with hoses or overhead water sources at the design benches), drains to accommodate water spillage, ample shelving, and an area to organize the flower orders, both daily and weekly.

13–16. The design room should have ample storage and a place to organize flower orders.

WEDDING CONSULTATION AREA

The wedding consultation area should be located where the conversation will be undisturbed by telephones or other people. A table and enough chairs to accommodate three or four people should be provided.

OFFICE

For convenience and supervision, the office should be located near the sales area and the design room. It should be adequately equipped with modern office equipment, such as a computer with Internet access, a fax machine, a copy machine, and a telephone with as many lines as necessary to handle calls efficiently.

REVIEWING

MAIN IDEAS

The love of flowers may not be enough of a qualification for running a successful flower shop. A florist should have floral knowledge, business skills, and important personal attributes. A floral shop owner should have extensive knowledge of flowers and plants, their care and handling, and floral design expertise. Display knowledge, trend watching, and creativity are other floral skills. Needed business skills include knowledge of advertising, marketing, delegating, buying and inventory, pricing, bookkeeping and accountancy, as well as knowing when to hire a professional in an area, communication skills, and computer skills.

The types of floral shops are a full-service shop, large-volume florist, carriage trade shop, party/wedding florist, stem shop, satellite operations, and franchises. Location is very important to the success of a retail florist. Research the geographic area—state, city, and neighborhood. Look at the number of competing businesses, the population and trends, the size of the trading area, and the traffic flow, parking, and availability of wholesale florists. Research economic and demographic information, such as employment, income, prosperity of community as well as the demographics of the distribution of age within the population.

A business plan is an organizational business tool to state the business' purpose and goals and estimate the financing needed to fund a new flower shop. The business plan includes introductory material, business data and research findings and projections, and financial data.

The business licenses and permits needed for being in a retail floral business are a fictitious name statement, a Federal Employer Identification Number, a resale license, and any professional or special use licenses. Affiliation with a wire service is an integral part of providing good customer service. The wire services are FTD, Teleflora, Florafax, American Floral Services, and Carik. Membership in trade associations and professional groups is a good source of continuing education and networking.

Marketing is the process of selling products and providing services that the customer wants or needs. The astute florist should seek an effective marketing mix. A marketing mix is a combination of activities and shop characteristics that a florist implements to attract and retain his or her targeted customers. A florist needs to define the shop's strengths and the targeted customers, determine the products the customers want to buy and know how to communicate the message, and decide the specific products and services to best suit the customer's needs.

Promotion is a variety of activities that lead to public name recognition. Advertising is just one part of promotion.

A good salesperson is a positive, motivated person who likes to work with people and plants. Good communication skills, enthusiasm, and the ability to think quickly and work under pressure are other good qualities in a super salesperson.

Packaging protects the design from the weather and promotes the shop's image. Protective packaging and secure positioning in the delivery vehicle help to guarantee that the design will arrive in the condition in which it was arranged.

The floor plan of a flower shop has a sales area and a design area. The traffic flow in the sales area should be open and encourage the customer to browse through all parts of the store.

Visual merchandising is a coordinated effort and plan to attract customers to the flower shop and then motivate them to buy something. Display is one component of visual merchandising along with advertising and coordinated planning and buying.

QUESTIONS

Answer the following questions using complete sentences and correct spelling.

1. What type of flower shop would you like to own? Define the type you chose. Tell why you chose that type.

2. What are important aspects of location to research before choosing a site? Be thorough.

3. What is a business plan and why is it important?

4. What are the important business licenses required before opening a flower shop?

5. How do wire services work?

6. What are the components of a marketing mix for a florist?

7. How are promotion and advertising different?

8. What are qualities of an effective salesperson?

9. What are the important parts in a flower shop floor plan?

10. Why is packaging important?

EVALUATING

Match the term with the correct definition. Write the letter of the term on the line provided.

a. marketing   e. carriage trade shop   i. satellite shop
b. gray market   f. clearinghouse   j. empty nesters
c. bucket shop   g. tax number
d. filling florist   h. demographics

_____1. A shop providing lavish, personal service to an elite clientele.

_____2. The license to register the business as a seller and to permit the collection of sales tax and buying wholesale.

_____3. Couples who are younger than 65, still employed, and their children are no longer at home.

_____4. A shop that sells flowers and foliage by the stem.

_____5. The florist who designs the wire service order and delivers it.

_____6. A second business location operated by a full-service shop.

_____7. The study of the size and distribution of population in a specific area.

_____8. The wire service's main office.

_____9. The process of selling products that customers want to buy.

_____10. People who are older than 65 and generally retired.

EXPLORING

1. Write a marketing plan for selling something at school. Interview prospective customers to help determine the products to sell.

2. Draw a floral shop floor plan for your dream florist, using the dimensions of your classroom.

3. In a floral design class, become a salesperson. With a classmate as the buyer, guide the buyer through his or her flower purchase.

14

Interiorscaping

OBJECTIVES

This chapter is about interiorscaping. It has the following objectives:

1 Define interiorscaping.

2 Describe the importance of green plants in an interior.

3 Learn the plants suitable for interiorscaping.

4 Discuss pleasing design using green and blooming plants.

5 Explain proper plant maintenance.

TERMS

acclimated
double potting
foliage plants
foot-candle
light intensity

interior landscape technician
interior landscaping
interior plantscaping
interiorscaping
plant care technician

service technician
soil probe
sub-irrigation

14–1. Green plants add beauty to an indoor space.

WALKING into a room that is lush with green and blooming plants gives a wonderfully satisfying feeling of being outdoors. The soothing qualities of green plants are beneficial in many indoor places such as the workplace, hotels, restaurants, shopping centers, and homes. Indoor areas that effectively use green and colorful blooming plants are considered more attractive, more upscale, and even healthier than places without plants.

In the United States, the use of plants indoors is a relatively recent activity. However, in Europe from the 1600s through the 1800s, wealthy families grew plants, such as orange trees and seasonal flowering plants, indoors. In the United States during the post–World War II era, plants were just beginning to be used in the work environment. The 1970s ushered in a huge expansion of the interiorscaping industry with the addition of shopping malls and office complexes that wanted "green" interior landscapes.

INTERIORSCAPING

Interiorscaping, also called *interior landscaping* or *interior plantscaping*, is the art and science of selecting, placing, and maintaining plants to improve and enhance the appearance of the indoor environment. Effective interior landscapes are artistically designed to create enhanced views and interesting plant placement. The scientific aspect of interiorscaping involves knowing about individual plants and their growth needs and care.

THE IMPORTANCE OF GREEN PLANTS IN INTERIORSCAPING

Interior plants enhance the indoor environment by providing aesthetics and function. The aesthetic aspects include providing beauty and unique textures, adding interest and variety to an indoor space, and serving as living sculpture and decoration. Studies have shown that employees prefer office spaces with green plants because they report higher morale and greater contentment with the work environment. Customers perceive businesses with interior plantscapes to be more upscale and inviting.

Equally important, the functional aspects of plants are to direct traffic flow, alter or hide views, provide enclosure to make a space more inviting and intimate, soften the architecture of the room, and to freshen or cleanse the air. How does a green plant cleanse the air?

14–2. Plants enhance a room by adding soothing greens and interesting textures.

14–3. Plants can direct traffic flow and soften architecture in an interior space.

Humans breathe oxygen and release carbon dioxide. Plants use carbon dioxide from the air and release oxygen. This process freshens and cleans the air, even removing air pollutants, and is mutually beneficial for both plants and people.

SUITABLE PLANTS FOR AN INTERIOR

The first step in creating a successful interiorscape is to select the right foliage or blooming plant for the indoor space. **Foliage plants** are tropical and subtropical plants, either woody or herbaceous (non-woody), that are successfully grown indoors. Foliage plants have a range of growing needs that should be matched to the specific indoor environment. The interior should have the appropriate light levels and temperature to support a healthy plant.

All foliage plants must be acclimated prior to installing in an interior area. A plant that is **acclimated** has become accustomed to a new and different environment. To acclimate a plant, the grower moves the plant from the lower-light growing area (not full sun) to progressively lower light levels before shipping to an interiorscaper. This process may take two weeks or two months depending on the type of plant. The interiorscape is the final step to acclimate or "shade condition" the foliage plant. Some plants that are not properly acclimated will drop their leaves (e.g., *Ficus*). A well-acclimated plant will be healthier and better suited to the interior environment.

Many types of plants can be selected to enhance an indoor space. Both tropical and subtropical plants are successful when placed indoors. These plants can be classified as trees, shrubs, or ground covers, providing short, medium, and tall forms for the interior landscape. Cacti and other succulents provide unique textures and are excellent for interior landscap-

14–4. A poorly acclimated plant, such as a fig tree, may drop its leaves.

ing. For seasonal effects, flowering potted plants such as azaleas, chrysanthemums, cyclamen, potted bulbs like tulips and daffodils, poinsettias, or orchid plants are also incorporated into interior landscapes.

LIGHT REQUIREMENTS

A successful interiorscaper should know the foliage plant's light requirements. Does the plant require low, medium, or high light levels? Some plants favor bright but indirect lighting; in other words, the plant needs good lighting but does not need direct sunlight near a window or skylight. Research each plant's needs to determine the proper location for that plant in an interiorscape.

An interior plantscaper must also be able to determine the light levels of indoor areas. **Light intensity** in a room refers to the amount of light per square foot per hour and is measured in foot-candles. A **foot-candle** is the unit of illumination that equals the light of one candle at a distance of one foot. Interior spaces vary from having very low light to having very bright spaces and lots of windows.

How does a plantscaper determine interior light levels? An accurate light meter can be used to measure light levels. Also, a practical test with a white piece of paper can reveal the answers as follows:

1. Place the white paper an inch or two under a leaf.

2. If the shadow has a sharp definite outline, high light levels are present (greater than 300 foot-candles).

3. If the shadow is fuzzy but with an obvious outline, medium light levels are present (100–300 foot-candles).

4. If there is no shadow, low light levels are present (50–100 foot-candles).

Check the area in several places and note the variation in the light levels within one

Table 14–1. Light Intensity in Foot-Candles

High light levels	> 300 foot-candles
Medium light levels	100–300 foot-candles
Low light levels	50–100 foot-candles

room. Select the appropriate plants for each area once the light levels have been determined.

Low Light Plants

Areas with low light are probably the most difficult locations to place foliage plants. Some office spaces even use silk or artificial plants due to low light or inaccessibility in caring for live plants. Some plants, however, will grow in low light levels, such as some Chinese evergreen plants, cast iron plant, golden pothos, some palms, and sansevieria.

14–5. Low light plants (clockwise from upper left)—Chinese evergreen *(Aglaonema);* cast iron plant *(Aspidistra);* golden pothos *(Epripemnum);* parlor palm *(Chamaedorea elegans).*

Table 14–2. Plants Suitable for Low Light Levels (50–100 Foot-Candles)

Short (< 3')	Medium (3–5')	Tall (> 5')
Aglaonema (Chinese evergreen)	*Chamaedorea elegans* (parlor palm)	*Chamaedorea erumpens* (bamboo palm)
Aspidistra elatior (cast iron plant)	*Howea forsterana* (Kentia palm)	*Chamaedorea seifriazii* (reed palm)
Epripemnum aureum (golden pothos plant)	*Schefflera arboricola* (dwarf palm)	
Philodendron scandens oxycardium (heart-leaved philodendron)		
Sansevieria trifasciata (sansevieria, snake plant)		

Medium Light Plants

Many foliage plants are suitable for medium light such as Boston fern, ivy, dracaena, and weeping fig. Medium light levels range in light intensities from 100 to 300 foot-candles. Some interiors will have medium light due to direct light but others will have medium light in the shade of taller high light plants.

Table 14–3. Plants Suitable for Medium Light Levels (100–300 Foot-Candles)

Short (less than 3')	Medium (3–5')	Tall (> 5')
Asparagus densiflorus 'Sprengeri' (sprenger asparagus)	*Dieffenbachia amoena* (giant dumbcane)	*Dracaena marginata* (marginata, red-edged dracaena)
Chlorophytum comosum (spider plant)	*Dracaena deremensis* 'Janet Craig' (Janet Craig dracaena)	*Ficus benjamina* (weeping fig)
Cissus rhombifolia (*Rhoicissus*) (grape ivy)	*Philodendron selloum* (lacy tree philodendron)	*Schefflera actinophylla* (umbrella tree, schefflera)
Hedera helix (English ivy)	*Pittosporum tobira* (Japanese pittosporum)	
Nephrolepis exaltata 'Bostoniensis' (Boston fern)		
Peperomia obtusifolia (oval-leaf peperomia)		
Syngonium podophyllum (arrowhead plant)		

14–6. Medium light plants—English ivy *(Hedera helix)* (upper left); Boston fern *(Nephrolepis)* (upper right); dumbcane *(Dieffenbachia)* (middle); red-edged dracaena *(Draceana marginata)* (lower left); and weeping fig *(Ficus)* (lower right).

High Light Plants

Foliage plants for high light areas prefer direct lighting that is greater than 300 foot-candles. Plants suited for more shaded sites will show browning or leaf damage in a high light area. Plants favoring high light will also provide needed shade to those plants requiring less light.

Table 14–4. Plants Suitable for High Light Levels (Greater Than 300 Foot-Candles)

Short (< 3')	Medium (3–5')	Tall (> 5')
Aechmea fasciata (urn plant, bromeliad) *Begonia rex* (rex begonia) *Cordyline terminalis* (ti plant) *Crassula argentea* (jade plant) *Tradescantia albiflora* (wandering Jew) *Zygocactus truncates* (Christmas cactus)	Cacti and other succulents *X Citrofortunella mitis* (calamondin orange) *Codiaeum variegatum* (croton) *Phoenix roebelenii* (miniature date palm) *Strelitzia* spp. (bird of paradise)	*Araucaria excelsa* (Norfolk Island pine) *Bambusa* spp. (bamboo) *Beaucarnea recurvata* (ponytail palm) *Dizygotheca elegantissima* (false aralia) *Polyscias fruticosa* (ming aralia)

14–7. High light plants—croton *(Codiaeum)* (left); bird of paradise *(Strelitzia)* (middle); and ponytail palm *(Beaucarnea)* (right).

DESIGN CONCEPTS

Plants add to the beauty and warmth of an indoor space. Beauty from plants is due to their textures, colors, forms, and size. Their effective use should be based on the design principles of proportion, balance, rhythm, and dominance.

The interiorscaper evaluates the space and lighting, takes measurements while noting furniture placement, draws a floor plan, and designs the plant placements to suit and enhance the environment in a cost-efficient way. The effective application of the design principles while keeping in mind the outstanding qualities of each plant will allow the interiorscaper to enhance and beautify interior spaces.

PROPORTION

Select the plant size to fit the space available. Large rooms or spaces can visually support large plants and bolder textures. Groupings of medium or small plants can also provide the needed scale to fit and fill a portion of the large area. Bright colors and bold textures combined with large and interesting plant shapes will add the proper scale and necessary interest in a large interiorscape. Soften the boldness with shorter, medium to fine textured plants used near seating areas, in mass in dividers and under the canopy of larger trees.

In contrast, a smaller space does not require large amounts of big, bold plants because their size and texture may overpower a space and make it seem crowded and uncomfortable. Use a single bold plant in combination with other varying textures and forms to add interest. The rest of the foliage plants will probably be medium- and fine-textured ones in keeping with the room's size. A tall, fine- to medium-textured tree could be used as an accent in a corner for variety in height.

BALANCE

An interior can be symmetrical or asymmetrical. The traffic flow through the room will determine where

14–8. Large, bold plants provide pleasing proportion and scale in filling a large area effectively.

plants and plant groupings can be placed. Formal rooms may indicate a symmetrically balanced design. Watch out for monotony! Even symmetrical rooms should have a pleasing variety of plants, avoiding mirror images of plant combinations. Asymmetrical spaces with unique architecture generally call for a counterbalanced placement of plants and groupings to create surprise, softening of architecture and enclosure.

For pleasing balance, try to position plants to enhance several areas around the room, not just on one side or area. A good balance of taller plants with shorter plants is welcoming and inviting. The use of hanging plants along with plants in containers is a pleasing way to counterbalance the use of green throughout the room.

Rhythm

14-9. Select plants of varying growth habit—trailing versus upright—and position them at differing plant heights for interest and contrast.

Rhythm implies movement. Green is soothing and the eye will follow that color throughout an indoor space. Therefore, foliage plants are excellent to lead the eye through a particular space. Positioning plants to direct the eye or to direct foot traffic provides visual rhythm. Variation in plant growth habits is pleasing to the eye; choose hanging and trailing plants along with taller upright plants to provide different staging or layers of green. Provide smooth transition between the layers, building smoothly from low or medium to tall.

Place plants on varying levels by using plant stands or tables of differing heights or simply by placing the plants on stairs or other architectural features that provide a change in height. Raised planters are often seen in shopping malls and offices; plants are placed within them, which elevates the display for enhanced viewing. The change in height allows each plant to be seen and enjoyed and moves the viewer's eye throughout the space.

The use of color in a repeating way throughout a space is another way to create pleasing rhythm and continuity. The change from fine to medium to coarse or bold textural plants also provides interest and effective visual flow in an interior.

DOMINANCE

Plant groupings of the same type of plant create pleasing dominance or focus within an interior. Avoid scattering a single plant here and there around a room; single plants do not usually have enough visual force to be effective. For variety, the use of three to five different types of foliage plants in a group can create quite effective emphasis within a room. Seasonal flowering plants positioned together focus attention and provide a dominant feature. Besides pleasing dominance, another reason to group plants in an interior is to increase the humidity near the plants.

An important exception to grouping for dominance is the specimen plant. A specimen plant can be used singly because it has outstanding characteristics of vivid foliage or flower colors, bold interesting texture, unique form or shape, and even large size. Beautiful large plants include the Norfolk Island pine or a bold banana plant.

The use of green is a wonderful emphasis or dominant feature. To give variety and contrast, introduce a variegated plant that has white or red edged or striped leaf such as spider plant or dracaena. Flowering plants provide exciting variety in color, shape, and even fragrance. Cacti make a definite statement of variety in texture.

14–10. Massing foliage plants creates pleasing focus and dominance to enhance the indoors.

DISPLAY AND INSTALLATION TIPS

The best plants to display in an interior are healthy ones. When the shipment of plants arrives, all should be inspected for quality and freedom from insects and disease. The leaves of the plants should be cleaned with a soft cloth before placement in the interiorscape.

Remove any damaged or aged leaves. A flowering plant should have faded or damaged flowers removed. For some flowering plants such as African violet and cyclamen, the flowers can be repositioned so all of them show above the leaves.

Each plant should be displayed or presented effectively to bring out its best features while keeping it as healthy as possible. Pots can be placed on saucers or into decorative pots or planters. Placing a pot into another one for decorative display or effective grouping is called **_double potting_**. To avoid noticeable gaps between the two containers as well as excess weight, add Styrofoam pieces between the two containers for stability. Some interiorscapers use moss, bark, or stones to cover the original planting pot if it shows within the decorative container. Used in another container, the original pot is considered part of the mechanics or "behind the scenes" part of the interiorscape.

Drainage into the saucer or decorative pot is important to avoid overly moist soil that may cause root damage. The saucer or decorative container also holds water to keep the draining water from ruining floors or causing falls. Any spills or leaks should always be immediately wiped and dried: a "Caution—Wet Floor" sign can be positioned there until the floor is completely dry.

14–11. These tulips are double potted. When the growing container or pot is placed into a decorative pot, it becomes a double potted plant. (Courtesy, Netherlands Flower Bulb Council)

14–12. Combine decorative pots in groups to effectively display seasonal plant materials in an interior. (Courtesy, Netherlands Flower Bulb Council)

Group several pots for a distinctive effect. Terra cotta pots as well as other glazed pottery are very effectively displayed with saucers. Decorative containers of differing materials can be combined for variety and pleasing effect.

Large containers may be heavy to move and install; a cart, wheelbarrow, or a moving dolly can be an effective implement to move and then position a plant in the plantscape. Cloths or tarps can be laid on the floor to protect it. Always sweep and clean the surrounding areas after installation or maintenance.

INDOOR PLANT MAINTENANCE

An interior landscape must be properly and consistently tended for the best results. The *interior landscape technician*, also called a *plant care technician* or *service technician*, tends and cares for the variety of foliage plants in an interior, including proper watering, fertilizing, cleaning, or removing leaves and/or flowers, and insect and disease control.

A maintenance contract is a service that interiorscaping companies provide for the client. The plant care technician may visit the site weekly or as needed to water, fertilize, and provide foliage and flower care. A flower or plant rotation program is another aspect of interiorscaping. Contracts for rotation or replacement can vary from once a month to every three to six months.

It is very important that the plant care technician is knowledgeable about the different types of plants and their care in each interiorscape. If a new problem or concern arises, a

14–13. An interior landscape technician performs many duties from installation to regular plant care and insect control.

good service technician will also seek advice from other professionals as well as from relevant web sites, journals, and books.

Proper Watering—When to Water?

Watering interior plants is a vital part of interior plantscape care. An experienced interior landscape technician learns by experience when and how to water the different types of interior plants. Plants vary in their water requirements from cacti that require very dry conditions to hydrangeas, ferns, Swedish ivy, citrus, and some palms that require moist soil. In general, most plants need soil moisture in the lower half of the container. The use of different types of soil media (soil mixes, soil-less mixes, other potting media) also determines when to water.

To determine when to water, use the following checklist:

1. Check visual signs—Test by looking.
   a. Note plant appearance.
   b. Check leaf color and condition.
2. Check tactile signs—Test by feeling.
   a. Feel the leaves for firmness (turgidity).
   b. Feel the soil surface for moisture.
3. Check the soil weight—Test by lifting the container.
4. Use technology—Test with a soil probe.

Visual Signs

The visual signs that a plant needs water include checking the appearance of the plant. If a plant is wilted, this is a sign of both overwatering and underwatering. Next, look at the plant's coloring. Overwatered plants may also develop soft, pale yellow foliage. An underwatered plant may exhibit browning at the leaf tips or the leaf edges (margins). Leaf drop is also a signal of underwatering.

Tactile Signs

To investigate further, use the sense of touch. A plant care technician can use tactile signs for determining watering, such as feeling the leaves as well as the soil. If the foliage feels limp or droopy, rather than firm, the plant needs to be watered. High temperature will also cause wilting so check for that condition before watering.

14–14. If a plant is wilted, look for other signs to determine the cause. Overwatering = yellow, soft foliage (left); Underwatering = leaf tip browning (right).

Test the soil by feeling it. Remember that each plant's moisture requirements are different. Most plants need moisture in the lower half of the container. Cacti would require less moisture; some plants, such as hydrangeas, require more water. Use the following general guidelines to determine soil moisture:

◆ At Soil Surface

- Moist—no water needed.

- Slightly damp—no water needed.

- Dry—check lower soil levels.

◆ ½"–1" below soil surface.

- Moist—no water needed, may be overwatered.

- Slightly damp—no water needed except for moisture-loving plants such as ferns, some palms, hydrangeas.

- Dry—check plant appearance; water if leaves are droopy and air temperature is not extremely warm.

◆ Lower half of container.

- Moist—probably overwatered.

- Slightly damp—some water needed especially for moisture-loving plants.

- Dry—time to water, except for cactus, some succulents.

Test by Weight

For small containers, test the water needs of the foliage plant by weight. A well-watered plant will be relatively heavy. Actually pick up the container and determine its relative weight compared to its well-watered state. A very lightweight foliage plant in its container is in need of water. Experience is the best teacher for this technique.

14–15. A soil probe is used to check soil moisture levels in potted plants. (Courtesy, Dr. Daniel Warnock)

Test with a Soil Probe

A *soil probe* is a useful tool to check the moisture levels of soil, soil-less mixes, or other potting media. The soil probe gathers small soil samples at varying levels when placed fully into the soil of the container, turned a ¼ turn, and pulled out. Check the upper soil sample for moisture first and then proceed to check each lower level. Keeping good notes for a particular site and its plants will help the interior plant care technician to develop a reliable watering system.

Watering Techniques

For each watering, the soil in the container should be completely saturated with some run-off through the drainage holes. Make sure that the water is not just running down the edges of the pot where the soil sometimes shrinks away from the side of the container. For a plant pot within another decorative pot, the sound of water draining out through the drainage holes can be heard. Avoid over-watering these closed decorative containers so that water will not stand near the root system of the plant.

Although top watering is the most common method of watering interiorscapes, sub-irrigation is another method. *Sub-irrigation* is a watering system in which water is added through a fill tube to a reservoir at the base of the container. This system utilizes the soil's natural tendency to draw water from wet

14–16. Water each plant adequately with water permeating the soil and allowing run-off into the saucer or additional container.

lower levels to the drier upper levels of the soil. Sub-irrigation decreases the time spent on watering because the interiorscaper merely needs to check the fill tube and add water every two to three weeks.

For small areas, watering cans are appropriate for watering. Larger areas may require watering machines with hoses, watering wands, and on/off valves. Watering in larger areas should be timed for off-peak hours.

FERTILIZATION

In general, plants growing in a container in an indoor environment need less water and less fertilizer than the same plant outdoors. With that in mind, don't over-fertilize these containerized plants. Most indoor plants are not actively growing during the winter months and should not be fertilized then. In spring, a dilute fertilizer treatment can be made. During the summer, watch the new growth for signs of needing fertilizer, such as yellowing, sickly growth. If the new growth looks healthy and is the appropriate color for its type, then do not fertilize.

Fertilizer can be applied as a water-soluble type during watering. For interior plants, use one-half to one-fourth the recommended amount. Look for a fertilizer that is low in fluoride or fluoride-free to avoid browning on the tips of the leaves. A 1-1-1 balance of nitrogen, phosphorus, and potassium is a common fertilizer type. Since nitrogen promotes good healthy leaf growth, fertilizers with a 2-1-2 or 3-1-2 balance are also effective.

14–17. Thorough cleaning of the leaves (both upper and lower surfaces) is important for the beauty and the health of the interior plant.

14–18. To create a neater appearance, a leaf with a brown edge can be trimmed to mirror the natural margin.

Foliage Care

Beautiful glossy green leaves and colorful top quality flowers are a pleasure to see in a well-tended interiorscape. Regular care and maintenance of the foliage plants is essential to the beauty of the interior. When needed, the plant care technician would provide the following care: cleaning of the leaves, removing yellowing or damaged leaves, trimming foliage, rotating plants periodically to encourage even growth, and pruning or shaping plants. Gently folding the leaf in half and trimming the brown edges away to mirror the natural shape of the plant can eliminate unsightly brown tips on leaves. The scissors should be disinfected before and after use.

INSECT AND DISEASE CONTROL

Prevention of pest problems in the interiorscape should be the goal of every plant care technician. Consistent, thorough leaf cleaning serves two purposes—beauty and controlling small amounts of pests. Another prevention strategy is to select cultivars that are insect and disease resistant.

Early detection is the key to controlling pests and disease indoors. Constantly check yellowed or discolored leaves for insects before removal. A small magnifying lens is a great tool to check for small insects. Position a piece of white paper under a suspicious-looking leaf and shake the leaf to check for pests. Spider mites can be detected early using this method.

Thorough cleaning may counteract a low-level infestation. Be sure to clean both the upper and lower leaf surfaces. Use horticultural soap for minor infestations. Larger infestations may require using horticultural oil or even spraying with pesticides. A pesticide applicator's license is required for interior pesticide usage. A heavy infestation may warrant the removal of

14–19. The early detection/observation of a mealy bug on this leaf will allow the plantscaper to clean the leaf and stop further spread.

the plant from the site. The plant can be more easily treated off-site. The use of biological controls such as beneficial insects may work at some sites.

Reference books about foliage insects with pictures, descriptions, and controls would be a great investment for a plant care company. Consult a local extension office for up-to-date recommendations for the timing of biological or pesticide control strategies.

Placing healthy plants in the proper light level and watering them properly is the best technique to control diseases. A weak struggling plant is highly susceptible to diseases. If a leaf looks unhealthy and fungal disease is the possible reason, consult a thorough reference guide or take a representative sample to a diagnostic plant clinic to determine the particular problem.

REVIEWING

MAIN IDEAS

Interiorscaping, also called interior landscaping or interior plantscaping, is the art and science of selecting, placing, and maintaining plants to improve and enhance the appearance of the indoor environment. Interior plants not only provide beauty through interesting placements and combinations but also function in directing traffic, hiding unwanted views, softening architecture, and cleansing the room air. Green and blooming plants used indoors boost morale and attitudes of employees and customers.

Foliage plants are tropical and subtropical plants that can be successfully grown indoors. Plant types may include trees, shrubs, and ground covers, as well as cacti, succulents, and seasonal flowering plants. For the best success, foliage plants should be acclimated to a lower light area before placing in an interior. A interior plantscaper should determine the light levels or light intensities of indoor areas.

An area of low light (50–100 foot-candles) is the most challenging location for a foliage plant. Examples of low light plants are Chinese evergreens and cast iron plants. Medium light intensities of 100–300 foot-candles are suitable for a broad range of plants, such as spider plants, parlor palms, and weeping figs. High light areas of greater than 300 foot-candles are suitable for cacti, bird of paradise, and Norfolk Island pine.

The design principles of proportion, balance, rhythm, and dominance should be employed to create beautiful and effective interiorscapes. The plant material should be a suitable size or scale for the room. A pleasing balance of plant placements, plant heights, and growing habits will create an interesting interior space. Green plants are excellent in leading the eye through an interiorscape. Plant groupings create pleasing dominance or focus within an interior.

The best interior plantscape starts with healthy plants. Plants should be cleaned and consistently maintained. Double potting and the use of moss or bark to cover the original planting pot are part of a professional-looking interior.

The plant care technician is responsible for proper watering, fertilization, foliage care, and insect and disease diagnosis and control. An experienced plantscaper will know the tactile and visual signs for water needs in plants and the proper watering techniques.

QUESTIONS

Answer the following questions using complete sentences and correct spelling.

1. What is a surprising benefit to people when plants are used indoors to improve the appearance of the space?

2. What are three functional aspects of interior plants?

3. Why is it important to acclimate a foliage plant? How is a foliage plant acclimated?

4. What is light intensity, and how is it measured?

5. What is the most challenging location for an interior plant?

6. How do you create the proper proportion when using plants in an interior?

7. What is an example of dominance when designing an interiorscape?

8. What are three tips for displaying foliage plants well in an interiorscape?

9. What are five ways a plant care technician can check if a plant needs watering?

10. How do you effectively water a foliage plant?

EVALUATING

Match the term with the correct definition. Write the letter of the term on the line provided.

a. double potting
b. interiorscaping
c. acclimate
d. sub-irrigation

e. foliage plants
f. foot-candle
g. soil probe
h. plant care technician

i. interior plantscaping
j. light intensity

_____ 1. The process of becoming accustomed to a new environment or different climate.

_____ 2. One who installs, cares for, and maintains a variety of foliage plants in an interior.

_____ 3. Unit of illumination equal to one candle at a distance of 1 foot.

_____ 4. Art and science of selecting, placing, and maintaining plants in an interior.

_____ 5. Placing the original planting pot into a decorative container.

_____ 6. Amount of light per square foot per hour.

_____ 7. Tropical or subtropical trees, shrubs, or ground covers that are suited to the interior.

_____8. Watering through a fill tube to the reservoir at the base of the container.

_____9. Tool to check soil moisture levels.

_____10. Another term for interiorscaping.

EXPLORING

1. Consider the living room of your home as a future interiorscape. Draw a rough sketch of the dimensions of the room and note the window locations and furniture placement. Determine the differing light levels using the white paper test. Select plants that are appropriate to the light level(s) and sketch in the placements of your favorites based on size, color, leaf shape, and texture.

2. Interview a plant care technician in person or on the telephone. Ask about a typical day's plant maintenance routine. List necessary supplies and tools needed on the job site. Find out their favorite reference books, resources, and web sites.

Glossary

Acclimated—To become accustomed to a new and different environment.

Advancing colors—Warm hues which look larger and seem to advance or move toward the viewer.

Aisle runner—Fabric or cloth-like paper covering for the center aisle for the bride to walk on during the wedding ceremony.

Aisle runner tape—Double-sided tape to secure an aisle runner.

Alkaline—A pH of 8 through 14.

Alstroemeria—Also known as Peruvian lily. Flowers of the *Alstroemeria* have a long vase life, two weeks or more, and come in many colors including yellow, orange, red, pink, purple, lavender, white, and bicolor.

Altar arrangements—Floral designs placed near the altar of the church to provide a beautiful frame for the bride and groom during the wedding ceremony.

American Colonial period—A simple style of floral design in the Colonies (pre-United States) that combined fresh and dried materials in arrangements.

Analogous—A color scheme incorporating colors of two or three adjacent hues on the color wheel and their tints, shades, and tones.

Anchor pin—A plastic, four-pronged design mechanic that is attached to a container and holds floral foam securely.

Annuals—Herbaceous plants that grow from seed to flower in one season before dying.

Arm bouquet—A grouping of flowers and foliages that is tied together and cradled in the bride's left arm.

Asymmetrical balance—Differing weights and placements of plant materials on either side of the vertical axis that appear to be visually balanced.

Balance—Physical or visual stability of a floral design.

Bent neck—A rose that wilts and bends over just under the flower or bud.

Binding—The technique of physically tying stems together for physical support and beauty.

Biological control—The use of living organisms to control pests.

Brick—The typical size of floral foam, approximately the size of a fireplace brick.

Broker—An agent who purchases flowers from growers and sells the materials to both wholesale and retail florists.

Bucket shop—Another name for a stem shop.

Business plan—An organizational business tool to state the business' purpose and goals and estimate the finances needed to fund a new flower shop.

Buyer—Person who locates sources of products and places bids or offers for purchase.

Calyx—The collection of the sepals of a flower.

Candelabra design—An arrangement of flowers attached to a candelabra for decoration during a wedding ceremony.

Candleholders—A plastic support for candles with a round fitted top for the candle and a pronged base to insert into the floral foam.

Capillary mats—Porous mats laid on a bench and wetted. The media in the pots absorb the water by capillary action.

Career success—gaining a favorable result in the job world with the help of effective skills and traits as well as appropriate knowledge

Carriage trade shop—A retail florist that offers lavish full service to a limited customer base.

Cascade bouquet—A bouquet with a full rounded central area and a trailing (cascading) line of flowers and foliages.

Casket inset piece—A small design displayed inside the casket lid.

Casket saddle—A container with a specially rounded base to fit the curving contours of a casket lid.

Casket spray—A floral tribute placed on the top of a casket during a funeral service.

Centering—Placing dominant plant materials along the central vertical axis.

Center of interest—An area that ties or visually pulls an arrangement together, located in the lower half of the design.

Chaplet—A garland or a wreath worn on a person's head.

Chenille stem—A wire covered with soft, fuzzy chenille fibers, also known as a pipe cleaner.

Chuppah—A canopy under which a Jewish bride and groom stand to be married.

Clearinghouse—The wire service's main office.

Colonial bouquet—A round bouquet.

Color wheel—A circular representation of the primary, secondary, and tertiary and their relationship to each other.

Combination method—A wiring technique that employs two methods of wiring to secure a flower or leaf within a corsage or boutonniere.

Combined pricing—A method of adding the total costs of typical supplies used for a specific arrangement in a particular vase or container.

Complementary—A color scheme of direct opposites on the color wheel and their tints, shades, and tones.

Conditioning—Preparation of plant materials before arranging them by allowing for uptake of water or preservative solution to extend the life of the flowers.

Conical centerpiece—A cone-shaped or three-dimensional isosceles triangle centerpiece, often designed as a tabletop Christmas tree.

Contemporary design—An arrangement designed using the latest styles and trends in floral design.

Contour—The three-dimensional radiation of an arrangement from the vertical to the horizontal, as viewed from a side.

Contrast—Objects or plant materials with striking differences in color, texture, shape, or size.

Cool hues—Blue (and sometimes violet) and its tints, shades, and tones.

Cornucopia—A horn-shaped container typical of the Thanksgiving season, also called a horn of plenty.

Cost of goods—The total wholesale cost or prices of materials that comprise the designs, plants, and giftware sold in a retail flower shop.

Counterbalancing—Balancing plant materials with visually equal ones on both sides of the central axis.

Covering method—A drying technique that employs a drying agent to maintain the shape of the flower as it is drying.

Crescent—A geometric design resembling a C shape.

Crescent bouquet—A variation of the cascade bouquet that is designed in a C shape.

Cut flowers—Flowers grown in a greenhouse or field, cut when they reach a certain maturity, and sold to a wholesaler. Roses, carnations, chrysanthemums, and orchids are a few common cut flowers. Another term used is fresh flowers.

Cut foliage—Leaves harvested for floral design work, often referred to as "greens." Leatherleaf, lemonleaf, pittosporum, podocarpus, asparagus fern, and huckleberry are common foliage materials used in floral work.

Daisy hook method—A wiring technique for daisies or asters for use in corsages or boutonnieres.

Deionizer—Used to remove the minerals in water.

Demographic study—A report of the size and distribution of population for a specific area.

Depth—The third dimension within a design.

Desiccant—A drying agent.

Design elements—Physical characteristics of plant materials.

Design mechanics—Techniques and devises that hold a corsage or arrangement together in a secure way.

Design principles—The rules and guidelines to follow in creating pleasing floral designs. Proportion, balance, rhythm, and dominance.

Dip dyes—Semi-transparent paints that change flower color by directly dipping the flower head in the solution.

Disease—A disturbance to the normal, healthy growth and development of a plant.

Dish garden—Differing types of potted plants in the same container.

Display—The pleasing visual arrangement of flowers and products.

Dominance—The prominence or prevalence of one element or characteristic with other characteristics being subordinate

Double potting—Placing one container into another one for decorative purposes

Dried flower—Plant materials that are successfully preserved or dried. Also called everlastings.

Drying agent—Holds the shape of the flower and draws the moisture from the flower as it dries. A drying agent is used for the covering method. An example is silica sand.

Dutch Flemish period—A style of floral design that featured large, flamboyant arrangements and accessories.

Easel—A tripod-like stand for holding sympathy flowers.

Easel spray—A one-sided sympathy flower arrangement placed on an easel.

Egyptian period—An early style of decorative flower use, valuing simplicity.

Empty nest couples—Couples who are generally younger than 65 and still employed with no children living at home.

English tradition—A style of floral design that featured fragrant bouquets and both formal and casual arrangements.

Equilateral triangle—A triangle with three equal sides.

Ethylene—A colorless gas produced in the nodes of stems, ripening fruits, and dying leaves. It causes the thickening of stems and speeds the aging of plant parts, particularly fruit.

Ethylene inhibitors—Treatments or chemicals that block or tie up the ethylene within the flower and reduce its impact.

Everlasting plant materials—Plant materials that can be dried or preserved successfully, also called dried flowers.

Feathering—A wiring technique for making smaller flowers from a larger carnation.

Fertilizer—Any material added to growing media that provides nutrients for plants.

Fictitious name statement—A document that must be filed with the county to register a business name and prevent another business from using that name.

Filler flowers—Small flowers that are used to fill space and provide texture, color, and depth within a design, also called fillers.

Filling florist—The florist who fills or designs a wire service and delivers it.

Finishing dips or sprays—Treatments applied to a finished corsage to minimize water loss and keep the corsage fresh for a longer period of time.

Fireside basket—A curved, open basket with handle.

Fixative—An additive to potpourri to hold or "fix" the scent or fragrances for an extended period of time.

Flat spray—A triangular, one-sided sympathy spray.

Floral arranger—People with the training required to make and copy floral designs.

Floral design—The art of organizing the design elements inherent in plant materials, container, and accessories according to the principles of design to attain a composition with the objectives of beauty, simplicity, harmony, suitability, and expression.

Floral designer—Person with the skill and training to make floral designs and unique floral art.

Floral industry—businesses that sell, distribute, handle, design and deliver fresh flowers, cut foliage, and foliage plants.

Floral foam—A porous material that holds water and provides stability for flower stems.

Floral foam holder—A wedding mechanic with floral foam encased in a plastic cage with a handle.

Floral sprays—Opaque paints that will completely change any flower color.

Floral tints—Translucent paints that allow some of the flower color to show.

Floriculture—Literally defined as the "culture of flowers," floriculture is an international, multi-billion dollar industry based on flowering and foliage (leafy) plants.

Florist—Person who works with cut flowers and foliage.

Florist shears—A cutting tool with short, serrated blades.

Flower exporter—Businesses that purchase and resell flowers and foliage to many parts of the world.

Flowers—The showy, colorful parts of plants.

Focal area—A center of interest.

Focal point—A center of interest.

Foliage grid—The overlapping and interlocking of leaves within a vase arrangement to give support to the flower placements.

Foliage plants—Tropical and subtropical plants grown for their leaves rather than for their flowers and selected for their ability to be grown indoors. They are also called houseplants.

Foot candle—A measure of light intensity based on the amount of light distributed by a single candle one foot away.

Form—The three-dimensional shape of a design.

Form flowers—Flowers with special forms or shapes that provide interest within a design and can create an effective center of interest.

Franchise—A flower shop that is purchased from and operated according to the parent company's operating specifications.

Free form—A style that allows the floral designer to convey creativity and individual expression by bending or breaking the rules of floral design.

Free, variable rhythm—Irregular, unpredictable use of plant materials to add surprise and interesting lines and forms with a floral design.

Freeze drying—A commercial method of freezing the flowers and then drying them.

French period or the Grand era—A refined and elegant style of floral design during the Louis IV period.

Fresh flowers—Another term for cut flowers, which are flowers grown in a greenhouse or field, cut when they reach a certain maturity, and sold to a wholesaler. Roses, carnations, orchids, and chrysanthemums are examples.

Full couch—A casket with a one-piece lid, which may be closed or open.

Full-couch casket lid spray—A large casket spray placed in the center of the open lid of a full couch.

Full-couch casket spray—A large casket piece that is placed in the center of a closed full couch.

Garland—Flowers and foliages woven or fashioned into a strand or a rope (roping).

Gauge—The thickness or thinness of florist wire.

Geometric form—Designs which mirror the shapes of geometry such as the circle and triangle.

Georgian era—An English style of floral design that developed the first centerpieces and miniatures.

Glamellia—A composite flower of gladiola florets made to resemble a camellia.

Glycerinizing—A preserving technique that replaces the moisture of a plant with a glycerin solution, preserving the plant material and causing it to remain pliable and flexible.

Golden mean—The Greek proportion of 1.6 to 1.

Grades—Flowers grouped according to size or quality.

Gray market—People who are older than 65 and usually retired.

Greek and Roman period—A style of flower use which includes the use of strewed or scattered flowers and garlands, wreaths, and chaplets.

Greening pins—S-shaped hairpins for securing moss or foliage in a design.

Green rose—A rose at a premature stage with the greens sepals prominently enclosing the bud.

Grid—A framework of materials at the top of a vase to provide support for flowers in a vase arrangement.

Gross sales—The total dollar amounts that the retail florist sells in a year.

Grouping—Placing flowers or foliages in sections or areas of just one type to repeat their growth in nature.

Hairpin method—A wiring technique for ferns or other compound leaves and for multi-flowered stems.

Half couch—A casket with a two-piece lid with the left side open during the visitation services.

Hand-tied bouquet—A three-dimensional grouping of flowers and foliages that are tied together with the natural stems showing.

Hanging method—A drying technique of bunching and hanging plant materials upside down to dry.

Harden—To condition or prepare flowers for use in arranging.

Hardgoods—Nonperishable supplies, such as vases, wire, or ribbon, used in floral designs.

Hard water—Water that contains high amounts of minerals.

Highly buffered—Resistant to a change in pH.

High-visibility colors—Warm hues, light values (tints), and bright intensities which are very noticeable from a distance.

Hogarth curve—A geometric shape resembling a slim S.

Hue—The name of a color.

Hyacinth stake—A long, green wooden stick used for extending height and supporting flowers and accessories within a floral design.

Ikebana—Japanese flower arranging.

Importer—A business that buys and brings goods "into their ports", that is, into their country from another country.

Integrated pest management (IPM)—Use of a wide range of strategies to control pests and diseases.

Intensity—The relative brightness or dullness of a hue.

Interior landscape technician—A trained person who tends and cares for the foliage and flowering plants in an indoor environment. Typical duties include watering, fertilizing, cleaning, removing faded or damaged leaves or flowers, and insect and disease control.

Interior landscaping—The art and science of selecting, placing and maintaining plants to improve or enhance the appearance of the indoor environment. Other terms include interior plantscaping and interiorscaping.

Interior landscaping company—Business that selects, designs, and maintains plants in an indoor environment.

Interior plantscaping—The use of plant materials to improve the appearance of the indoor environment. Other terms include interior landscaping and interiorscaping.

Interiorscaping—The art and science of selecting, placing and maintaining plants to improve or enhance the appearance of the indoor environment. Other terms include interior landscaping and interior plantscaping.

Interiorscaping company—Business that selects, places, and maintain plants in an indoor environment.

Inverted T—A variation of the isosceles triangle that incorporates more space and fewer flowers.

Isosceles triangle—A triangle having two equal sides and a narrower width than the equilateral triangle.

Italian Renaissance period—An early style of flower arranging that is considered the beginning of flower arranging in vases.

Japanese influence—A style of floral design emphasizing space and significant placement of each type of plant material.

Joining point—The place where the wired and taped stems of a bouquet converge and are eventually taped together.

Kneeling bench—A bench provided and decorated for a wedding ceremony in which the bride and groom kneel as a part of the wedding ceremony.

Labor—An operating expense, a cost of manufacturing (designing) an arrangement.

Language of flowers—The tradition of assigning meanings to flowers to convey messages which was initiated and became popular during the Victorian era.

Leader pricing—A pricing strategy of offering commonly purchased items at a significantly reduced price compared to the competition.

Leadership—The ability to direct and influence other people to meet individual or group goals.

Leaves—Plant organs responsible for the production of food (sugars) for the plant. Usually green or variegated. Also called foliage or "greens".

Light intensity—The amount of light per square foot per hour. Measured in foot-candles.

Line—The visual movement between two points within a design.

Line arrangement—A design that is based upon the Japanese ikebana designs and emphasizes space, rhythm, and line.

Line mass—An American design style that combines the line and space of the Japanese influence with the colorful mass style of the Europeans.

Line materials—Flowers or foliage that are very tall or long compared to their width that are useful in creating the outline of a design.

Lines of opposition—A design with a high contrast use of two different design lines or forms, sharing a center of interest.

Low-visibility colors—Cool hues, dark values (shades), and dull intensities which do not seem to show up very well from a distance.

Marketing mix—A combination of activities and shop characteristics which a florist implements to attract and retain targeted customers.

Marketing—The process of selling products and providing services that the customer wants or needs.

Mass arrangement—A design of many flowers, usually in a geometric shape that is based upon the lavish European flower arrangements of the 17th and 18th century.

Mass flowers—Round or solid flowers that are useful in filling out the shape of the design.

Mini carnation—A type of carnation. Mini carnations are ½ to ⅓ the size of standard carnation flowers.

Monochromatic—A color scheme including only one hue and its tints, shades, and tones

Mottled foliage—Leaves with flecks of a differing color throughout the entire leaf.

Multiple price points—A pricing strategy of displaying and pricing several related designs or products in varying sizes and prices to provide the customer a choice.

Multiple unit pricing—A pricing strategy offering the customer price advantages for purchasing additional items.

Narcissus—Also known as daffodils. This bulb produces brilliant yellow flowers, with some varieties available in white, two-tone colors, and peach.

National FFA Organization—The premier student organization for young people interested in the floral industry, promoting leadership, personal growth, and career success.

National Junior Horticultural Association (NJHA)—A youth organization for those interested in the floral industry. NJHA programs focus on Horticulture, Youth, Careers, Education, and Leadership (HYCEL).

Naturalistic form—Designs repeating and suggesting nature, often using groupings of plant materials.

Needlepoint holder—A design mechanic with a heavy metal base and sharp, closely spaced pins for holding flower stems. Also called pinpoint or even frog.

Nested baskets—Containers which are three different sizes with each one placed inside another.

Nestled boutonniere—A boutonniere with a smaller flower placed within the center of a larger carnation.

Net profit—The income at the end of the year after expenses, the return on the florist's investment.

Nosegays—Fragrant handheld bouquets of flowers, herbs, and foliages.

Novelty design—A whimsical, imaginative arrangement of flowers designed to resemble animals, birthday cakes, or clowns.

Odd end pricing—A pricing strategy of rounding a product's price to a set price just below a whole dollar amount, for example $9.99 or $9.95 instead of $10.00.

Operating expenses—The costs of running a retail flower shop.

Ornamental horticulture—The practice of growing and using plants for decorative purposes.

pH—The measure of acidity or alkalinity.

Paddle wire—A continuous length of wire wound onto a piece of wood (paddle).

Papier-mache—Sturdy, molded, paper-like material which holds water and is used to fashion a container used for sympathy flowers.

Pattern—The coloration of plant materials and arrangement of the plant parts.

Pavé—The technique of placing plant materials very close together in rows or sec-

tions to completely cover the foam and fill in the design.

Percentage mark-up—A pricing method of dividing the wholesale cost of goods by the cost of goods percentage, based on the retail shop's financial statement.

Personal growth—Understanding and developing skills such as citizenship, social skills, and self-esteem.

Pest—A living organism that can cause injury or loss to a plant.

Pesticide—Chemical used to control pests and diseases.

Petals—Structures located just inside the sepals. Petals appear leaf-like and are often very colorful to attract pollinators.

Pew decorations—Bows, flowers, or floral designs attached to the ends of the pews in the aisle where the bridal party walks

Physical balance—The secure, stable placement of plant materials within the container.

Pick machine—A flower design tool that attaches a metal stem to a dried or silk stem to add length or strength.

Pierce method—A wiring technique for corsages or boutonnieres that requires inserting a wire horizontally through the thickened calyx of a flower, such as roses or carnations.

Pillowing—The technique of placing flowers close together and very low in a design, forming undulating peaks and valleys.

Plant care technician—A trained person who tends and cares for the foliage and flowering plants in an indoor environment. Typical duties include watering, fertilizing, cleaning, removing faded or damaged leaves or flowers, and insect and disease control. Other titles include interior landscape technician or service technician.

Plant health—Refers to plants that are free of pests and disease.

Plush animals—Stuffed animals that are suitable for accessories within an arrangement.

Polychromatic—A color scheme the incorporates a wide range of colors, both warm and cool.

Poly foil—A foil with a thin plastic covering on the silver side.

Potpourri—A scented mixture of dried petals, flowers, leaves, buds, fragrances, and a fixative.

Pressing—A drying technique that preserves plant materials in a two-dimensional form.

Pricing strategies—Well planned methods and practices of pricing to attract customers and motivate them to buy something.

Primary colors—The foundation colors of red, yellow, and blue, which cannot be created by mixing any other colors.

Principles of design—The rules and guidelines to follow in creating pleasing floral designs.

Promotion—Activities that lead to public name recognition of the flower shop.

Proportion—The pleasing relationship in size and shape among objects or parts of objects.

Radiation—The appearance of flower stems emerging from one point.

Raffia—The fiber of a palm tree used to tie objects together or to add a decorative flair in packaging.

Ratio mark-up—A method of pricing which relies on a predetermined increase from the wholesale cost of goods.

Receding colors—Colors such as blue and violet which are not highly visible from a distance and seem to become smaller or disappear (recede) because of their color.

Regular, repeated rhythm—Repetitive, predictable placements of plant materials to create a bold, strong visual pathway through a design.

Repetition—Repeating one or more of the design elements throughout a floral design.

Resale license—A permit registering the business and allowing the business to collect sales tax and purchase for resale from a wholesale business without paying tax.

Respiration—The process of the plant using its stored food.

Retail floral manager—Person who has the responsibility of coordinating the operations of the business. Tasks associated with this position include managing personnel, working with budgets, and maintaining the store's inventory.

Retail florist—Provides floral design services, cut flowers and other floriculture crops. Retail florists have typically been small independent businesses.

Retail price—The florist's selling price based on the wholesale cost and predetermined pricing methods and strategies.

Rhythm—The related, orderly organization of the design elements to create a dominant visual pathway through a floral design.

Right triangle—An L-shaped asymmetrical triangle.

Rosettes—Foliage placement technique of placing all of the stems emerging from one point to mimic the growth of ferns.

Salesperson—Person who has direct and usually frequent contact with the retail florist. The salesperson takes orders and arranges delivery of the products.

Satellite shop—A second business location that is operated by a large, full-service flower shop.

Scalene triangle—An asymmetrical triangle with three sides of differing lengths.

Secondary colors—Colors creating by mixing the adjacent primary colors, orange, green, and violet.

Sending florist—The florist who sells a wire service order and then sends the order by phone, computer, or fax to the florist in the city and zip code of the person who is receiving the flowers.

Sepals—Green, leaf-like structures on the exterior of the flower. The sepals fold back as the flower opens.

Service technician—A trained person who tends and cares for the foliage and flowering plants in an indoor environment. Typical duties include watering, fertilizing, cleaning, removing faded or damaged leaves or flowers, and insect and disease control. Other titles include interior landscape technician or plant care technician.

Set pieces—Sympathy designs in special shapes, such as wreaths, crosses, hearts, or organizational symbols, that are displayed on easels.

Shade—A dark value of a hue, the hue with black added.

Shape—The two-dimensional term for form, the outline of a design.

Shattering—The breaking apart or the falling out of petals.

Silica gel—A type of drying agent available as white crystals (sand-like) or color-indicator crystals that change colors when the desiccant is too moist to effectively use.

Silica sand—A type of drying agent, white builder's sand.

Snapdragon—Cut flower with an elongated floral inflorescence that comes in a variety of bright colors. White, pink, and yellow are very popular. Other colors available include red, bronze, and purple.

Softened water—Water that has been treated with salts to remove minerals.

Soil probe—Tool used to check moisture levels of soil, soil-less mixes or other potting media. Used by plant care technicians to determine watering needs.

Spadix—A spike with a thickened, fleshy axis, usually enveloped by a showy bract called a spathe. Anthurium is a spathe and spadix.

Spathe—A flower with a showy bract with a central axis called a spadix. The anthurium is an example.

Split complementary—A color scheme which combines one hue with the two hues that are on each side of its direct complement.

Split calyx—The biggest problem with harvested carnations. This condition, when the calyx tears or splits, petals spill out and the flower appears misshapen, is caused by fluctuations of temperatures and is more common with some cultivars than others.

Staging the bow—Arranging the bow loops so the bow appears balanced and full or rounded.

Standard carnation—A type of carnation. A large, solitary flower that has been disbudded.

Standing spray—Another term for an easel spray.

Stem blockage—An obstruction of the xylem due to air, bacteria, or other microorganisms, salts, undissolved particles, or other debris such as sand or soil.

Stem dyes—Color solutions that are transported through the xylem of a plant to change the flower color.

Stem shop—A cash and carry operation the offers a variety of flowers and foliages by the single stem or as bunches.

Stitch method—A foliage wiring technique.

Strewing—The scattering of flowers and loose petals on the ground.

Styrofoam—A lightweight form made of synthetic polystyrene material used to attach flowers for creating sympathy designs or other stylized designs.

Sub-irrigation—A watering system in which water is added through a fill tube to a reservoir at the base of the container.

Supervised experience (SE)—Valuable work experience to apply classroom instruction through on-the-job training in the floral industry.

Sweetheart rose—A smaller rose that grows as a spray, but can also be a single, smaller rose (because it is disbudded). Sweetheart roses are used extensively in wedding work, corsages, and centerpieces. Yellow, red, white, and pink make up a large percentage of those produced. New cultivars also offer many pastel colors and bicolors.

Symmetrical balance—Similar weight and appearance of plant materials on either side of the vertical axis within a floral design.

Sympathy flowers—Flowers that are sent to a funeral home or funeral service to honor the deceased and to comfort the bereaved.

Tape grid—The placement of waterproof tape across the opening of a vase at 90-degree angles to form a support grid.

Tax number—Another term for resale license or permit.

Terracing—The technique of placing plant materials in differing levels, one above another.

Tertiary colors—A mixture of a primary and a secondary color.

Texture—The visual and tactile qualities of plant materials.

Tie-in pricing—A pricing strategy to encourage customers to buy related items by offering special discounted prices when the items are purchased at the same time.

Tint—A light value of a hue, the hue with white added.

Tip spraying—A special spray technique that applies color to the edges only of the petals.

Tone—A full spectrum hue with gray added.

Topiary—A formal pruned tree or shrub fashioned into shapes; also a two-tiered floral design.

Toss bouquet—A small, wired and taped bouquet that is thrown by the bride to unmarried friends during a traditional part of the wedding reception activities.

Transition—Smooth, gradual change from one thing to another.

Transpiration—The movement of water vapor out of the plant (through the stomata).

Triad—A color scheme combining three equally spaced hues on the color wheel, such as the primary colors or the secondary colors.

Tulip—Bulb plant from southwestern Europe and the Near East. They are available in practically all colors with the exception of a true blue, and are grown for cut flowers or as potted flowering plants.

Tulle—Florist netting, available in many colors and finishes.

Turgid—Tissues full of water.

Turgidity—Water pressure in the plant cells.

Tussie-mussie (tuzzy-muzzy)—Another name for a nosegay.

Unit cost of goods—The wholesale price of a single item.

Unity candle arrangement—A centerpiece featuring a candle which the bridal couple light during a wedding ceremony.

Up-selling—The sales practice of persuading a customer to make a larger purchase than originally planned by suggesting a range of prices and offering related products.

Value—The lightness or darkness of a hue.

Variable mark-up—A pricing method with differing increases based upon the type of design or the type of flower and the labor required to design with it.

Variegated foliage—Leaves with lines, stripes, or areas of a differing color along the leaf edge or center.

Variegation—The different color patterns of leaves caused by pigments.

Variety—A diverse mixture or differing components.

Vase life—The length of time cut flowers and foliage live after they have been cut.

Victorian era—The period during the reign of Queen Victoria of England known for establishing floral design as an art form and the language of flowers.

Virus—Symptoms of infection include discoloration of plant tissues, stunting of growth, and deformed growth. Tobacco mosaic and Aster yellows are two common viral disease associated with greenhouse crops.

Visual balance—The perception of an arrangement looking stable.

Visual merchandising—The coordinated effort and plan to attract customers to the flower shop to motivate those customers buy flowers and related products.

Visual weight—Perceived lightness or heaviness of plant material based upon its combined characteristics of color, shape, pattern, size, texture, and spatial arrangement.

Votive candles—Short, stocky candles placed in holders to give a soft light and festive effect.

Warm hues—Red, orange, and yellow and the tints, shades, and tones of these hues.

Water tubes—Small, rubber-capped, plastic tubes which hold water and a single flower or cluster of small flowers

Wholesale cost of goods—The price of all materials in a floral arrangement, determined from the prices paid at the wholesale florist or from a broker.

Wholesale floral manager—Person who oversees the operations of the business by supervising the staff, estimating retail demands for products, and preparing long-range plans.

Wholesale florist—A business that buys from growers or brokers and sells to retail florists at wholesale prices.

Wholesale price—Another term for wholesale cost of goods; the amount or cost of materials based upon their purchase price from a wholesale florist.

Wilting—A drooping condition and a lack of firmness to the plant tissues caused by inadequate water.

Wooden pick—A narrow, pointed piece of wood with a wire attached at the top to attach to dried or silk stems to add length or strength.

Wrap around method—A wiring technique for securing small bunches of foliages or filler flowers.

Wreath—Flowers and foliages woven or fashioned into a circular shape.

Wrist corsage—A lightweight corsage designed to be attached to a wristband for wearing on the wrist.

Xylem—The conductive tissue in the stem that transports water and minerals from the roots to the leaves.

Bibliography

Biondo, Ronald J., and Dianne A. Noland. *Floriculture—From Greenhouse Production to Floral Design.* Danville, Illinois: Interstate Publishers, Inc., 2000.

Briggs, George B., and Clyde L. Calvin. *Indoor Plants.* New York: John Wiley & Sons, 1987.

Collins, Barbara L. *Professional Interior Plantscaping.* Champaign, Illinois: Stipes Publishing Co., 2002.

Flowers by Design. Lansing, Michigan: The John Henry Company, 1998.

Hunter, Norah T. *The Art of Floral Design.* Albany, New York: Delmar Publishers Inc., 2000.

Noland, Dianne A., and Talmadge McLauren. *Florist's Review Seasons of Flowers.* Topeka, Kansas: Florists' Review Enterprises, Inc., 2002.

Noland, Dianne A., and Ken McPheeters. *The Principles of Floral Design.* Urbana, Illinois: Information Technology & Communication Services, 1983.

Professional Floral Design Manual. Oklahoma City, Oklahoma: American Floral Services, 1989.

Royer, Ken. "Buy Like A Professional," *Florists' Review*, March, 1987.

Royer, Kenneth R. "What Kind of Florist Are You?" *Florists' Review*, October, 1998.

Rutt, Anna Hong. *The Art of Flower and Foliage Arrangement.* New York: The MacMillan Company, 1958.

Teleflora. *Advanced Floral Design—Encycloflora Series.* Leachville, Arkansas: Teleflora, 1993.

Teleflora. *Basic Floral Design—Encycloflora Series.* Leachville, Arkansas: Teleflora, 1993.

Teleflora. *Marketing and Promoting Floral Products—Encycloflora Series,* Leachville, Arkansas: Teleflora,1994.

Teleflora. *Purchasing and Handling Fresh Flowers and Foliage—Encycloflora Series.* Leachville, Arkansas: Teleflora, 1994.

Teleflora. *Selling and Designing Sympathy Flowers—Encycloflora Series.* Leachville, Arkansas: Teleflora, 1994.

Teleflora. *Visual Merchandising for the Retail Florist—Encycloflora Series.* Leachville, Arkansas: Teleflora, 1994.

Index